Dil Se Samarpit
... a heartfelt tribute to Maa

'Love is the highest emotion,
all other emotions can be transformed with love'
—**MAA**

Faith & True Love

Dear Preeti

With love

Sangeeta Maheshwari
19.03.18

Faith & True Love

Journey
to
Inner Peace

Sangeeta Maheshwari

RUPA

Published by
Rupa Publications India Pvt. Ltd 2015
7/16, Ansari Road, Daryaganj
New Delhi 110002

Sales centres:
Allahabad Bengaluru Chennai
Hyderabad Jaipur Kathmandu
Kolkata Mumbai

ISBN: 978-81-291-3741-8

First impression 2015

10 9 8 7 6 5 4 3 2 1

The moral right of the author has been asserted.

Printed at Replika Press Pvt. Ltd., India

To Maa

When I close my eyes and think of Maa, I visualize an ocean filled with calmness, soft waves of love gently washing away the harshness of life and a rainbow emerging with rays of truth, peace and hope.

On connecting with her, the fog of my thoughts lift and clarity emerges. Although I cannot physically speak to her anymore, yet I feel her presence around me and I know she is looking after me like always.

Maa held my hand since I was five years old and became my umbrella, sharing her wisdom and guiding me with compassion. Her simplistic, yet profound advice helped me overcome the hurricanes in my life. Today, forty years later, she continues to be in my conscience. I feel her presence inside the core of my heart guiding me to undertake the less travelled road in order to reach a higher destination.

Maa conjures a larger-than-life image with patience, kindness, faith and true love.

She led two lives at the same time: the worldly life and the spiritual life.

It was intriguing and magical to see how she integrated both the worlds at all times.

Maa did not preach but practised her philosophy as a way of life.

Through this book an attempt has been made to assimilate learnings of life she imparted to all as a way of living. I requested Maa to guide me through the book and it has been an extremely fulfilling experience to be led by her from an astral level.

Please join me in my fascinating journey with Maa.

Contents

Introduction to Shyam Baba

*I*n many ways this book is as much about Shyam Baba as it is about Maa, since she became a vessel for Shyam Baba to guide us.

According to Hindu mythology, the cosmic functions of creation, preservation and destruction are personified by the three primary Hindu gods, also referred as the 'the Hindu trinity': Lord Brahma (the creator), Lord Vishnu (the preserver) and Lord Shiva (the destroyer or transformer).

Lord Vishnu, the preserver and protector of the world, rests on a huge serpent, Sesha, which floats in a cosmic ocean. A beautiful lotus flower grows out of Lord Vishnu's navel. Lord Brahma, the creator of the world, sits on this beautiful lotus flower. Lord Shiva, the destroyer or transformer of the world, meditates on Mount Kailash in the Himalayan range and destroys the world when a new era needs to come in.

The cycle of creation, preservation and destruction is never ending.

Lord Vishnu and Lord Shiva have reincarnated as different deities on earth.

Lord Krishna is a reincarnation of Lord Vishnu, who helped the Pandavas in the epic war, the Mahabharat (around 3000 BC).

Shyam Baba was originally known as Barbarik. Like his father Bheem, Barbarik was extremely strong and powerful. His mother Ahlayawati (a devout Lord Shiva devotee) had raised him on her own. As a child he had curly hair and thus his mother named him Barbarik, which means someone with curly hair. She taught him to be respectful towards saints and brahmins (sages); to be kind and generous.

During the Mahabharat war, Ahlayawati sent Barbarik to participate, instructing him to support the losing side.

As Lord Krishna was supporting the Pandavas, they became the stronger side. It meant that Barbarik was obliged to fight against Lord Krishna and the Pandavas.

Barbarik carried his bow and three divine arrows gifted to him by Lord Shiva, which could conquer the whole world and achieve the impossible.

Lord Krishna realized that Barbarik's participation would hugely impact the consequences of the Mahabharat. So he disguised himself as a brahmin to test Barbarik's strength and realized Barbarik could win the battle for the opposing Kauravas.

This would have been an injustice and would have allowed greed, jealousy and anger to succeed. Lord Krishna asked Barbarik to donate his sheesh (head). As Barbarik was taught by his mother never to deny any priests and sages, he cut off his sheesh immediately.

Lord Krishna was so moved by this gesture that he blessed

Barbarik. 'In the next era, the age of Kalyug (era of strife), you will be worshipped under my name. You will be called Shyam.'

Shyam happens to be one of the many names of Krishna.

Lord Krishna had proclaimed that in Kalyug, just by taking the name of Shyam Baba with a pure heart, his devotees would be blessed. They would be granted all their wishes on the basis of their true devotion to Barbarik/Shyam.

Shyam Baba is worshipped and revered as an extremely generous and gracious deity. He has hundreds of thousands of devotees and his main temple is in Khatu in Rajasthan, where his sheesh had reappeared, according to a legend. He is known as 'sheesh ke daani' (one who has donated his head) and 'haare ka sahaara' (always supportive of the losing side).

Every year at springtime, the fagun mela (a fair held in honour of Shyam Baba) is celebrated in Khatu attended by hundreds of thousands of devotees. Many devotees walk barefoot several kilometres with a nishaan (flag) in their hands as a way of expressing their devotion and gratitude for the fulfilment of their wishes.

Shyam Baba

SECTION 1

Chapter One

Early Years

S avitri Sharma was born on 27 February 1930, in a small town called Alsisar in Rajasthan, India. As she was born on Shivratri (Lord Shiva's birthday), her parents named her Savitri. She would come to be known as Maa to all in the later years, and I will use that name throughout this book.

Maa came from a privileged background. Her parents were Shri Manmohan Lal Sharma and Shrimati Sita Devi Sharma. Maa's father was friends with Mahatma Gandhi (Father of India). He was an advocate and also took active part in the Indian freedom movement. Mahatma Gandhi had gifted him a signed charkha (spinning wheel) for his efforts.

Maa's mother was a housewife and the mother of four children.

Maa's parents were known to the Nehru family. Pandit Jawaharlal Nehru (India's first prime minister) had visited their *house.*

In 1934, aged four, Maa moved to live with her maternal grandparents in Rajgarh, Rajasthan. Her grandmother, Champa Bai, was a spiritual and pious lady. Maa was influenced by her grandmother and learnt to worship and pray from her. She also learnt to cook during her time with her grandmother.

Maa grew up in a village and studied at the local Hindi-medium school in Rajgarh until she was fourteen years old. Mama, her uncle, was a very kind, simple, soft-spoken man who was a teacher at the same school she attended. She accompanied him to school every day.

In 1944, Maa moved back with her parents.

It was around 8 p.m. on a Tuesday night, in the year 1972, when my father said he had to go and meet Sharmaji to seek some advice on an official matter.

My whole family had just returned from London earlier that year after living there for three amazing years, and we were still in the process of adjusting and resettling in New Delhi.

'Can I come with you too, Papa?' I asked, eagerly. My father did not have much choice. I was five years old. I liked spending time with my father and enjoyed meeting people.

Both my father and I sat in a huge living room on the first floor of a sprawling plot house in Kailash Colony, south Delhi, which had a private front garden covered with red roses. I thought it was an enormous house and that they must be very wealthy people.

'Be on your best behaviour. Sharmaji is a very senior man in our organization and a very respectable and honourable man,' my father had alerted me before entering their house.

I was a bit intimidated by the height of the ceiling in the living room and the reverence my father used to describe our host. He must be very powerful and maybe very strict, I thought to myself.

'They are in their prayer session, so please wait here. Would you like to have some water or tea to drink in the meantime?' asked a member of their staff.

After a few minutes, Sharmaji and his wife entered the living room. I addressed them initially as Uncle and Aunty until later, when I realized everyone addressed them as Bauji and Maa.

'We were in the temple, doing puja (prayers)', said Bauji while greeting us with a big smile.

Bauji introduced me to his eight-year-old daughter, Anita. I liked her straightaway. I smiled back shyly feeling slightly embarrassed by the attention Bauji gave me. Then I saw Maa and I instantly felt a spark of a connection.

'We have prayers every Tuesday and Saturday from 6 p.m. till 8 p.m. and an all-night-long prayer on ekadashi (the eleventh day of a Hindu lunar month)', informed Bauji.

Despite being warned to be at my best behaviour, my inhibitions melted away in front of Maa.

'Can I please come for the prayers too?' I enquired shyly.

'Of course, anyone can,' assured Maa with a smile.

Perhaps she was slightly amused by my question and tone. Suddenly, that room did not look that humungous, such was the impact of Maa's first smile.

When the day of the puja came, I was very excited. For

the fifteenth time that evening I had asked my mother the time. Somehow, the hands of the clocks seemed to move in slow motion and my heart was running faster to make up for the slow pace of each minute.

'Why is it not 5.30 p.m. yet? You said we'll leave for the puja then?'

I kept pestering my parents to go. There was something about the house that kept calling me.

My father was happy to take me, expecting it to be a one-time event. My mother stayed home to look after my brother who was seven at the time. Finally, the time caught up and we left for the puja.

We reached early and met Maa, Bauji and Anita.

The temple was built in one of the large square-shaped rooms of their house. As I entered the room I saw a wooden carved temple, in white, taking the whole length of the wall. We had a very small temple at home where my parents worshipped every day and I was familiar with most deities. However, this temple was enormous in comparison.

All the deities present in the temple were adorned with flowers and some deities had chattar (silver umbrellas) hanging over them. Prashad (offerings of Indian sweets) was served in silverware and jal (holy water) in a small silver kalash (jug). The fragrance of sandalwood incense sticks and rose petal incense filled the room. I was standing near the entrance of the temple room and felt incredibly peaceful. Soon the devotees entered the room facing the temple. They bowed in front of the temple with folded hands and then sat on the floor on small rugs. There were two rugs right in front of the temple, next to each other.

Maa and Bauji came and sat on those two rugs, Bauji sat to the right side of Maa, both facing the temple. As I walked in with Anita, everyone had already taken their places. Anita sat on the left side of Maa. I followed Anita and sat next to her. We were sitting right between Maa and the temple. I was able to see Maa in meditation. She was wearing a yellow sari in the Rajasthani style and had covered her head with a pallu (the loose end of the saree). I noticed she was wearing a gold chain and gold bangles in both her hands. Maa and Bauji started their prayers and the devotees sang beautifully with them. I felt like I was in heaven.

Maa sang all the aartis (devotional songs) with everyone and while singing bhajans (hymns), she closed her eyes. She had a divine smile on her face. After some time she stopped singing and started meditating. Her body seemed to surrender and her eyes flickered. Suddenly in the middle of bhajans, she started talking. The singing stopped. The devotees knew Shyam Baba had arrived.

Maa had her back towards the devotees, so she could not see anybody. She started calling people by their names and answering their questions without being prompted. While talking, her eyes remained shut and her eyebrows moved, creating waves of a frown across her forehead. She told them their problems and gave them their solutions, one by one. Each time she finished with one devotee, he or she nodded in agreement and there was never any confusion or cross-communication. When the devotee was satisfied he bowed down towards the temple.

All the devotees would sing together,

'Bol Shyam Baba ki jai! Bol Khatu naresh ki jai!'
(Salutations to Shyam Baba!)

Not once did Maa open her eyes. At five, I was surprised that all her predictions and answers appeared to be spot on for each devotee. She even knew what the devotees were unaware of. I thought she was GOD. I mean only God knows everything about everybody. That's how my journey with Maa began.

Faith has the power to move mountains

—MAA

Chapter Two

Marriage

During 1944, at the age of fourteen years, Maa married Shri Banwari Lal Sharmaji, addressed as Bauji, who was born on 11 November 1926, and was eighteen years old. Maa was given lots of gold jewellery by her parents at the time of her marriage.

Rajasthan is a more conservative state with joint families working and living together. Marriage customs in Rajasthan are very important, and in those days a woman had to compromise more in a marriage than the majority of women of the country. The wife was expected to help look after her husband's parents and their home.

Maa always covered her head with her saree and along with Bauji supported his family in every way they could. They lived together in Brajrajnagar, in Orissa (now Odisha).

In the beginning, Maa and Bauji lived a simple and frugal life together.

Bauji was a commerce graduate and started his career as a storekeeper. His salary was Indian ₹65 Indian per month out of which he used to send ₹35 to his parents.

When Bauji started working, his father retired. Bauji was the only earning member of the family and the oldest sibling. He educated his siblings and looked after his parents, with Maa's support. He helped his sister with her marriage. Maa bought jewellery for Bauji's sister and saved for the marriage expenses. She also helped educate and settle Bauji's brothers.

I wanted to visit every Tuesday and Saturday evenings to see Maa and participate in the prayers.

On Tuesdays, my poor father would come home from work tired and despite his protests, I would drag him to Maa's house. I think he relented as I never really asked for anything and yet for this one thing I was relentless. If he declined, I would be devastated. I don't think he could bear to see me so disappointed. He used to give in and say, 'Oh, okay, let's go.'

I would jump with joy and tell him, 'You are my favourite. You're the best.'

My mother usually stayed home to look after my brother and only occasionally accompanied us with my brother.

Once we arrived, I would sit and close my eyes and feel amazing. I loved hearing people's stories and the answers they would get. I loved joining in with the singing and chanting. I found devotion fascinating and felt an instant connection with Maa and felt bliss there.

I was very sensitive to Maa's responses to me being there. Maa would smile at me between prayers, which made me feel welcomed.

I continued going to Maa every Tuesday for two hours and Saturday for another two hours with the same vigour and enthusiasm. Once a month I attended jaagran (all-night-long prayers) on ekadashi, three days before the full moon, from 9 p.m. to 5 a.m.

My mother and father became concerned about the amount of time I was dedicating to prayers. They were worried about my schoolwork, even though I did very well at school. I was usually amongst the top few students in my class. They felt it was not normal for a child to be such a devout devotee.

I even wanted to go to Maa's house in between. I just loved being there. Maa's husband Bauji, was much more senior than my father in Taylor Instruments. Father began to worry that my too frequent visits could be misunderstood and affect their professional relationship.

Even Anita seemed to find it amusing that I wanted to attend so many prayers.

Eventually, my father spoke to Maa about his concerns. Maa then spoke to me, with a lot of love, 'Beta (child), you are most welcome to attend the prayers, but you must do your studies, play with friends and listen to your parents.'

Since I had so much respect for Maa, although a bit disappointed, I kept my faith, and did not complain. I followed Maa's advice and did not go to her house more than necessary.

It is only recently that my mother told me that Maa said to my parents at that time, 'Don't worry, let her come to prayers. She was very spiritual in her past life.'

At the prayers, the other devotees would smile and acknowledge me in a kind way. I now imagine it must have been unusual and amusing to see a little girl so engrossed in spirituality.

I went to every prayer, and of course, my father had to accompany me as I was too young to be alone in such a big crowd.

I often wonder why I became so enthusiastic about the prayers at Maa's home. I am still not sure what led to the dramatic events that followed. Looking back I feel it was something about the way Maa was with me.

Men and women were equal in Maa's eyes. Maa's daughters chose their own husbands. Her daughters were educated and Maa supported them and gave them a lot of space. This was quite different from the culture of our common ancestral home Rajasthan, even though, we all lived in New Delhi at that time.

I was drawn to Maa's soft, contented nature. Maa accepted me as I was and gave me a lot of space and unconditional love. She had abundant patience with everyone. My Naniji (maternal grandmother) was very patient and compassionate like Maa and I always felt very close to her, too.

The first step in my spiritual growth was to recognize and acknowledge Maa's kind gesture of giving. At some point this led me to the practice of the Art of Giving.

Maa's mantra was 'Giving is living' and she practised it

with full zest. Her smile reflected smiles on others. I noticed her quietly eating without ever complaining and living with no ulterior expectations. Her cool temperament and non-judgemental nature gave me and everyone the confidence to express themselves freely. Her wisdom gave people the clarity to make decisions.

In my forty years of knowing Maa, I never saw her holding any grudge against anybody. She gave with both her hands compassionately, without interfering, thus creating the freedom and space, to be oneself. She never sought acknowledgement for her contribution and never held any grudge against anyone. My impression was that if someone did not have love and gratitude, she poured more love and understanding in that person rather than holding it against him or her.

Maa expressed her views with utmost sincerity.

I now feel when we hold something against someone, not only do we make it difficult for that person and other people around us but also more importantly, become discontented within ourselves.

I watched Maa patiently listening to the discontentment of a person, in her home, and then lovingly say, 'Leave it for Shyam Baba to deal with it, let us move on, and let go.'

She never appeared to embroil herself in other people's dramas or disturbances. Instead, as they would talk about their problems, the discontentment or anger would slowly give way to calmness. That was the magic of Maa's presence.

I marvelled at the way Maa did not impose authority. She helped thousands out of difficulty but never took any credit for it. She always helped people feel so good about themselves for achieving their own resolution.

'I have done nothing, it is all Shyam Baba's blessings and your destiny', Maa would say to anyone who would come to thank her.

I never saw the toxin of ego enter her pure consciousness.

In those days our family would go for an evening walk in the local park, quite often.

I recall on one particular summer evening in 1973, as we walked past a sea of roses, I saw Maa and Bauji walking. They were talking and smiling, and to me they seemed to have a deep companionship.

I got excited and exclaimed, 'Look, there's Maa and Bauji.'

As we walked towards them, they stopped and nodded and smiled.

As is our custom, the four of us folded our hands and bowed in front of them to seek their blessings. Maa and Bauji gently placed their hands on our heads to bless us.

The adults talked whilst I happily listened to their conversation. After some time, my parents respectfully made an excuse to leave and give them their privacy.

After that, when we met them in the park, Bauji would sometimes insist we accompany them. I would get very excited, running and jumping beside them as they walked. Bauji later explained that, like us, they went for a walk every evening for an hour to have time alone with each other and to reflect on the day.

If someone plants thorns in your life,
you make sure to sow flowers for them.
Your goodness will always remain
with you and so will your plantation of flowers

—**MAA**

Chapter Three

Challenges of Married Life

There was concern that Maa had not conceived for five years since her marriage. However, she delivered a beautiful daughter, Shashi on 22 July 1949.

Later Maa delivered her eldest son, Satish, on 5 November 1954 in Jharsuguda in Orissa, where Bauji's brother and his family lived.

In 1952, Maa and Bauji moved from Brajrajnagar to Kurnool in Andhra Pradesh. Bauji was designated as an officer so he got an 'A-type Quarter' accommodation for the family to live in. Maa learnt to speak the local regional language, Telugu. She had a hands-on approach and was keenly interested in local culture.

Then they moved to Sirpur, in Madhya Pradesh, so that Bauji could work at the paper mill in Kagaznagar. Bauji was the main commercial brain in the paper mill.

Most of the employees lived in a colony and their wives interacted with each other socially. Maa enjoyed playing cards and Tambola (Bingo) with the other wives and led a normal life. She had support at home with staff for cleaning, cooking and taking care of the house. In Sirpur, the mill would sound a siren to call employees to work and later, another to announce the lunch break, which gave Maa enough time to rush home. Maa and Bauji were vegetarian. Maa would get Bauji's hot chappatis ready, along with an ayurvedic thali (vegetarian platter) usually including dal, vegetables, yoghurt and salad. The siren would sound again when Bauji had to return to work and finally, again when work finished, so Maa would know when Bauji was returning.

By the time I was seven I had become so devoted that during a channelling session during prayers, Shyam Baba spoke to me through Maa, 'Come here.'

Maa gestured me to move closer. As I was sitting next to her daughter, Anita, I assumed she was talking to her. I nudged Anita, but Maa shook her head, with her eyes closed, and pointed at me.

I moved closer, conscious that we were not allowed to be between Maa and the temple.

Next Maa touched me and made me sit in front of her. I was feeling unsure and a bit nervous. I did not know what to do or what was happening. Normally, we were not to touch Maa during channelling as it distracted her and could break her connection.

I was sitting facing the temple with my back to Maa.

Shyam Baba asked, 'Do you want to see me?'

I turned to look at Maa. She was smiling with her eyes shut. I glanced at my father who was sitting with the devotees and saw him nod at me.

'Yes, Baba,' I replied.

I was still very confused. I felt everyone's eyes on me. I froze. I looked at my father again. He gestured to indicate that I should fold my hands together and close my eyes. I turned back to the temple and closed my eyes.

I saw the indigo colour swirling, leading to an image of Krishna. I felt blissful. I turned to Maa and saw her make circles with her hand, still smiling with closed eyes.

Baba asked, 'Did you see me?'

'Yes, Baba.'

'What are you going to give me now?' he asked affectionately.

'Whatever you want,' I replied, while wondering what one could give God.

'Tell your mother to make homemade butter and serve it with sugar crystals on the day after ekadashi, that is on dwadashi, and I will come.

'Whoever comes for prayers has always asked me for something, you are the first one who has only given your devotion and pure love. I am so happy with you that I want to bless you. You are protected by me and no one can harm you.'

Baba had blessed me. I felt peaceful and humbled.

One way of paying respect in India is to bow and touch the other person's feet. After prayers and channelling, Maa's devotees would touch her feet while standing or kneeling or lying down for blessings.

After the incident there was a little celebration in the corridor. Some devotees wanted to touch my feet for a blessing from Shyam Baba, and others seemed really happy for me. Anita smiled and gave me a big hug. I was swept away by everyone's happiness and felt something special had happened to me. Maa and Bauji nodded with pride.

The next time I came for the prayers, devotees started touching my feet. I felt intimidated and I insisted they went to Maa and took her blessings.

Yet they continued touching my feet whilst smiling. I started to feel uncomfortable and a little angry.

I pointed to Maa and said, 'That's Maa, that's Baba, take blessings from them. Don't touch my feet.'

'Don't get angry with them. Bless them,' Maa said.

I put my hand tentatively on their heads, feeling uncomfortable.

When we were home, my father asked me to bless him and I started to cry. It was as though our roles had changed. I still wanted to be his little girl and for him to look after me.

'No, no, no, I can't bless you,' I said.

'Just put your hand on my head,' he insisted. But he stopped asking once he realized it was disturbing me.

Each time we went to prayers some devotees would continue to seek blessings from me. After a month, I cried in front of Maa.

'I don't want Baba to bless me in front of people. I want a normal life like others. I want to see the world. Please tell Shyam Baba not to do miracles on me in public,' I requested.

Maa asked people not to seek my blessings and over time they forgot the event with Shyam Baba.

After that time I sometimes felt I could see through the masks people were wearing. I felt disappointed at times by the false lives people were leading. Maa made it clear that everyone was equally special, through her behaviour. Reflecting on Maa's life over the last two years, I have been trying to be less judgemental and more accepting, following Maa's example.

If someone does injustice to you,
make sure you do justice to them otherwise
what is the difference between the two of you?

—MAA

Chapter Four

Murari's Birth—Turning Point

On 31 December 1956, Murari, Maa's third child and second son was born. He was born with no voice box and had difficulty moving. Maa and Bauji were very worried about his health. Although the family were pure vegetarian, Maa applied fish oil to massage him to strengthen Murari's bones.

When Murari was nearly five years old they met Shri Bagariaji in Sirpur, who was a devout devotee of Shyam Baba. He suggested that Maa should vow to follow and worship Shyam Baba for Murari's healing.

Maa spoke to her in-laws and Bauji about Shyam Baba. Bauji agreed to carryout the ekadashi prayer and light the dwadashi jyot (holy fire). This was the ritual that they had agreed to follow every month in order to pray for Murari's voice, strength and mobility. Murari started talking after the first month of their following the ritual although his speech was unclear initially. After three months, he started walking without any surgical intervention.

To express her gratitude Maa went on a pilgrimage to Khatu, Rajasthan and her faith grew stronger as she saw Murari's miraculous healing. She and Bauji walked bare foot for seventeen kilometres on uneven desert sand and roads. The temperature would range from 2 degrees to 50 degrees Centigrade. The journey from Ringas to Khatu could take up to five hours, but they walked barefoot to express their gratitude and devotion.

After the pilgrimage Murari healed completely, except he was a slow learner, which made excelling at academic studies a challenge. Despite this Murari made it through school.

As a result of the miracle of Murari's healing Maa became devoted to Shyam Baba. She started meditating and praying even more, which was a huge turning point in Maa's life.

In February 1978, when I was eleven years old, I went on my first pilgrimage to Khatu. I had been pestering my parents to take me but they always insisted I stay at school. As the pilgrimage fell over a weekend my parents finally gave in. My excitement built as the big day approached. I packed and prepared for it in advance.

My parents and I took a train to Ringas. I remember looking at the mountains, looking through the window, whilst singing my bhajans. A passenger seated opposite to us was amused.

He smiled and asked me, 'Where are you going?'

'On a pilgrimage.'

'As a brother, I can help you even climb the mountains.'

His polite words added to my joy and encouragement in my adventure.

Next we took a bus to Khatu. The bus was full of Rajasthani women, some with children. They were dressed in cotton sarees with long-sleeved blouses and kept their heads covered. The colours of the sarees were bright with strong yellows, pinks and greens. The men wore white turbans. I stared at them with open curiosity as this was all new for me. It was very hot and dusty and I guess their clothing must have protected them. The bus rattled along the uneven roads. People clung onto the roof and some were even hanging on the sides.

We walked to the dharamshaala (pilgrims' rest house). It was set up for community living and people contributed what they could to help run the houses.

Maa used to walk seventeen kilometres with some devotees, as part of her pilgrimage, from the train station in Ringas to the dharamshaala in Khatu, holding a nishaan.

We walked into the courtyard. I looked around the rooms set on two floors. All were painted pale yellow. Maa also had a room on the ground floor.

Maa went to the temple that very night but my parents and most devotees waited until the next day.

I woke up the next morning to people singing salutations to Shyam Baba and getting ready to queue at the temple. The temple was only five minutes' walk away. People came from all over India to the temple. It was packed. Many policemen were present organizing the crowds. We all stayed in a group, behind Maa. We walked into the temple for darshan (seeing/

praying to the deity in the temple).

Just as going to the temple was important, so was sitting in the dharamshaala chanting, singing, dancing and listening to Maa channelling. I would sit near Maa and participate happily.

I felt here I could be with Maa more, as she was with us all the time. I loved to watch her as she interacted with hundreds of her devotees. It was an interesting contrast to witness Maa so different from being a mother at home.

Positive mindset and willpower
is necessary to fight life's challenges

—**MAA**

Chapter Five

Another Miracle

On 10 November 1962, Maa's fourth daughter Sunita was born in Sirpur and in 1964, Maa's fifth daughter Anita was born in Sirpur as well.

In 1964, Bauji had a massive heart attack in Amlai and doctors declared that he would not recover and never get up. Maa started crying and called Shyam Baba to seek his blessings. Suddenly Murari, Maa's second son, started singing bhajans. He lit incense sticks and asked everyone to leave the room. Shyam Baba channelled through him and Murari took the ashes of the incense sticks and rubbed them on Bauji's stomach. Bauji got up with Murari's help and urinated almost two buckets full.

Maa started sleeping on a mat and stopped combing her very long hair, seeking Shyam Baba's blessing for Bauji to fully heal. Bauji healed steadily and led a normal life. This was another *miracle in Maa's life.*

In 1979, when I was twelve years old, my brother Sanjay who was thirteen years old, injured his left eye while playing with a friend in school. They were playing 'cops and robber' and he was a robber. The friend who was playing the cop's role had a compass in his hand, which he was using as a prop for a gun. He was pointing it at my brother who was lying on the desk. As Sanjay was getting up, his friend aimed his hand at him and the compass pierced Sanjay's left eye.

When Sanjay came home from school with his left eye bandaged, my parents panicked.

He went through medical tests and doctors said he would lose his eye. My parents and I were shocked. Sanjay was a bright student and a budding artist, but he could now lose his left eye forever. We all went to the prayers at Maa's house, seeking a solution.

Shyam Baba said, 'I have saved Sanjay's eye from blindness and he will not lose his vision, although he will not regain his old vision.'

'How can my son not get better, despite you being there?' my parents pleaded. They prayed for a miracle, for their son to recover completely.

'Sanjay will be operated twice and then will get better,' said Baba finally.

My parents were very confused with that prediction as even one surgery was unlikely due to the complexity of the case.

Sanjay was getting treated at AIIMS (All India Institute of

Medical Sciences). The doctors were trying to save his vision. Someone recommended that we consult a world-acclaimed eye surgeon who used to visit Delhi once a week from Aligarh Eye Hospital.

After a number of tests the doctor agreed to perform a surgery on request, despite stating the case's complexity.

Sanjay was transferred to Aligarh, which was a five hours' train ride. Those were tough times for us. My father had to commute back and forth between Delhi and Aligarh for work and my mother stayed with Sanjay for several weeks in Aligarh. Meanwhile I stayed with my maternal grandparents in Delhi and then moved in with my school friend, Amit and his sister Rachna, in order to carry on with my schooling.

After surgery, the doctor reviewed the eye and surprisingly remarked, 'Repeat operation.'

After the second surgery, he met with my father and said the surgery had been successful. Sanjay was able to see clearly with a contact lens. It was indeed a miracle.

It cost my parents a lot of money, time and dislocation, but Sanjay's healing gave them greater faith in Maa and Baba. This helped them feel better, despite the financial challenges for the future.

Sanjay missed a year of school due to his eye treatment. I used to get notes for him from his school friends and read them to him. Then my mother and I would write a copy of the notes for my brother's reference.

Baba said, 'I will not let him miss a school year. Don't worry he will go back with his old friends and get promoted.'

We wondered how it was possible? He had not been to

school for a year. At that point I had nightmares about whether he would ever study normally.

When the time came, the school let him re-join his friends, without losing a year.

'I will make him a doctor and he should help underprivileged people,' Baba predicted.

Sanjay became a doctor at an early age of twenty-three years after being selected in the Delhi medical entrance examination in the first attempt. It was an immensely proud moment for the family. He later went to the US for further specialization.

He now lives in Delhi, working as a radiologist. Recently, he had laser surgery so he can see well with both his eyes without the aid of contact lenses.

Be patient,
have faith and face the challenges of life with grace
—MAA

Chapter Six

Shyam Baba's Channelling

S hyam Baba started channelling through Maa in 1966. Maa kept the channelling a secret for two years as she was not sure what was happening. At the beginning she started seeing another dimension but did not test the potential.

   Maa and Bauji moved to Calcutta (now Kolkata) with their family. Aloo Singhji was a devout devotee of Shyam Baba and used to channel Shyam Baba. He lived in Khatu and met Maa and Bauji there. He used to visit Calcutta to attend Shyam Baba's kirtan (collective prayers and singing) where there were a lot of devotees of Shyam Baba. He used to take Maa and Bauji to these prayers.

   Once when Maa and Bauji went on a Shyam Baba pilgrimage to Khatu, after taking a dip in the holy Shyam kund (pond) Bauji lost his gold ring. They told Aloo Singhji and he said he would look for it when the staff cleaned the Shyam kund. They found the ring, whilst Maa and Bauji were present. Shyam Baba told Aloo Singhji that Maa could also channel but she was unsure of this possibility. Aloo Singhji asked Maa to channel for the workers and she did. Bauji was surprised and tried to stop Maa as he was unsure of what she was doing, but she continued. This is when it was publicly established that Maa could channel Shyam Baba.

Devotees started coming to attend the prayers with Maa and started benefiting from Baba's guidance.

Devotees used to hear sounds of a horse galloping and could smell the fragrance of rose incense even though there was none at home. Shyam Baba is said to ride on a horse called Leela and devotees used to hear the horse riding when he used to channel through Maa.

Bauji woke at 4 a.m. every morning. He was punctual, intellectual, intelligent and spiritual. Bauji was very particular and systematic, always following a strict timetable.

Their house had to be cleaned every morning by 6 a.m. Soon after that they both did their prayers and did not like any disturbance at that time. Children knew they had to keep their voice down during their parents' prayer time.

Bauji was very particular and liked things to be in a certain order. He was extremely caring about Maa and did not like her to go even to her parents as he missed her. Their companionship was amazing. When Bauji got angry, Maa kept quiet and never reacted. To make it easier to go through his annoyance she kept drinking tea and finally, Bauji would give up his annoyance.

When he came home from work he always wanted to see his children. They could go later to play but at that time they had to be home to get a cuddle from Bauji. Bauji loved his family.

One day, Maa saw a snake with a chakra on its head, sitting on top of an onion in her kitchen garden. As snakes are considered sacred due to their association with Lord Shiva, she folded her hands and promised never to eat onion or garlic. She continued to give Bauji two cloves of garlic every morning for his heart, for medicinal purposes although she completely gave up eating onion and garlic herself. She was devoted to her cause whilst retaining a pragmatic view.

They moved to Delhi when Maa conceived their sixth child Shyam. He was born on 28 January 1969 in a Delhi hospital. By now they had a huge house in one of the finest locations of South Delhi, Kailash Colony. They had cars and drivers and staff to serve them. Their house had a rose garden and staff quarters. Bauji was now the Commercial Director of Taylor Instruments (an Indo-American company).

On 11 December 1969, Shashi got married and moved to Patna. As the eldest, Shashi was the most favourite child and Bauji wanted her to visit home every month. However, Maa did not think it was good for Shashi's married life so she discouraged Bauji from expressing his wishes.

On 25 August 1971, Neetu, Maa's seventh and youngest child was born. Bauji travelled to London on work in 1971 and 1973 and also visited Nairobi during that period. This was a special event for someone working in India at that time. Bauji balanced his spirituality as well as family and career responsibilities.

Since 1972, Maa's prayers were attended by many devotees on every Tuesday, Saturday and ekadashi.

In 1976, Maa and Bauji went for a drive to look for a house to buy for retirement. They really liked a street in Faridabad near

Maa's brother's house.

In 1977, Maa built a dharmshaala, within two-minute walk from the temple.

On 9 November 1977, my father came from work, looking very upset. I saw him sitting and crying on the sofa with my mother. Then my mother started crying too. They told me not to come into the room.

I thought something had gone wrong at work. Fearing I would provoke them at a time of distress, I stood outside and tried to listen with my ear pressed against the door, but their voices were too muffled to hear anything.

The next day my parents took my brother and me to a relative's house. They left us there saying they had to see some friend in the hospital who was not well. My brother and I were very worried, assuming the worst. Then I overheard the relative telling their daughter that Bauji had passed away.

I was completely shattered. My brother was also shocked. We went into their garden and hid in a corner and wept. Both of us cut a strand of our hair as a mark of respect. It is a custom in India to shave or cut hair when a father or grandfather has passed away.

For some reason I could not express my condolences to Maa. Now, I wish I could have given Maa greater comfort. At the time I felt frightened to go and care for her. It felt too big a reversal of roles.

I saw much less of Maa during the following year. She stopped channelling for some time. She became busy making decisions to uproot her family and house as they were staying in a house provided by Taylor Instruments Company where Bauji worked.

Despite all the challenges Maa never lost her faith. 'Shyam Baba will take care of everything,' was Maa's implicit faith.

Now Maa was the head of the family.

Within a year Maa moved from Delhi to Faridabad with her five unmarried children, who were still studying.

My first visit to Maa's Faridabad home was about a year after they moved. My parents drove me. We parked in a wide road near a market. Maa was living in a white single-storey home with a terrace on the roof.

We climbed two steps and walked into the living room. It seemed quite simple after her previous home. I hoped Maa was coping with her new environment.

When I saw Maa, she was just the same. She smiled, radiating warmth, and suddenly my concerns melted away. I realized she was beyond such human frailties.

The back of the home had been converted into a small temple. The devotees made the long journey to her new home and were joined by new devotees from Faridabad.

All her children seemed to have adapted to the change very well.

Once I was around Maa again I felt as reassured as ever. The change of circumstances made no difference, I realized it was Maa who made the difference to those around her, not the house.

Recently, Maa's son, Shyam, told me how she used to get some payment from insurance policies to assist her to run her household.

She taught her children to follow the right path and never endorsed any luxury expenses. This lady who had once two cars outside her driveway, with drivers, and domestic help at her disposal while her husband was alive was now travelling alone in state buses to get her legal and insurance papers organized.

Maa insisted on travelling to Delhi alone by bus. She did not want to inconvenience anyone. She could not read English, and only recognized buses by their colours. Devotees would meet her in Delhi to help with sorting out her financial affairs. She would understand where to get off by a landmark described by either her sons or the devotees. She had no idea of the roads and the geography of the place. She distinguished the files of the banks by colour-coding. She applied simple common sense to her finances. When Baba used to channel through her she seemed to know everything and other times she was a very simple, homely lady.

She did not preach but actually practised her philosophy as a way of life. Her simplicity and humility were her strength. Her authenticity was her robe and her faith and true love were her horses that led her chariot through her Mahabharat, that is, the battle of her life. Maa lived her private and public life at the same level of authenticity and sincerity. The energy around her was so pure and positive that it charged and uplifted anyone who met her.

If you have accepted defeat in your mind, you have already lost. However if you have won in your mind you will surely be victorious

—MAA

Chapter Seven

Maa's World Changed

O n 9 November 1977, a day before Diwali (the biggest festival of Hindus) during prayers in the office of Lord Ganesha (deity worshipped for removing obstacles) and Goddess Laxmi (goddess of wealth), Bauji offered flowers, bowed and then collapsed. He died of a heart attack immediately.

Maa's world changed instantly.

As mentioned earlier, in 1978, Maa started looking for a new home and found a house on the same street she had seen and liked with Bauji when they were planning his retirement. Maa bought that house. She moved with her five children to Faridabad in 1978, just two streets from her brother's house.

Maa had no training for work. She went through very tough times. Some people even said, 'If she is so devoted, then why does she have so many problems in her life?'

Her own children challenged her and asked how Shyam Baba had not helped them despite all Maa's devotion. Maa felt she had to go through her journey and karma, and kept her faith in her Shyam Baba.

'Don't say anything to my Baba, he will take care of everything,' she would quietly respond.

Her daughter Anita recalls an incident when Maa carried her youngest son Shyam, who was running a high fever, in her arms to the doctor. Anita asked, 'Maa, why are you carrying Shyam in this heat? He is twelve years old and is no more light in weight.'

'He has no strength to walk, and he has to see the doctor. I will walk slowly and carry him,' replied Maa.

She did not ever show to her family that she avoided taking an autorikshaw or taxi due to financial constraints. She protected her family from any such fears and insecurities. She also travelled regularly to the wholesale market to buy vegetables and groceries to run the house more economically. During her children's exams Maa would wake up at 5 a.m. and make tea for them before they started to study. Quietly, she kept on living every moment with her inner strength and faith.

Maa continued with her open house prayers. Her devotees were given the same warmth and welcome as before. They would help themselves with refreshments and would use her house freely to rest and sleep during ekadashi prayers. Maa welcomed everyone and made them feel as if it was their own home. The change in financial circumstances made no impact on Maa's kindness and hospitality towards her devotees.

Two years passed before Maa was ready to organize another

pilgrimage with her devotees. I was then fourteen years old. I had only seen Maa a few times since Bauji passed away. In that period Maa was still there; as my guardian, however, I was growing and my life changing. I was very social and had developed my own group of friends, apart from my family. I had become more independent. I was determined to succeed at school and by now I represented my school in elocution and other extra-curricular activities. I won a trophy for the entire Delhi area in elocution and acted in a leading role in my school theatre production.

As we approached the spring season, I had an urge to join Maa in the fagun mela pilgrimage. I asked my parents if I could accompany them and they were happy for me to join them. By now they had accepted my devotion to Shyam Baba and realized it was not disturbing my academic or social life.

A coach was hired annually for the devotees to go to Khatu for the pilgrimage together. Those who had money shared the cost, and those who could not came for free.

My parents and I drove to Maa's house as it was the meeting point for the journey. There were about a hundred devotees packed into Maa's house, singing salutations of Shyam Baba whilst packing everything to take for the pilgrimage.

I went to the temple, bowed, and took blessings from Maa. After prayers I saw Anita and was excited that she was coming too and we would spend three days together.

One of the highlights for me was that Maa travelled in the coach with everyone. We sang bhajans, talked and slept during the seven-hour-long journey. Anita and I sat together, for the whole journey.

Some devotees had brought food and they passed samosas and kachoris around the coach. Eventually, feeling a little tired, we arrived in Ringas in the evening.

I wanted to do the seventeen-kilometre barefoot walk with Maa, Anita and other devotees, but my mother did not allow me. I was hoping Maa would overrule my mother but she clearly did not want to interfere. I think my mother thought it would be very tiring for me. I respectfully sat in the coach and carried on to the temple, feeling disappointed. On the coach Maa's daughter-in-law complimented my mother for how well she had brought us up, noticing my obedience. By the time I arrived at the dharamshaala, I forgot my disappointment.

After a few hours we heard salutations from the distance and ran out to the gate to welcome everyone. I ran up to take Maa's blessing, touching her feet. Then I ran to Anita and we hugged.

'Oh, you should have come, it was so much fun walking in the night, barefoot, looking at the stars. We sang and stopped for Maa to channel,' she said.

I was happy for her, whilst feeling I had missed something special.

Back in the courtyard there was a buzz of excitement with stories of miracles. It had a festive atmosphere. Maa would stay up until the end. Anita and I shared a room with other family members, sleeping on mattresses laid on the floor. Although the day had been hot, the night was cold and we pulled blankets around us.

In the morning I woke up to the sounds of devotees serving tea and humming bhajans. We got up and had our masala tea. We washed and got dressed before going to the temple for darshan. Maa reminded us to be very kind to others, including those not in our group.

After darshan we sat together and ate lunch. In the afternoon we gathered for more prayers and singing. It was so exhilarating and I loved the way I could just be myself. As it was ekadashi we stayed up all night meditating, singing and even dancing with joy and bhakti (devotion). Maa would channel and all the devotees sang bhajans. The bhajans would get faster in pace and beat, and higher in pitch, leading to lot of excitement. Devotees would get up and start dancing. There was a festive mood and soon they started playing with dry colours to celebrate Holi (festival of colours).

The next day was dwadashi. The ritual was to take jyot (holy fire). I sat and sang with the devotees. Maa sat crosslegged on her special rug. She lit a cotton bud soaked in ghee, next to hot charcoal, and soon the charcoal caught fire. Maa made a special offering of churma (wheat ground coarsely and roasted with ghee and sugar), kheer (rice pudding), mishri (sugar crystals) and makkhan (homemade butter). This ritual was called dwadashi jyot.

There was more singing and dancing to celebrate with Maa, Baba and the devotees. There was intense, positive and vibrant energy in the hall.

We all had lunch at the dharamshaala in the afternoon. After lunch we started packing up and got on the coach. I sat

next to Anita again. By then I was so tired, I slept for most
of the journey.

Whenever you raise your hand, raise it to give

—**MAA**

Chapter Eight

Change of Role

On 20 February 1980, Murari got married to Santosh. He had twin daughters on 13 February 1982. *Unfortunately, his wife Santosh went into a coma. She never recovered and passed away on the eleventh day after delivery. Maa brought the twins home and her brother Shri Mahender Kumarji offered to raise one daughter Chinu, while Maa raised Meenu.*

On 8 February 1985, Murari married Neelam and they were blessed with a son on 23 February 1987. He was named Rahul, nicknamed Sunny by his older sister Meenu.

Sunita got married on 4 December 1985 and Anita got married on 26 June 1989. After that, Maa only had Neetu and Meenu to get settled.

In 1983, I went through a very bad attack of acne. I was sixteen years old. It completely shook my confidence. My entire face broke out with pus-filled pimples. It was so painful, I could not eat or smile and my skin would crack when I moved my facial muscles. My face looked puffed up and it used to bleed. Relatives started commenting that my face would never get better and how would I get married?

I began to look down in an attempt to hide my face. There were no medications in India in those days that would heal my face. New pimples would emerge as the doctor would puncture the old ones.

After about a year of going through this trauma, it all stopped. I was given Shyamjal (holy water from Shyam kund) by Maa (after channelling Baba), and was asked to apply it on my face. Pimples completely stopped and slowly my face started clearing up from the redness. My mother was very worried that I would have problems in getting married because of the remaining marks on my face.

'Do not worry, carry on applying Shyamjal and she will be absolutely fine,' said Shyam Baba.

Within one year most of the marks vanished.

In 1987, when I was studying for my undergraduate degree in Economics honours at Delhi University my mother started worrying about getting me married and settled. She kept asking Shyam Baba about when I would get married. In our community, marriage is usually an expensive affair and I was principally against dowry. She was also concerned about how I would get married without spending enough money.

'Why are you worried? I'll take care of Sangeeta. She will decide who she wants to marry. There will be no obstacles,' said Shyam Baba to my mother every time she asked him.

My mother would still worry. It seemed to her that Baba was just trying to pacify her. When the destination is nowhere to be seen it is hard for the passenger to believe he will reach there soon. You need a high level of surrender and faith.

In February 1989, during the fagun mela pilgrimage, Maa called my mother over while she was channelling.

'You have doubt, don't you?' Shyam Baba asked my mother.

'No, Baba, I'm sorry.'

'Within one year she will get married. You don't have to worry, they will come to your home and will ask for her hand. The boy will be living abroad. He will have one brother and one sister. His name will start with 'S'. He will be a chartered accountant by qualification. After Sangeeta's twenty-second birthday the real proposal will come.'

'Baba, I only have one daughter. Why are you sending her abroad?'

'Ask her, she is the one who wants to live abroad.'

My mother asked me once she was back home and I did share my desire to live abroad, so I could enjoy a more broadminded, liberal life. I was very clear that I wanted to marry a professionally qualified man with a broader outlook on life. It was most important for me to be treated with respect and dignity. However, I was disappointed to hear he would be a chartered accountant, as I was looking for someone who would travel to see places instead of a stationary job that I perceived that profession would entail. Somehow I had the opinion that accountants were very money-focused in their outlook and was hoping for someone more holistic and less materialistic.

The initial marriage proposals had come from engineers and business management professionals. There was none from accountants.

After my twenty-second birthday, Baba asked me to fast for five Thursdays. I had to eat something yellow and give jaggery to a brown cow to eat. I did this for four Thursdays and got engaged before the fifth Thursday.

Two proposals came close to each other. Both were chartered accountants living abroad and had one brother and one sister each. Both their names started with 'S'. One was working in the US and the other in Trinidad and Tobago (will be referred to as Trinidad). Both were focused on their careers and came from traditional yet professional backgrounds and the same community as mine.

Baba said, 'It's your daughter's choice. Both will say yes to her.'

The man living in the US was to meet me in December 1989. Suddenly some complication with his green card emerged and he had to delay his visit.

The chartered accountant working in Trinidad was to meet me in January 1990, which he did.

It was 18 January 1990, when father went to receive Sudhir along with his parents at the New Delhi railway station. He called me from a local pay phone while they were collecting their luggage, describing Sudhir as a respectful and decent young man. There was an excitement in my father's voice, and I felt the joy in his words.

Sudhir came to our home with his parents and relatives to meet me. He was wearing a crisp light blue shirt under a navy blue suit and black leather shoes. I liked that he cared to dress appropriately for the occasion. As he walked in, he gave me a warm and sincere smile and said, 'Hello'.

I smiled back and said, 'Hi.'

Sudhir later confessed he was exhausted after a forty-hour journey from Trinidad to Mumbai, via London, followed by a train journey to New Delhi. But my smile wiped away his tiredness. He had instantly fallen for me. It was love at first sight for him and he made up his mind to say, 'Yes'.

He told me how he wanted to see this smile every time he came home.

For me, Maa and Baba had already predicted my marriage with him and as my faith was so high, it was a matter of just making sure I felt comfortable with him.

We all sat in the living room and although everyone was trying to be light-hearted, I was a bit tensed, being the focus of attention. I walked around the room with a tray of drinks and snacks wearing an orange-coloured Indian suit. I had designed my own outfit and felt very elegant.

I sat near Sudhir's family and spoke to Sudhir's father. He asked me general routine questions. The rest of Sudhir's family were listening intently and I felt I was under the spotlight.

I felt like I was on the precipice of a life-changing event, but despite it I was strangely serene, feeling reassured that Maa and Baba were with me and had blessed this event.

When I finished talking, my parents asked Sudhir some questions. My trust in Sudhir rose as I watched him respond with respect and sensitivity. I liked his poise and mannerisms. He seemed very calm and self-assured.

My father had already liked him from their meeting at the station and my mother liked him so much that she kept calling me in the kitchen to ensure that my answer would be affirmative.

'He's very good. Don't make excuses,' she said.

So far Sudhir and I had not spoken to each other. We had just caught each other's eyes once or twice.

After about half an hour Sudhir's uncle spoke up. He said, 'Either all of us should move to another room and leave Sudhir and Sangeeta here, or send them to another room to get to know each other.'

Everyone laughed and Sudhir and I went to another room. I was relieved as his uncle managed to break the awkwardness of such an obviously staged event.

We went to my room and Sudhir sat one end of my bed, while I sat at the other end.

'You've been hearing me talk so much. I would love to hear more about you,' Sudhir said with a smile.

'What would you like to hear about?' I asked shyly.

'Anything,' he replied with a smile.

Once I started, the conversation flowed as though we were in sync. I felt very comfortable. We laughed and chatted like good friends. After an hour, my brother knocked on the door and joined in the conversation. A bit later, Sudhir's father came and called him.

Sudhir came back and my brother suggested we all go out for coffee. Once I was ready to leave, my father called me into his room and asked, 'Do you like Sudhir?'

'There is nothing wrong with him. He seems very nice. I guess it is a yes,' I replied. My father looked relieved.

I was not in love with Sudhir, but there was something about Baba's prediction that I knew love would come. My faith in the divine power was such that I trusted that Sudhir was genuine, and made the most important decision in my life.

The three of us left in our car to a modern stylish café in Panchsheel Enclave. When my brother had finished his coffee he left the table to visit the washroom.

'What is your plan from here?' I asked Sudhir.

'I'm leaving for Ajmer tonight with my parents to visit my grandfather. I believe you are coming tomorrow with your parents and we are getting engaged tomorrow,' Sudhir informed me with pride.

Our fathers had obviously already made arrangements and Sudhir was aware of them. It would have irked me that my father had not told me first, but I was enthusiastic as our relationship had been blessed by Shyam Baba and Maa. Nothing could spoil the moment.

The next morning we took the early train for a seven-hour journey to Ajmer. Sudhir's first cousin was getting engaged that day, and it was decided Sudhir and I would also get engaged at the same event.

My mother was beaming with joy during the whole train ride. She had brought a beautiful golden brocade saree for me to wear that was given to her by her mother.

The next day, Sudhir and I got engaged and in less than five weeks, on 20 February 1990, we got married. There were so many changes in my life, so quickly and so dramatically. Despite all the last minute arrangements to be taken care of, Sudhir's family looked after me the whole time.

There was a short ceremony where a Hindu priest blessed the engagement and Sudhir's mother gave me jewellery and sarees. After that I had to touch everyone's feet to take blessings, and was handed money as a form of good wishes for the marriage.

That night Sudhir, my brother and I took an all-night coach back to Delhi. While sitting next to Sudhir, I told him about Maa and Shyam Baba and narrated the whole story of them predicting and blessing our relationship. He keenly heard the whole story and wished to meet Maa.

For the first time we held hands. I began to feel close to him. I started to fall in love with him.

Do not worry, be happy,
with time everything will be fine

—MAA

Chapter Nine

Worldly Responsibilities

Maa stayed at home most of the time. Both Meenu and Sunny assisted her with preparations for her prayers. People usually came to meet her at her house. As years passed, Maa could give answers without meditating.

Anita lived in Faridabad with her husband and visited Maa almost everyday.

Both her sons Murari and Shyam lived with Maa with their wives and children.

In 1996, Maa's youngest daughter Neetu got married.

After that, Maa's prime responsibilities for the family and house were over and she could dedicate more time to helping others.

Maa still had her granddaughter Meenu to get settled. She was also very fond of her grandson Sunny.

In February 1990, Maa had travelled with us to Calcutta by train for over twenty hours and stayed with us for the entire duration of eight days to bless my marriage. It was very unusual for her to leave her home to go anywhere, especially for that long.

We were all staying in a guesthouse in Calcutta. My parents-in-law wanted the wedding to take place in Calcutta. It was a new city for my family, so my father-in-law helped with all the arrangements.

The day before I got married, Maa said, 'You are getting married tomorrow. Come here, I want to tell you something.'

These private moments with Maa were the best moments of my life. I could happily trade any worldly pleasure for her wisdom. My joy seemed to rise sky-high.

We were sitting in the common room in the guesthouse. The relatives left the room when they realized Maa wished to speak to me privately. Maa was always in a saree with her head covered and she was wearing a green saree at that time. I was wearing a green and pink Indian suit and had henna patterns applied all over my hands and feet.

Maa sat on an armchair and I sat on the carpet on the floor.

She was calm and affectionate. We smiled at each other. However, when I sat she became more sober and I could tell she was going to tell me something very important.

'These days girls seek ways to separate the boy from his family,' she said. 'They look for ways to break familial relationships. You shall not do that.'

Maa continued, 'Never expect anything from anyone. You will get disappointed if you do. You haven't come to this world to take, but to give. Give as much as you can.'

'But how much do I have Maa that I can keep giving?' I asked innocently.

'You just ask Shyam Baba, he will give it to you. How that would happen you leave to him. Why are you worried about that?' she reassured me.

'Can I ask my husband if I want something?' I asked her, a bit worried.

'If you ask your husband for something, he will surely give it to you. But remember you'll only get what you ask for. It's when you don't ask him for anything that he will start taking an interest in you. He will wonder why you are not asking for anything. He would want to understand you and your likings and want to discover your world and then he will give you the world. Be patient as this will take more time and will require more tolerance and resilience but the respect and love will be long-lasting,' she replied.

As time passed I tried to remember and to my best ability, follow her pearls of wisdom. Initially, my husband wondered why I did not express my desire for things and even got annoyed with me for not letting him buy gifts for me.

'What am I working so hard for? I want my wife to have everything,' he would say with love.

But then he did get very curious about my life, values and perspectives. I felt the difference. He built a deeper companionship with me and it is true that it took time and a lot of trust, but he has embraced my world and for me that was his biggest gift.

After my wedding, I stayed with my in-laws for five days

and found it challenging to adjust to the new lifestyle in a joint family. Each one of us had different expectations from each other. One day, I got really upset and took it out on my husband. After an open discussion, our differences got resolved.

I returned to Delhi on 25 February 1990 and the next day I went to seek Maa's blessings. She was delighted to see me with my husband. I was wearing a silk saree with gold jewellery and Maa was very pleased to see me looking so elegant and feminine.

She asked me to sit next to her alone when the others were talking to Sudhir.

'What happened in Calcutta shouldn't have happened,' she said. I was a bit surprised as I had not spoken about the incident to anyone and had almost forgotten about it.

'Yes, Maa,' I replied with my head down.

'But Maa, you know what happened, I felt undermined,' I said.

'No one can undermine you, you are who you are. Keep yourself away from drama. Who can take away your brightness and light from you, beta?' she said with love.

'Why did it affect you? Make yourself so strong that you do not need to be reactive.'

Maa looked into my eyes with compassion.

'So what are you going to do now?' she asked compassionately.

'What do you want me to do?' I asked politely.

Maa said, 'When you go home, call your parents-in-law and apologize and make sure you do not just say sorry but mean it.'

'No one becomes small by asking for forgiveness,' she added with a smile.

When Sudhir came back into the room, Maa smiled at him and said, 'Sangeeta has made a mistake, she'll never do that again.'

Maa's wisdom and her approach always felt like magic to me. I reached home and booked a telephone call to Calcutta and apologized to my parents-in-law. They were pleased and said they had also forgotten the incident and had forgiven me.

That was when Sudhir began to understand Maa's impact on me and her sensibilities.

Maa's explanation of the matter and situation with such clarity and simplicity in a non-judgemental fashion showed me that life could be viewed in a transparent and objective manner. Her unconditional love never wavered. What was unique was her affection to all yet detachment from controlling and imposing her views on anyone.

I wondered why I always felt more significant when I was with her! It was because she gave the space and allowed the person to connect to his or her own self and assured them that she supported them, just like a mother. Whenever I needed guidance I knew Maa was the person to speak to.

We are all equally special. No one else but our own thoughts and actions make us small or big

—MAA

Chapter Ten

Spiritual World

As time passed, Maa's life was set in a routine. On a typical day, Maa would get up in the morning, bathe and then meditate in the temple on her own or with her grandchildren and some devotees. They would sing devotional songs, for around an hour.

She usually rested after lunch. Her physical body could not keep up as it used to, and Maa developed high blood pressure. Yet she practised an open house policy with no prior appointments required. She would leave her house to bless a new house or to a wedding on a special request by a devotee, but otherwise preferred to stay at home.

People would come to meet her and seek her wisdom in the afternoon after her nap. Anita would visit her mother after work. In the evening her sons would come home and after meeting them, she would do her evening prayer. She patiently listened to people's problems and applied wisdom and channelling.

Twice a year Maa went on a pilgrimage with hundreds of devotees to Khatu in Rajasthan, to Shyam Baba's temple. After reaching Ringas, Maa would, like always, walk through the night with a nishaan from the railway station to the dharamshaala. During this time, Maa expanded the dharamshaala so more devotees could stay with her.

My husband and I lived in Trinidad after marriage and my contact with Maa became an occasional phone call as I did not want to disturb her. She also discouraged it as she wanted me to settle in my new life. During my annual trip to India, I used to make it a point to visit her. I felt as close as ever to Maa and her love and warmth remained unaltered. I had a sense of security that Maa was there, just a phone call away to patiently enlighten and comfort me, when I needed it the most.

In the first year of my marriage, I was like most other newly married wives getting to know my husband better. Since I was nine years old, I had been fasting every Monday and it just made me feel good and was like a part of my life. I used to eat around 5 p.m., the only meal for the day. My husband did not like my fasting as he felt I was depriving and straining myself and also he did not enjoy eating his dinner alone. I sensed his displeasure on every Monday. When I visited India after a year, I asked Maa for her opinion and explained how as a Lord Shiva devotee I like fasting for him. I was in a dilemma.

'My child, there is no point in making your husband

unhappy to please your God. Lord Shiva's statue is made of stone but your husband is human. Shivji will not love you more or less by your fasting. He will see the purity in your heart and your good intentions. You can continue your devotion to Lord Shiva but keep your husband happy by eating with him and maintain harmony in your married life,' Maa explained patiently.

I realized that there was no point fasting for a more peaceful life, if the fasting itself was creating conflict. I stopped fasting for a few years. Sudhir was happily surprised to see the change, but later came to accept and understand my desire for fasting.

In 1992, I lost my first newborn daughter Stuti. We were devastated. Stuti was treated in Mount Sinai Hospital in New York, due to congenital problems. She was exposed to Rubella, also known as german measles, in the first trimester of my pregnancy. She was born with glaucoma and calcifications in her brain. We did not have the finances for the treatment but the hospital made it a research case so they absorbed all the costs, which went into hundreds of thousands of US dollars. The doctors were most baffled by how an infant could be such a fighter and withstand three lengthy surgeries. Stuti taught me how to fight and to accept what life has to offer. The experience of seeing our baby and many other children in the hospital go through so much suffering built my compassion and humility. Of course, at that time I did not see it that way. I suffered and was disheartened and shattered. Stuti fought for six months.

Sneha, our second daughter, was born two years later and

survived for only two weeks. I was in shock and could not believe this could happen to me despite all medical theories suggesting otherwise.

Maa always said, 'Shyam Baba helps understanding and accepting the situation better, though miracles take place, you still have to go through your learning. We have to go through our karma and lessons in order to grow and evolve to be a better person.'

I had trouble accepting the words at that point, and it took me a long time to appreciate them fully.

'If you don't go down how are you going to come back up? If you want the rose, you have to accept the thorns as well,' Maa had compassionately shared her wisdom at the time.

We were blessed with Angana, a beautiful bundle of joy in 1994. She completely changed our lives, filling it with joy and laughter. She never cried, only giggled, chuckled and played with us. I believe she came to us to replace our tears with laughter.

In 1997, Ayush our son completed our family. He is such a blessing in our life, justifying the name we chose for him. The name 'Ayush' means blessings and he added a new dimension and perspective to our family.

Maa later told me, 'You were always meant to get the joy from Angana and Ayush.'

'Then why did I have to go through the pain and suffering of seeing two of my babies suffer and die?' I asked helplessly.

'Have you got it written that you will only see good things in life? How will you appreciate goodness if you do not live through tough times? Even Lord Ram had to go for fourteen years in exile. He as God did it, so why do we humans expect no difficulties?'Maa explained patiently.

I felt my first two daughters came to teach me compassion, surrender and acceptance.

I spoke to Maa in early 2004 during my visit to her about supporting young underprivileged children and enabling them to study. Maa was very pleased with my intentions and blessed the worthy cause.

We set up two preschools in two villages near Calcutta in 2005 to look after underprivileged children from age two to six years old. On an average there are around fifty to sixty children between the two preschools. They learn to read, write, share, care, draw, sing, learn basic hygiene and get healthy lunch to eat. By the time they turn six years old, they are more capable of being absorbed in the mainstream schooling. Some of our children have got admission into English-medium private schools in Calcutta. We have trained teaching staff and qualified and dedicated social workers looking after the children. My father-in-law helps us look over these two preschools.

We also set up a day care centre called Stepping Stone on the premises and in collaboration with Leonard Cheshire Home in New Delhi in 2011. It looks after economically deprived children with special needs. We have over eighty individuals from the age of five to twenty-five years of age. Their challenges range from visual impairment, autism, hearing and speech impairment and other challenges.

We have physiotherapists, trained teachers, music and arts teachers to enhance their creative side and serve healthy meals for the day. A coach picks them from their houses in the morning and drops them back in the evening at 6 p.m. They participate in interschool competitions and feel valued with the participation and appreciation of their work and efforts.

Sudhir and I have since set up a charity, The Maheshwari A2Z Foundation. Through our foundation, over 800 children in total have benefited in various ways. Over the years, we have learnt so much from them. These children have taught me how to live and appreciate life. We try to help them become more independent and prepare them to compete in the real world.

All these experiences in my journey have taught me to acknowledge and appreciate what I have and try not to control outcomes in life. To see that, life is already how it should be. Life is beautiful and everything happens for a reason. If we learn to embrace it, we would be at peace. That is our journey, struggle and alchemy.

Live life simply and serve humanity generously
—MAA

Chapter Eleven

Shashi's Cancer and Impact on Maa's Health

*M*aa's eldest daughter Shashi was diagnosed with breast cancer in 1998, but she hid it for eighteen months and only revealed the cancer to her family when she developed high fever. Shashi did not want to undergo any treatment due to the fear of the unknown and wanted to stay home and carry on with her domestic responsibilities.

Once Maa found out about Shashi, she went to fetch her from her home for treatment. By then, Shashi was at the last stage of cancer and doctors in Delhi unanimously discouraged surgery, as according to them there was no hope left. Maa was devastated to see her daughter's plight. She pleaded with Shyam Baba for Shashi's recovery, as she did not know how to face the impending death of her daughter. She begged Baba to give her

Shashi's troubles instead.

They were given no hope at all at Delhi's hospitals. Baba asked Maa to go to Rohtak, a small town with basic facilities. Maa with Shashi and Shashi's family decided to go to Rohtak where doctors agreed to perform a surgery in July 2001. Everything went surprisingly smoothly. There was a devotee of Shyam Baba working in the hospital who helped them.

Maa took Shashi's problem on herself and had a brain haemorrhage around the same time as Shashi's surgery in 2001. Despite this, Maa went to see Shashi at the hospital regularly and constantly prayed for her speedy recovery. Due to her brain haemorrhage, she developed spotted memory loss and took to resting a lot. Her channelling stopped due to her health issues, as she would feel confused and disoriented, though she continued to attend prayers with her grandchildren and devotees.

Despite that, Maa insisted on keeping Shashi with her and took care of all her needs, nursing her like any caring and doting mother would during Shashi's chemotherapy sessions. She kept her for six months under her care and fed her food that revived her taste buds and brought Shashi back to health. At the same time Maa's CT scan became normal again.

Maa started channelling again after eight months once she had fully healed.

In 1999, we had completed nine years of marriage and by then my husband's career had taken us from Trinidad to Hamburg (Germany), to Dusseldorf (Germany) and to Luxembourg. Alongwith our two children, Angana (almost five years old) and Ayush (two years old), and my husband who was always travelling, I felt there was no certainty when and where we would move. I could not commit to any studies for myself nor had a work permit. I was getting very frustrated and annoyed with my state of not having anything substantial to do. Every time we moved I had to make a new friends circle for the children, look for right schools and rebuild our life. I also had to familiarize myself with the local language and culture. Having done the routine so often, I soon lost desire to move to a new country. I wanted to go to an English-speaking country, or back to India, and settle with my children for them to study and have stability. As a result, my relationship with my husband got strained. It was all about my husband and his career.

I asked Sudhir if we could move to London, an English-speaking cosmopolitan city, where I thought it would be easier to fit in. He curtly replied there was no chance of his move to London.

So I decided to move back to India with my children. I contracted an architect to build a house in Delhi and organized my children's school admission. Then I decided to phone Maa and take blessings from her on my decision.

I thought Maa would happily bless me and it would be great to be near her, but she absolutely refused.

'If you come back you will have to move back within a year. You are not meant to live in India. So why create all this disruption?' Maa asked.

I explained my dilemma to her and told her that I had no desire to make any friends and settle in Luxembourg as I was frustrated for moving so often and felt lonely.

Maa said, 'It's Sudhir's time, he's doing this for you.'

'When will my time come, Maa?'

'It will come,' she reassured me.

I kept insisting and Maa felt I was being impatient.

'Why don't you understand? If you come back you will not settle and will be torn between your husband and children,' she said.

'Your children will not be able to adjust in India at this stage.'

For the first time I insisted otherwise. She put the phone down after saying 'no' once more.

I made Maa upset, I told myself in a rather unforgiving tone. I did not call her out of shame and decided to meet her and apologize to her in person during my next trip to India.

I do realize now that I was being impatient, as I had previously wished to get married to someone who would travel and show me the world. Be careful with what you wish for, was my lesson here. There is no perfect balance. We have to find the balance and make it happen. In hindsight life was how it was meant to be.

Three months later, during the Christmas holidays, I went to India and visited Maa on 1 January 2000.

As soon as she saw me from a distance she said, 'You are going to London.'

I was not interested in anything but forgiveness from her.

I sat near her and said 'Maa, please forgive me.'

'Don't worry,' she smiled and said.

I asked her if she was still angry with me.

'Can you ever be angry with your daughter Angana? How

can I be angry with you?'

Her warm radiating smile brought out my hidden emotions as tears rolled out of my eyes.

'Please, Maa, never leave me. I will never argue with you. I'm so sorry.'

She put her hand on my head.

'In six months you will move to London,' she repeated.

There was no possibility as far as Sudhir was aware of at that moment.

In March, Sudhir's bosses flew to Luxembourg and asked him to move to London quite unexpectedly. Although Maa had predicted it, the news still came as a surprise. We were told it would be a permanent move and we would be living in London while Sudhir would travel as required. Everything happened at a superfast pace.

We had moved around the world and due to the temporary nature of our stay we always lived in rented accommodation. I told my husband that I wanted to buy my own house now. We'd been moving around for nearly ten years.

We flew to London to look for schools and houses. We found very good schools, and they also offered Angana a place straightaway.

Sudhir thought I was being very ambitious by expecting to buy a house in London in four weeks, while still living in Luxembourg. We saw houses over two trips to London over two weekends. By the third weekend, the house was finalized.

In July 2000, on my birthday, we arrived in London officially on a work permit and moved into our own house. I was gifted my own house keys on my birthday in London only six months after Maa had predicted the shift.

I could still remember glimpses of London from the years we all lived near Gunnersbury Park, when I was a child. It was one of those incredible repeating cycles where during their visits, my parents took my children to the same places they took me and my brother to when I was three years old.

Within a year, both my children moved into excellent schools after appearing for entrance exams in London, even though my friends said it would be difficult to compete due to the difference in their education system in Europe.

Whilst writing this I was reminded how the unhappiness put a big strain on our relationship, when everything was moving towards bringing me to London. Life can be a joy when we see it with a bird's-eye view. We suffer when we get too caught in our desired outcomes and thus cannot see beyond them.

After we were settled, a business idea sprung in my mind and I started my own business in 2001. I set up an IT training centre with a close friend, Jhankhana. I became really busy and I realized my time had come just as Maa's prediction indicated. We ran the centre for three years and we had over 450 students before we sold it.

During that period, in 2002, my father-in-law was diagnosed with thorasic aortic aneurysm. Sudhir was really upset as this was a very serious and risky condition to treat. After a lot of deliberations and research it was decided to bring him to London for his surgery. His condition was serious and unique. It was said to be twenty times more complicated than open-heart surgery and the risks were fatality or paralysis as the blood supply is stopped during the surgery.

I was very worried for my father-in-law and he had asked me to donate all his organs, should something happen to him, just before he was leaving home for the surgery. Relatives had flown down from all over the world to support him. Emotions and anxiety filled the rooms.

I called Maa, frantically, to explain the situation on my way to the hospital on the day of the surgery.

'Don't worry the surgery will go absolutely fine and he will heal in your house.'

Sudhir was driving, listening in on our conversation. He nodded as an acknowledgement. Maa continued, 'Take ₹101 and make a circle around your father-in-law before he is wheeled in for the surgery and wish for his good health and speedy recovery. Keep the money in front of Shyam Baba's photograph in your home temple. Baba will take care and all will be fine,' she continued.

He was operated by a world-renowned surgeon, in John Radcliffe Hospital in Oxford. The surgery lasted eight hours during which my father-in-law's lung was taken out and compressed completely to access the aorta. A new aorta was inserted. The doctor told my father-in-law after he came back to consciousness, 'You are extremely fortunate, it was a miracle that you are alive.'

The aorta had bloated to ten millimetres in width, and anything over three millimetres was considered dangerous. The surgery was recorded and aired on BBC television in a programme based on doctors' miracles, *Your life in our hands.*

My father-in-law fully recovered in our house in London

in about two months after the surgery. He has been leading an active life pursuing philanthropy and his professional career. He recently retired from his professional career and keeps good health.

*Fill yourself with gratitude and
all the blessings you receive*

—**MAA**

Chapter Twelve

A Grandmother

Maa was very keen to get Meenu married so that she could fulfil her responsibilities as a mother.

While Meenu's mother, Santosh, was pregnant with Meenu and her twin, Santosh's childhood best friend, Laxmi, was raising her two-year-old son, Vikas. The two friends promised each other to let their children marry, if Santosh gave birth to a girl. Santosh had told Maa about the two friends' wish. Although Santosh passed away eleven days after Meenu was born, her best friend still honoured her promise.

Laxmi was a devotee of Maa and attended the annual kirtan in Orissa. In 2000, Laxmi was reminded of her promise to Santosh in a dream. She approached Maa at the kirtan and told her the whole story.

Maa told Meenu she had found a suitable match for her and she should meet him.

When Maa channelled Baba, Meenu said, 'I do not know this boy. You will have to come with me to see him.'

'I will come with you and you will like him,' said Baba.

In November 2003, Maa took Meenu to a wedding in Calcutta where she met Vikas. Later, Maa telephoned Laxmi and told her the children liked each other. Laxmi graciously asked Maa to bless their union even though she had still not met Meenu. The next day the children got engaged. Maa gave Vikas a gold coin and blessed them as a couple. The marriage date was scheduled for a few months later. Maa was very happy.

It was early afternoon on 14 December 2004. I had invited a few of Ayush's school friends' mothers for lunch. I had prepared an Indian meal for the diverse nationalities I was hosting. I always enjoy having people over and everyone was relaxed, admiring the Indian cuisine and the Indian artifacts in my house.

Suddenly the phone rang and I picked the receiver with excitement in my tone. I recognized my mother's voice.

'Sangeeta beta, there is very bad news,' she said.

I knew it was not terrible news about my father, as my mother would be too distraught to call me.

'Maa passed away.'

My body froze in shock and my mind became numb.

'What! What are you saying? This cannot happen!' I said in disbelief.

I ran upstairs to my bedroom, leaving my friends in the living room with the cordless phone in my hand.

I walked to the bedroom window.

'How did this happen?' I asked.

'It was very sudden. We've just come from her funeral. She passed away late last night.'

'Why didn't you tell me straightaway?' I complained, choking on my tears

'We rushed to the funeral and what would you have done anyway?'

'It doesn't matter what I would have done. I should have known as soon as it happened. I would have attended the funeral.'

'We only found out just before the funeral."

I was annoyed that she did not tell me. In my mind I would have somehow got to the funeral in time. I felt I was one of the people closest to Maa and I was not at her funeral. My mother tried to console me.

'We will all miss her dearly. No one can take her place.'

I started howling and my mother passed the phone to my father.

'Sangeeta, it is sad news, but you have to collect yourself together and look after Angana and Ayush,' he said.

I just wanted to cry. I stood looking up at the sky. The earth shifted beneath my feet and the sky had given way. How am I going to live now, was my biggest question.

I was a mother of two children living a very independent life, moving to different countries, making new friends despite language and cultural barriers, and yet then I stood helpless. I felt like a child. It was after all when I was only five that my journey with Maa began and now it had all come to a sudden end.

After a few moments I phoned my husband. He was in

Romania. I broke down. I stuttered and could not form proper sentences but Sudhir got the essence.

'Maa gone… Su-Sudhir,' was all I could utter through my sobs.

'Oh my God, I'm so sorry. I can understand how you feel.'

'What do I do?' I sobbed.

'We'll make sure you go to pay your respects as soon as possible.'

I had to return to the guests who were clearly wondering and concerned about the phone call I received.

I spoke little with words although the silence expressed more. My friends offered help to drop Ayush home and asked how they could be of assistance. I just wanted to be alone. I needed someone who knew Maa to talk it all through with. Maa was like God to me. How could my God leave me? I had several long phone calls with Anita.

Sudhir cancelled his meetings and flew back to London immediately. Waiting for Sudhir were the most difficult and longest hours of my life. I was sailing on waves of disbelief.

When we love someone so much and we look on that person for wisdom and as our supreme guide, I guess we believe that person will outlive us.

As I was writing this book I tried to remember what I was doing before the phone rang with the terrible news. Till date my memory has blanks. Angana recalled that I hosted the lunch and Ayush was dropped by a friend's mother. She remembered everything vividly as she had never seen me so upset. I had told her everything when I went to pick her up from her school that fateful afternoon. All I remember of that afternoon are my conversations with my parents, Sudhir and Anita about Maa. I guess when we go through an emotional trauma, our mind protects itself by creating a memory block.

Sudhir arrived, having already booked me a flight to Delhi. We drove immediately to Heathrow airport and I said goodbye to Sudhir, Angana and Ayush.

I reached Maa's house on the morning of 16 December, the third day after she had passed away. Once I reached Maa's house there was a stillness and calmness that surrounded me. It was almost as if I was draped by Maa's energy. I sat in her temple to pray with Sunny and Meenu. It felt as though Maa was leading the prayers, the way she always did. When I shut my eyes I felt her presence and our singing had Maa's tone and pitch. I was strangely at peace rather than being emotional; I felt all was well.

Anita and I consoled each other and it was good being with her as she and I had shared some of our journey with Maa.

Sunny gave me a photograph of Maa and said, 'Didi (elder sister), take Maa with you.'

When I returned to London I told Sudhir that Maa hadn't gone anywhere and she was with me.

Time passed and I missed talking to her and her physical presence. I felt spiritually I disconnected with myself. I had lost Maa and I had lost part of myself in the process. With time my fear of loss escalated. I started clinging on to my family and my parents.

Accept what you cannot change

—MAA

Chapter Thirteen

Her Last Moments

On 11 December 2004, Neetu came to visit Maa. She gave Neetu a saree, money and sweets, and blessed her to stay happy. As Neetu lived nearby, it seemed unusual. It seemed like she was saying goodbye.

Three days later Maa became unwell. She sat with Sunny and said, 'Finish your studies otherwise people will say Maa's grandson only did prayers and did not study.'

Sunny said, 'You are there to fight with the world. Why should I worry when you are here?' Maa did not say anything.

She made everyone eat dinner and asked tea to be made for Anita who had come to visit after dinner.

She kept feeling unwell. Sunny brought some honey mixed with black pepper for Maa. She tried to drink it but her hands were shaking, so it dripped. Sunny asked if he could feed Maa and she agreed. He fed Maa and she blessed him. He was told by Shyam Baba later, that it was that moment he was given Guru diksha (blessings) by Maa.

Maa's health deteriorated further and Sunny called Somani Bua a high soul, like Maa and was very close to Maa.

Somani Bua came within few minutes with Shyamjal, ghee and vibhuti (holy powder). As soon as she entered, she channelled Shyam Baba.

Somani Bua went to Maa and called out 'Maa!'

Maa saw her and it seemed as if she saw her God, her Shyam Baba in Somani Bua.

She looked in Somani Bua's eyes and said, 'Meenu'.

Maa's last responsibility was Meenu and she was concerned about her marriage. Somani Bua's eyes silently assured Maa that it would be taken care of. Maa seemed to be a little relieved and then Somani Bua immediately put vibhuti and Shyamjal in Maa's mouth and Somani Bua gently stroked Maa's head to give her comfort.

She then asked Sunny to put one hand on Maa. At that point, Maa seemed to have allowed herself to go. Maa had requested Baba to let her leave this world in Shyam Baba's devotee's hands and not her children. She put her grandson in the Shyam devotee category before she left.

Her last words were, 'Hey Ram! Hey Shyam!'

In December 2013, I visited Khatu with my son Ayush, to visit Shyam Baba's temple. I arranged to meet Maa's grandson, Sunny Bhaiya (elder brother), at Maa's dharamshaala. I had been through some difficult times and promised myself that once everything was resolved I would go to make an offering, to Baba. Sunny Bhaiya organized everything.

After visiting the temple we were sitting in the dharamshaala drinking tea. I was describing my struggles over the past year and I wondered how Maa coped with all her challenges. I became very emotional.

'Maa went through so many struggles in her life. But we never saw her distraught or worried. She was always giving comfort to everyone around her. She did so much for everyone with no expectation of any kind from anyone. She always gave so much love and solace to all. How many really thought of giving anything to her? In fact, some never thanked her and when they needed her again, they would come back. But it never seemed to affect her. She was always kind to people's gestures, grateful or ungrateful.'

'I did not do anything for Maa,' I sobbed.

Everyone looked down and gave me space to open up.

'Then why should I feel upset when my good deeds and kind gestures are not acknowledged? Why should I suffer when I do not get valued? Why do I give other people so much power to value me? Why do I not recognize and reward myself? Why have I not learnt this from Maa?

'She demonstrated it so well by her actions. She did not expect any acknowledgement from anyone. But with time I got so consumed with my own story that I got trapped in the worldly illusions. I want to rise above expectations of acknowledgement and approval from people and try to follow Maa's example,' I said as I wept.

'No, Didi, please don't think like that. You have done your

bit for Maa, and for everyone,' Sunny Bhaiya comforted me.

I looked up and spoke to Maa and Baba.

'Please help me liberate myself. Release me from the dramas. I do not want to be stuck and want to rise above the illusion and attachment.'

'Please help me do something meaningful for you, Maa'.

My son gave me a big hug and I started to feel better.

In Maa's room in her dharamshaala, her photo was radiating so much energy that I felt I could communicate with the photo. As I was leaving to go back to Delhi, Sunny Bhaiya called me and said, 'Didi, Maa wants to go with you to London.'

I was stunned! He draped that photo of Maa in a holy cloth and gave Maa to me. I felt an energy run through my body, when I held her photo.

By Maa and Baba's blessing I have a beautiful temple in my house in London where I meditate and pray daily.

Two months later, on 23 February 2014, Sudhir and I returned to Maa's house to wish Sunny Bhaiya on his birthday. We sat in the temple to pray. Suddenly I had the inspiration to write a biography on Maa. I did not say anything to anyone, as I was overwhelmed by the task I had in mind.

Later that evening Sunny Bhaiya cut his cake and whilst we sat eating, we discussed what we could do for Maa's tenth anniversary of her passing. Sudhir suddenly spoke out, 'Why don't we get a biography written about Maa.'

I jumped with excitement.

'When did you think of it?'

'During the prayers,' he replied.

'Oh my God, I had the same idea during prayers. That must be Shyam Baba sending us a message.'

I felt relieved as this was one way I could give something back to Maa.

'Please, I want to write it myself,' I pleaded to Sunny Bhaiya.

Sunny Bhaiya laughed and said, 'Who else knows Maa better than you? Of course, you can.'

Writing the book was like a journey through profound emotions. It took me months before I could be more objective and pen it down. It helped me get a bigger perspective and better focus on Maa's values.

I met Simon Brown, my macrobiotic teacher, who had authored eighteen books himself, and asked him to help me write this book. He asked me tell my story by using real life events to describe Maa. Simon encouraged me to be more descriptive and make the book a more engaging story.

To write this book I travelled to India several times to interview people who were either close to Maa or her devotees. I wanted to get different perspectives and be able to see Maa through other people's eyes.

The biggest learning that the devotees got from Maa and Baba was to accept the present and find harmony in it. Life is what you make out of it. If you live it with peace and appreciation you liberate yourself from your karmic cycle. I was amazed at how each devotee I spoke to felt he or she was most special to Maa. All the devotees were her children, irrespective of their age.

As a mother, wife, daughter, daughter-in-law and many

other roles, I am torn between my worldly responsibilities and spiritual journey. Whilst writing this book I reflected on how Maa managed to harmonize these aspects of her own life.

I am finding that the more I can detach myself from worries, and give myself and others their own space, the more I can trust in life. For example, with my eighteen-year-old son Ayush, I had strong maternal opinions, like any mother, regarding important decisions, yet I now realize that if one of us needs to make a shift, why not me? It has helped both of us discover ourselves and value each other more. It compels me to surrender and accept, which saves me a lot of unnecessary dramas.

To lead a worldly life and fulfil worldly obligations is a task on its own and most people struggle to justify their role and relationships along with the boundaries that come with it. How many hats do we wear? How much do we give and where do we draw our line? How do we deal with each other's sensitivities and sensibilities? Can we first share and love and care and then let go and forgive?

Through the process of writing this book, I feel better equipped at detaching myself from disturbances. Now I feel I have opened up and embraced life, with greater acceptance. My relationships are deeply connected through love and understanding. I feel I can listen better even when people are upset. I can be empathetic and compassionate yet not feel obliged to solve their problems.

My spiritual life helps me embrace my inner stillness, while still being able to enjoy the material world.

In the past I have put other's needs before mine in fear of

disappointing people. I am learning to love myself rather than seeking love and acceptance from others. I am committing myself in service to people with joy, rather than obligation.

It is a delicate balance between my inner spirituality and external relationships that has to be maintained, to create the integration of the two.

Life is beautiful and simple. We complicate it by overanalysing every thought and action of ours. We are souls who have come to experience human life and enjoy every aspect of life, like wealth, career, relationships, love and so on without becoming victims of it. Many of us get so attached to pleasures that we then identify ourselves with them and thus create fears and insecurities regarding losing them. There is no pleasure without pain and pain teaches us how to appreciate and grow. The challenge is to enjoy both and yet be able to transcend both.

Letting go and forgiveness liberates
you and accelerates your spiritual growth

—MAA

SECTION 2

Chapter Fourteen

Maa Through Her Grandson's Eyes

*M*aa was taken to the hospital but the doctors announced that she had passed away some time ago.

Maa's body was brought back to her house. She seemed at peace, radiating the same light and divinity and Maa looked as if she was sleeping.

She used to say, 'Live a life of service and die like royalty'.

She meant live by serving others, performing your duties with full sincerity and compassion.

When her body was taken for final rites, she was decorated with the most beautiful sarees, shawls and finally, a red spread covered her.

Maa used to say 'a red carrier will come to fetch me when I finally leave this world for another journey.'

All her wishes were coming true. Hundreds of devotees walked with Maa to the cremation ground. There were constantly four shoulders carrying Maa's body. No shoulder got a chance to carry her for more than five minutes and no shoulder got a second chance. The entire procession seemed like a floral river where flowers were being placed on her body by the devotees and the path of three and half kilometres was carpeted with flowers.

When the procession reached the cremation ground, a pure sandalwood pyre was prepared for her and she was adorned with flowers and the final sheet with 'JAI SHREE SHYAM' (Praise to Shyam Baba), written across. There was an outburst of emotions and many devotees wanted to go with her. Sunny wanted to sleep next to her like he used to as a little child.

Pure ghee was poured on the pyre. One of the sandalwood sticks with a nail sticking out, had accidentally been put on the pyre.

Vinod, one of Maa's devout devotees, scolded the man, 'Don't you know Maa will get hurt with the nail? Quickly remove the nail.'

In accordance with Hindu tradition, Maa's eldest son Satish was asked to light a fire on the pyre. At the last moment the priest called for her grandson to join Satish.

Sunny and Satish held burning sticks to light the fire. The entire place blazed with Maa's warm love. Such was the energy and power of Maa's body.

She truly went like a Queen of all hearts. Innumerable hearts wept that day and heads bowed in reverence.

My first interview for the book was with Sunny Bhaiya. He had taken on the responsibility of looking after Maa's temple.

We met at Maa's house.

As a toddler, Sunny used to crawl to Maa for comfort. Sunny and his sister Meenu were extremely close to Maa. She was a doting grandmother and was seen as the head of the family by her family. She kept everyone together by being sensitive but firm.

Sunny was influenced by her spirituality from a very young age. Maa had him in her lap when she was praying. He and Meenu used to sleep with Maa in her room and got pampered and showered with her love.

His toys were a flute, bangles of Maa, and all prayer accessories. He used to decorate his toys with old costumes of deities and create a little spiritual fantasy world around them.

Maa discouraged him from spending so much time in prayers. She was very keen for her children and grandchildren to become self-sufficient, independent and educated.

Sunny was allowed to attend prayers on weekends only as Maa insisted he must spend the week on his studies and homework.

When Maa used to go for jaagran and kirtan and would channel Baba, she used to come back home late. But Sunny would keep awake no matter how late it was. He could never sleep without Maa. That place was vacant and he struggled to move on without her for the longest time.

Maa did not train Sunny in meditation techniques. He was just fascinated by shringaar (decoration). He would devote himself to bhakti through decoration. He used to make flower garlands and Maa started decorating Baba with only Sunny's garlands.

Both Meenu and Sunny used to take turns in conducting evening prayers and Maa used to conduct the morning prayers. When Baba used to channel through Maa, they were never interested in asking Baba questions but just immerse themselves in singing and praying and feel the higher soul within. Through this experience, Sunny learnt the unique beat of bhajans. He knew which bhajans helped in concentration and lead to channelling and which bhajans broke the concentration.

While Maa was alive, Sunny had some experiences where he felt his subconscious mind had awakened. A devout devotee, Mr Dalmia (who also helped Maa with organizing her finances), one day found that his car was stolen in Connaught Place in Delhi. After not finding his car anywhere, he visited Maa at Khatu. Sunny had remained silent about his spiritual awakening during Maa's time, as he did not want her to feel that he was copying her. But that day, he picked some flowers, offered them to the deities and gave a flower to Mr Dalmia. He told him, 'Go back to the same place and you will find your car.'

Sunny was around eleven years old. Mr Dalmia took the flower and with full trust he went back to the same place and found his car. After the incident, Mr Dalmia started addressing Sunny as Sunny Baba.

Mr Dalmia narrated this incident to Maa, but she did not encourage this much in children as she wanted them to enjoy a normal life. She knew that would lead them to a different path.

Time went by and Sunny's normal and spiritual life ran parallel with each other. He continued decorating the temple with more keenness and vigour. Maa was quite strict about his studies and very keen for him to go to university and be self-sufficient. Maa had seen how difficult life could be without academic qualifications and a career.

His spiritual world evolved with Maa when he shared a grandson's role and stepped in for Maa at the temple when she was unwell and unable to get out of bed.

During the prayers, devotees offered money to deities, especially Shyam Baba, as a token of gratitude. Maa never allowed anyone from home to touch that money. That money was Baba's money and it used to go to the temple in Khatu at the time of fagun mela.

One day a devotee offered money and Maa kept it in front of Baba's photo. Sunny came from school and, as always, was excited to see decoration of the temple. Later, Maa went back to do her prayers and noticed the money was not where she left it. She got very angry at Sunny and scolded him. He has always been sensitive and felt very upset. He kept pleading with her to trust him.

Maa looked again to make sure, and found the money behind Baba's photograph. It must have slipped behind. Sunny felt very angry and humiliated that Maa had doubted him. He said, 'I will never enter your temple again. Give me another photo of Baba and I will make a small temple in the store room next to the temple and worship alone. I don't need to touch your money because I get whatever I want from you. You provide us with everything. Then why should I look for it elsewhere and why should I take Baba's money?'

He went into Maa's room and locked it and started crying.

For him, his God was Maa, and to fight with his God was painful enough and what was worse was that his God doubted his integrity. He was devastated.

Maa apologized to him by saying, 'You were right, now open the door.'

But Sunny was so upset he just could not stop crying, feeling the injustice of Maa's false accusation.

Sunny's misery continued until the evening.

'Open the door for my life's sake,' Maa pleaded.

For Sunny there was nothing more important than Maa's life. He opened the door.

Maa said, 'Come, eat dinner.'

'I will not eat dinner, you go ahead and eat.'

Maa became very serious. In Maa's room there was one bed on which Maa used to sleep and two mattresses on the floor, for Meenu and Sunny.

That night around midnight, Sunny saw Shyam Baba and Baba showed him Maa covered in white on her pyre.

Sunny said, 'Who are you scaring, Baba? If Maa dies I will also die.'

Baba said, 'If you trouble my devotee like this I will take her.'

'Why are you telling me this? I have not troubled her. She wrongly accused me,' Sunny replied, defensively.

Baba repeated, 'I will take my devotee away.'

Suddenly, Sunny realized what was happening. He stopped in shock and burst into tears. He went and lay down on Maa's feet and wept profusely with remorse and regret.

'Please forgive me Maa, I have hurt you', he said.

Maa had also not slept. It was 2 a.m. and she was up, feeling terrible that she had hurt her closest person. Overwhelmed, she was unable to speak. He put his head on her feet and pleaded again. 'Maa, please forgive me?'

Maa got up and looked at Sunny with her compassion and painful heart. He begged for forgiveness and promised he would never ever trouble or hurt her in any way.

'Maa, please do not ever leave me and I promise I will never argue and get angry with you again.'

She put her hand on Sunny's head and blessed him. She wept with him and they hugged each other.

'I will not leave you but I wanted to teach you to respect and honour the money left for Baba's offering. Any misuse of the devotee's gifts will bring bad karma to the family and we will all suffer. I know you did not take the money but I really wanted to impress upon you the value of money, integrity and honesty,' she told him.

Maa never shared her worries and stresses with her family as she never wanted them to be troubled.

Since that day Sunny feared that if anyone troubled Maa, Baba would take her away. He began to treat Maa as his Guru more than a grandmother. He became more respectful and his attachment to Maa kept increasing as his faith and divine love increased.

Maa had a soft corner for Meenu, as she was her grandmother and mother. She was quiet and rarely shared her hurt with Maa. Maa would look visibly shaken if Meenu had an outburst.

Meenu had also quite a protected upbringing and when

she went to university, she enjoyed going to college festivals and get-togethers like other girls of her age. Maa gave her consent, although would always be watchful as Meenu was naïve and innocent. She wanted her to get settled while she was alive.

Maa's faith in Shyam Baba had no boundaries.

She always said 'Baba will take care.'

Maa would innocently ask Baba in the hour of crisis, 'Why, Baba?'

She would then let go and say, 'Baba, I've left it for you to take care'.

Her faith in Baba and surrender to him was second to none. She kept pushing her own limits of devotion and divine faith and true love till she reached a point where there was no difference between Maa and Baba. They had almost become one. Despite all this, her responsibilities in her house did not waiver. Love, good deeds and compassion filled her heart.

Try to light everyone's path with joy and blessings

—MAA

Chapter Fifteen

Maa's Absence and Difficulties Faced by Her Grandson

Maa's dream was to always help humanity through Shyam Baba's prayers and channelling. She had taken up a mission to help, guide and support people during their difficult times and she desired it to continue even after she was gone.

Sunny, later addressed as Sunny Bhaiya, took it upon him to try to fulfil Maa's dreams of carrying on the devotion and good deeds.

With Meenu's wedding, Maa's last family responsibility also got fulfilled. Meenu's in-laws looked after her very well, just the way Maa had wished for her.

After Maa's passing away, life at her house completely altered. Most devotees stopped coming. Some could not handle her loss, some lost their relationship with the house.

However, there were some devotees who continued to come and kept her flag flying high.

Vinod Jindal had met Maa in 1972, when she blessed him for the first time, and he felt an instant connection. Maa helped him at every stage of his life. He is so indebted to Maa and Baba that he found it overwhelming to narrate his innumerable miracles to me.

Vinod still organizes pilgrimages and carries out the work involved in looking after a few hundred people for three days twice a year.

He like the other devotees was devastated over Maa's death. But his conviction to continue with Maa's dreams of carrying on the good work meant that Maa remained alive through the prayers and pilgrims. He continued attending every prayer. His younger son, Nitin, who grew up with Sunny Bhaiya as best friends became Sunny Bhaiya's right hand man. Vinod's older son Amit also continued to attend prayers regularly and helped his father organize the pilgrimages and prayers.

It was really challenging in February 2005 to do the fagun mela pilgrimage preparation. Hundreds would bend backwards to help and organize the pilgrimage while Maa was alive, but then there were only a handful left. Yet, Sunny Bhaiya kept his faith and his will power increased and so did his detachment from the material world. At a very young age the veil of maya (illusion) was removed and he recognized the truth. He took his responsibility and ownership of his life and his emotions. He knew he had to stand up for himself and not rely on others. Maa kept blessing him and kept reassuring him from an astral level.

'Give it time and it will all be fine,' Maa kept saying.

With the support of some ardent devotees, he kept faith and his good work. Ultimately they were blessed.

Since 1985, every December a jaagran was organized. Thousands of devotees attended it. Singers from all over the country came to sing Shyam bhajans and a huge marquee was set out with beautiful decorations. Dinner was served for everyone and hundreds of volunteers helped organize this event.

In December 2005, for the first time Shyam Baba channelled through Sunny Bhaiya. He jumped three feet high when he channelled Baba. He had no idea what happened.

In February 2006 during the fagun mela, Baba came and spoke and started giving directions about how to do everything.

Sunny Bhaiya started channelling Shyam Baba. Shyam Baba came back to Maa's temple and Maa was delighted from the astral world. Slowly, the word spread and devotees started coming.

Sunny Bhaiya developed a more structured approach and set out how rituals should be followed. He decided to keep his distance while helping the devotees and not get attached to them. Some old-time devotees found it challenging to accept him and the changes. They had known him as a child and compared him with Maa's magnanimity. The family also found it difficult to accept that Sunny Bhaiya was channelling.

From Sunny Bhaiya's point of view it was a big challenge

to accept this responsibility, as Maa was his God too. He was devastated to hear accusations that he was ambitious and trying to benefit from Maa's glory.

In 2009, he was so upset that he tried to end his life. People's doubt on his authenticity kept scarring his pride. He swallowed a lot of sleeping pills without telling anyone. He was at Nitin's shop in Delhi. Baba immediately started channelling through Sunny Bhaiya and told Nitin what had happened he asked him to make Sunny Bhaiya drink a Limca (soft drink) and allow him to sleep. Sunny Bhaiya drank the Limca and woke up the next afternoon. When he sat in his temple, Baba reminded him of the last night.

'You are fine but this had an impact somewhere. Do you want to see?'

Sunny Bhaiya saw an image of himself swallowing the tablets and the tablets falling on Baba who was sitting in his heart. Baba was turning darker in colour every time a new tablet came. Sunny Bhaiya understood that Baba always took the pain of his devotees and just like all parents protect their children, he protects his devotees too. Sunny Bhaiya wept and apologized and promised he would never do this again.

By Maa and Shyam Baba's grace, blessings and guidance, Sunny Bhaiya continues to help devotees through their life struggles.

In 2008, Sunny Bhaiya's father, Murari, passed away.

I decided to go and visit Sunny Bhaiya and his mother to offer my condolence. When I reached Maa's house there were many devotees and Sunny Bhaiya was already in the temple praying. I learnt then that Sunny Bhaiya had started channelling Baba. I was unaware of the developments in the family since Maa's passing away as I did not have the heart to go to her house and not find her.

I was called to come inside the temple. I sat down, not quite sure of what was happening.

Sunny Bhaiya's eyes were closed and he started talking to me. I thought I was talking to Baba through him. I was overwhelmed as I had not spoken to Shyam Baba since I last saw Maa in February 2004 and I started to cry. Sunny Bhaiya told me later, 'Didi, that was Maa you were talking to. Maa has come back and she has been waiting for you.'

After four years it was so joyful to hear that Maa was back. Maa was very happy that I had come back to her temple. She helped me overcome the depression that I had gone into after her physical loss.

She revived my energy, my spirit and enthusiasm slowly but surely in the right direction. I started reconnecting with myself and also with people. I slowly started opening myself to both the inside and outside world.

Every year, since 2008, I go by myself to a retreat for detoxification and yoga for about one week. I try to choose a different venue each time for an out-of-comfort-zone experience. It gives me time for myself and helps me get some introspection. I am discovering myself beyond external relationships. I have started listening to my inner guidance more and Maa reconnects with me now at a different level. I feel Maa's energy around me.

We all have a Maa and inner voice that we can hear if we connect to ourselves at a deeper level, that tells us to take a higher path. It is up to us if we want to listen and believe in the guidance and ourselves.

I remember an instance, when Maa passed away, my parents advised me, 'You should not interrupt the thirteen-day mourning period, go after two weeks when you visit India over the Christmas break.'

I shut my eyes while I was in London and asked Maa for her guidance. The answer came, 'Listen to your heart.'

The message that came with full conviction from my heart was, 'Go now for your own sanity and pay your respects.'

Feel the supreme energy around you by thinking positively and you will realize the Almighty around you

—**MAA**

SECTION 3

Miracles

Since 1972, when I first started going to Maa, new devotees or anyone with a serious question used to bring a coconut with them. They used to whisper their question to their coconut and place the coconut on a wooden step next to the temple in front of Maa's rug. When Maa used to channel Baba, Maa was given a coconut, one by one, and she would answer the question. No one ever disclosed their question to anybody else so there was no way others would know whom that coconut belonged to. Devotees used to put their own secret mark on the coconut to recognize their coconut amongst many, and remember the question too.

SURENDER GOEL

Recently, in November 2014, I went on an annual pilgrimage

to celebrate Shyam Baba's birthday in Khatu. Vinod Jindal recommended I speak to Surender Goel, a devotee, about Maa's miracles. I had known Surender since I was five. We met in Maa's dharamshaala, very early in the morning before prayers for the interview. We sat on a bench in a big central hall. Surender is a very tall, muscular man in his sixties and spoke with a deep voice. His tone was measured and stable. He remained serene through the interview, although once or twice he did choke on his words.

In August 1972, Surender met Maa for the first time.

He had been diagnosed with cancer in his legs. His condition was so deplorable that when he stood, pus would flow out of his legs like water. One could see his bones. He had no skin from the knee to his ankles. Both his legs were covered with open lesions.

He decided to take a coconut and ask Shyam Baba to help him as all the doctors he had consulted had given up hope and told him that he would lose his legs. Maa picked his coconut but Baba's reply was similar to the doctors. Surender was disheartened. Bauji put his hand on Surender's shoulder and consoled him, urging him not to give up.

Bauji said, 'Speak your mind. Say whatever comes to your mind to Baba.'

Surender then spoke to Baba and challenged him, 'If Baba is divine, why did he deny me any healing?'

Surender agreed that we have to go through our karmic debt but the divine power can intervene at some point.

'There cannot be a "never" or "no" in God's eyes. There may be a delay due to our karmic balance. Baba, you can test our commitment and determination but then after that you have to help us,' he said.

Baba asked Surender, 'How confident are you about your commitment?'

'I am very confident.'

Previously, Surender underwent treatment in a Delhi hospital for ten months without improvement. The pus was tested in Chandigarh (Punjab) and the results also showed an advanced stage of cancer. They said his legs would need to be amputated.

The doctors said he would need to fill a disclaimer waiver form and be admitted for surgery in Bombay (now Mumbai). Surender asked for a few minutes to think but decided to scrap the form as he would much rather die. Seeing no end to his misery, he decided to let the cancer fully consume him, and he decided against the treatment.

Then, Baba asked him what he thought was his level of devotion.

'I come from a very humble and modest background. I'm a student with no earnings. Although I am confident of my inner strength, I would not do anything that would burden my family.'

That made Baba smile. He said he would treat Surender but on the condition that he would not be allowed to drink water anywhere outside his own home for eight years (it could be challenging during the Indian summers).

'Put ₹5 away and when you get better, donate a warm piece of clothing to a poor needy person,' Baba told Surender.

Surender started attending prayers every Tuesday,

Saturday and ekadashi. After the prayers Maa used to serve dinner to Bauji and then spend an hour applying herbal oil to Surender's legs gently with her hands.

Surender did not trust in the power of healing for the first three months, but he wanted to believe as Maa was his only hope. Maa channelled Baba and took ghee from the jyot and applied it to Surender's lesions.

Maa would alternate between coconut oil and jyot ghee, every three weeks to apply to his legs. She looked after Surender, as a mother would do, for eight months. Slowly, his skin started returning and the pus reduced.

When Surender saw the improvement in his condition, his faith in Shyam Baba's powers grew. Finally, he had darshan of Baba in December 1972 and his faith was solidified. He was able to walk the seventeen kilometres to the temple, with Maa, on the following fagun mela pilgrimage.

He started fasting without a drop of water every Tuesday for fifty-three weeks to express his gratitude and did not drink water outside his house for nine years.

Surender organized a bus service for all devotees attending the pilgrimage, as a token of thanks. Anyone who could not afford it would still go with the help of others. He ran this service for twenty years.

I remember observing Surender and thinking he was dedicated in his devotion. He used to stand all night long and offer ghee in the jyot during ekadashi. When he narrated his story I was impressed by his perseverance and his faith in Baba.

*Remember the supreme power in
both your highs and lows*

—MAA

❖

ARUN BOTHRA

Sunny Bhaiya recommended I talk to Arun Bothra, who is presently the Inspector General of the Cuttack Police Crime Division. I called him from London in the afternoon, that was around 10 p.m. his time. I was a little apprehensive, due to his position. Arun put me at ease instantly, by straightaway apologizing that he had missed my previous calls and complimenting me on taking up such a noble project. He came across as a humble, no-nonsense man of few words. He came straight to the point, as though essentially a man of action. I felt he was more touched by Maa's values, pure love and compassion, than the miracles.

In 1986 his mother started visiting Maa in Faridabad. They were in a bad state financially as their printing business had shut down. They started attending ekadashi prayers regularly every month. Arun told me how he developed faith in Maa, when he witnessed her solve problems and offer solutions to devotees through channelling, and shared a few instances with me. Slowly, Arun's life started to change. He used to be very upset as he wanted his younger brother to get work. They wanted a Hero Honda agency for his brother. This was very difficult at that time. Maa visited their house and asked them to give besan (chickpea flour) to any cow for five Thursdays. By the fourth Thursday his brother got the agency contract. During this period his youngest brother got a job in the police department, his sister got married and Arun started working in the Crime Bureau of Investigation (CBI). The whole family's faith increased as they saw what seemed impossible becoming possible.

Arun said he prayed with full faith and surrender.

'Baba, I have come in your darbar (temple) to seek blessings, bless me with what you think is appropriate. All is humbly acceptable to me as your blessings,' he prayed.

Maa told him, 'Never accept anything that is not right. Follow the path of truth.'

He followed the wisdom with all sincerity through his life.

One day Arun, who was a Deputy Inspector General in the CBI at that time, went to raid a house. As soon as he entered the house he saw Shyam Baba's photo and he realized this person was a Shyam devotee.

He prayed to Shyam Baba, 'Baba, I will follow the path of truth but I do not wish to harm a Shyam devotee, especially when you are there.'

Fortunately, they did not find anything in that house.

Being an Inspector General of Police, Arun was surrounded by people wishing for an appointment with him. He confessed how irritating it was when people came in without prior appointments insisting on meeting him, sometimes without a real reason.

He remembered how Maa accommodated one and all without ever having a frown on her forehead or losing her divine smile. She was calm, serene and patient. People came with no appointments and called on the phone to talk about their sorrows; however, Maa's patience and love remained unperturbed and at the same level of sincerity for all.

Arun also commented that it was his duty to serve and meet people and despite that, it was frustrating and overwhelming at times. Maa was not obliged to serve or help anyone. Yet, she did it with undying love and compassion.

It reminded me that it is not only what we do but how we do it that makes the biggest difference.

Spread love and joy with no expectations
—MAA

MRS SUSHILA SHARMA

I met Mrs Sushila Sharma, a traditionally dressed rural woman. She led a simple life, yet she was a wise and religious-minded brahmin lady. We met in November 2014 in Khatu for the interview.

The first time she met Maa was in 1996. She had no money, no food, absolute poverty and had three daughters at that time. Her husband was a brahmin priest. They lived in a small dilapidated house and experienced abject poverty yet lived a life with pride in Delhi. She did not believe in ever asking anyone for any help.

During the monsoon season, the ceiling of her house began to collapse.

People rushed to help and a devotee suggested that she should seek Maa's blessings. Not knowing what to expect she made the journey to see Maa. During Maa's channelling, Baba asked her to join the pilgrimage during the springtime fagun mela.

She had no money and she thought to herself, 'Baba has asked me to go, how will I pay for the ticket that costs ₹350. I will not ask anyone as it is against my principle.'

'Don't worry, you do your preparation and I will get your ticket organized,' said Maa, reading her thoughts.

Sushila attended Shyam Baba's pilgrimage with Maa and the other devotees. After she returned from the pilgrimage, she told Maa about her broken house. She had been too embarrassed to tell Maa on her first visit.

'I'm scared we will die as wind blows so much and the rest of our roof will collapse,' Sushila said.

'Start the work latest by ekadashi,' said Baba, which was two weeks from then.

'I can barely eat a meal and feed my family, how can I think of repairs and renovations?'

Baba repeated, 'By next ekadashi your renovations will start'.

Two days before ekadashi a wealthy man came to her hut. He was wearing a yellow kurta (Indian long shirt) and white dhoti (linen cloth) and a 'Jai Shree Shyam' stole around his neck. His forehead had a sandalwood tika (oblong dot on the forehead) and he was wearing a turban on his head. He brought a red tote bag full of money.

As Sushila was a brahmin lady, she thought someone had come to visit her husband. Perhaps he had come to give a donation. She covered her head with her saree in accordance with her traditions. Being very shy she looked at the ground and remained silent. Her daughters asked him to take a seat.

'I will not sit but I have come to deliver money. Your mother had spoken to Maa about roof repairs and that you had no money. I have come to give her money. Please ask her to start the repairs to your roof now.'

He opened the bag on the bed and took out bundles of money. The family was shocked to see the money. The daughters asked him his name.

The mysterious man said to one of the daughters, 'Maa has sent me and I will come again during your wedding.'

'I do not know anyone, how will I start the work?' said Sushila, still in state of surprise.

'I will send people to start your work and they will bring whatever you need,' said the mysterious man.

She was so overwhelmed that she could not speak. He then gave squashes, fruits and sweets.

Then she offered a place for him to sit but said she had no sofa.

'I'll send a sofa,' he said, before leaving.

For the next eight months, someone brought baskets of fruits and grains to their house. People supplied all the material for their renovation and it was completed without any hitch.

There was no electricity in the entire street where she lived. There was an electric pole but they needed permission from the government to connect to the electricity.

Soon, a man came and said, 'You will need a stamp from the prime minister's office to get electricity.'

In those days, Mr Atal Bihari Vajpayee was the prime minister. He sent his approval promptly after the request was sent and the entire street was lit. Her quality of life leaped to a completely different level of happiness.

Her neighbours commented, 'They did not have a morsel to feed themselves and now they have a sturdy house with electricity and variety of food. How did they become so prosperous?'

Sushila spoke to Maa, 'I had only asked for about ₹20,000 but you have sent an unlimited amount for me.'

Once the building work finished, the supply of food and money stopped. But the family got used to spending and living a new lifestyle and they soon ran out of money.

Time passed and Sushila's first daughter got married. Sushila's husband died soon after and to add to her misery she lost her second daughter through illness. She went back to Maa and said, 'My husband's died and I have no money or contacts to find a groom for my third daughter. I've always been a mother and don't know how to look after myself.'

'Don't worry, I'll help you. Your third daughter will get married and I will find her a husband. He will come and take care of you,' Baba replied.

In three months' time a suitable boy came and Sushila took him to Maa.

'Baba has sent him and he will take care of you and your house,' said Maa. The preparations of the wedding were done without any hurdles.

Maa attended the wedding along with many people. Baba and Maa assured her that she would get a son-in-law who would be more than a son and would take care of her. It has been many years and until now her life has been well taken care of by her son-in-law and daughter. They live happily together.

Before I met Sushila, I had heard her story from Nitin. Yet, when she narrated her story, I was amazed.

Since Sushila was seven years old, she had been worshipping Shyam Baba. She had known of him since childhood and was really drawn to him. This reminded me of my attraction to Maa and Baba when I was a child. So after listening to her childhood story, I felt a connection and I could relate to her much better.

Miracles occur only when we truly believe in them, like Sushila did. She was a very simple village lady who had no idea about the world but her world came to her doorsteps. She confessed they became lazy and slowly they spent everything, but that was their lesson. I spoke to other people who witnessed Sushila's struggles and triumphs.

Through her story Sushila helped me open up to unlimited possibilities in life. Who knows what is around the corner, and sometimes just when everything seems hopeless, help knocks at our door.

Later Maa told Sushila that it was Shyam Baba who came

in disguise with the money and pulled all the strings to change her life. Sushila still wishes she had the courage to have spoken to him more.

> *Your thoughts make your destiny.*
> *You will reap as you sow*
> —MAA

❖

RAJESH SHARMA

I met Rajesh Sharma from Rajgarh, Chhattisgarh on December 2014 at Maa's temple when he had come to attend prayers in Faridabad.

I found Rajesh to be a soft-spoken, calm and compassionate human being.

He had always been a Shyam Baba devotee as his whole family has been worshipping Shyam Baba for generations. He used to sing bhajans for Baba with his gifted melodious voice.

Later he was instrumental in getting Baba's temple built in 2011 by singing bhajans for devotees and raising donations towards the temple construction in his neighbourhood in Rajgarh.

Life was good for Rajesh in Chhattisgarh. He was happily married, had a good stable accounting job. His singing spiritual songs and devotion to Baba gave him peace and joy. However,

Rajesh and his wife Deepa had something big missing in their lives. They did not have any children. As years passed by, their desire to have children increased and they decided to seek medical intervention.

All the possible tests in Rajgarh proved that they could never have the family they dreamed of. They did not give up and went to Mumbai for a second opinion. Despite having all the advanced medical facilities and specialist doctors, they were told they could not have children.

Rajesh's sister was Maa and Baba's devotee and used to live near Maa's house. She could not bear to see her brother go through so much of agony and disappointment and she urged him to come once to meet Maa. Rajesh came to visit Maa in the year 1998.

As Rajesh narrated his first meeting with Maa to me, I noticed his eyes started to sparkle and shine and his face lit up with joy. He was so attracted by the divinity of the temple and Maa that he started coming every month from Rajgarh to attend every prayer on ekadashi. He sang bhajans and found so much solace with Maa and Baba.

Baba was so pleased with his devotion that he said, 'I will bless you not with one but two.'

Rajesh continued his devotion and after two years he was blessed with a son in the year 2000. As his birth was a miracle and blessing from Shyam Baba, Rajesh and Deepa named him Shyam.

Rajesh continued his devotion to Maa and Baba. Two and a half years after their son's birth they were blessed with a daughter.

Rajesh and Deepa were over the moon. Their family was complete and they came to thank Maa and expressed their gratitude.

Maa laughed and said, 'You cannot stop this. Baba has already blessed you with two, he meant two sons. You will have another son.'

They were blessed with a second son on the same day as Baba's birthday. They named him Kapil.

Rajesh is so pleased and grateful for the blessings he received that has made him and Deepa proud parents. His children are kind, loving and caring.

I was particularly moved by Rajesh's faith and humility.

Be grateful and humble.
Do not take credit for your or others' achievements

—**MAA**

MINAL SAPANI

Minal and Sunil have been Maa's and Baba's devotees since the 1980s. In fact Baba blessed their alliance.

Like all Maa's devotees they, too, felt they were Maa's children and were blessed by her love and sincerity.

Sunil Sapani lost his brother on 20 July 2000, at the age of twenty-two years, in an accident and the family was devastated. They went to Khatu on ekadashi to seek courage to deal with the loss.

Maa channelled Shyam Baba.

Baba said to Sunil, 'I can understand your grief in losing your brother. I cannot change that but I will give you your brother back.' They were so consumed in their grief that they did not pay attention to this. They just thought Baba was consoling them. After the pilgrimage they returned to Faridabad. Sunil's wife Minal went straight to her parents to stay and Sunil returned to Bikaner, in Rajasthan. She wanted to stay with her parents for some time.

Minal's parents were Maa's devotees and Minal had been visting Maa with them even before she got married.

Now Minal went to visit Maa with her mother and Maa stopped her at the entrance.

'You are pregnant,' Maa said.

Minal was stunned as she and her husband had not been together with Minal staying at her parent's house. Minal denied any such possibility. But Maa kept insisting that she was pregnant. Minal went back to her husband and met her doctor. The doctor sent her back saying it was too early to detect. Minal went back after a few weeks and the doctor declared that she was not pregnant. They called Maa but Maa kept to her prediction. The couple were very puzzled. They had three ultrasounds and each proved that she was not pregnant.

Minal was getting very anxious and the doctor was getting annoyed. Sunil got really confused and decided to meet Maa personally. Maa sat in prayers and Shyam Baba said, 'Take this garland of forty roses and ask Minal to eat one rose every morning. No need to go to doctor till then and only after forty days should she see the doctor'.

After forty days Minal went back to the doctor.

'The baby is growing healthy,' said the doctor in amazement.

Her doctor was stunned and confessed it was a miracle. The doctor kept asking throughout Minal's pregnancy what Maa and Baba had to say now, out of curiosity. Her faith started growing towards Maa and Baba and she wished to accommodate Maa and Baba's blessings.

They were blessed with a baby boy during July 2001. He is now fourteen. Sunil had lost his brother in July 2000 and was blessed with a son in July 2001. Their son has habits similar to the brother they lost. They do feel they have the brother in their son's form.

The lesson for me is to keep faith and patience. We only stress ourselves and suffer when we try to navigate and expedite our desired outcomes.

Man proposes and God disposes. We cannot understand everything with our human mind. When the right time comes, clarity will emerge

—MAA

ANITA'S SECOND LIFE

In November 2009, Anita was diagnosed with stage one breast cancer and was immediately operated on. Doctors gave her very strong chemotherapy after the surgery to ensure no relapse in the future.

In June 2010, she was diagnosed with jaundice which kept getting worse. When the doctors conducted liver function tests such as SGOT, SGPT, bilirubin and albumin, the results were alarming. They found that she had developed liver cirrhosis, as a result of her chemotherapy. Her liver started shrinking. Due to her history of cancer she could not get a liver transplant and there was no other treatment to cure her liver. Her body weight started dropping down swiftly.

According to the doctors she had at the maximum three months to live. Her whole body was filled with fluid. During her tests Anita started feeling breathless and extremely restless. She was transferred to the Intensive Care Unit.

Neetu (Anita's younger sister) went to Sunny Bhaiya and pleaded for Anita's recovery. Sunny Bhaiya channelled Shyam Baba.

Baba said, 'She will come out of the Intensive Care Unit by 9 a.m. the next morning. Give her Shyamjal to drink.'

Anita drank Shyamjal, which Neetu brought for her.

That night Anita saw bright light like rays in her room and the next morning the doctors surprisingly found her condition stable. At 8.30 a.m. she was shifted from the Intensive Care Unit to a normal room for further tests.

Doctors had given up all hopes on Anita as her whole

body was filled up with fluid, and she was sent home. Her husband and both children were depressed and felt helpless. She was incapable of getting up herself. She had to be assisted by someone to get up.

One night Anita was crying profusely and worrying about how she would manage everything now. She was most worried about her daughter, Neha. Anita really wished Neha had got married and settled while she was alive.

Finally, Anita fell asleep. In the middle of the night she recalls Maa spoke to her.

'Get up, baby, and go to the washroom.'

Maa held Anita's hand and took her to the washroom. Three or four times in the night Maa woke up Anita and took her to the washroom.

'Maa, I do not need to go to the washroom any more,' Anita said in her sleep.

Neha, Anita's daughter, was sleeping next to Anita and was woken by her mother's talking.

'Mummy, who are you talking to?'

'I'm talking to Maa.'

'But Maa is long gone, Mummy.'

Anita insisted that Maa took her to the washroom three to four times in the night and each time Anita went to the toilet. Everyone in the house was stunned as Anita was incapable of getting up herself let alone going to the toilet by herself.

They went to the hospital in accordance with the doctor's advice to take the fluids out and make her last few months more comfortable.

She was lying down and all machines were attached to her to take the fluid out. Surprisingly no fluid came out. She had no excess fluid in her body. The doctors were stunned.

Her healing started and her bilirubin levels started jumping down. Within three months all her tests showed SGOT, SGPT, bilirubin and albumin as normal. Her body weight started improving and stabilized.

Neha got married in 2014 and I had the pleasure to invite all of them for lunch. Five years later Anita looks well, and as always, a positive, kind-hearted and loving person.

Have purity and goodness in your thoughts.
Always keep your morale high

—MAA

ANGANA MAHESHWARI

When Angana, my daughter, turned fifteen years old in 2009, she contracted a bad case of an acne attack similar to what I faced twenty-seven years before. It completely shook her confidence, she became a loner at the time and started walking with her head down. I was shattered and very worried to see her in such a state.

I went to Maa's temple and her grandson Sunny Bhaiya said, 'Didi, wait for two years and Angana will touch the sky.'

'I will take care of her. She will be absolutely fine,' blessed Shyam Baba when he channelled through Sunny Bhaiya.

She was given Shyamjal and was blessed by Maa from an astral world.

That night Angana felt Maa's presence in her bedroom empowering and protecting her.

Slowly Angana started recovering and her confidence grew. She chose to challenge herself and undertook the International Baccalaureate programme in 2011. She stood for student council elections in her new school where no one knew her. After presenting a speech and a video on herself in front of the entire student body and teachers, she won hands down.

Angana's face cleared of acne completely and her posture improved. It all took place within two years—as Sunny Bhaiya had predicted.

Today she is studying media culture and communication in New York University. The relatives and friends, who witnessed her going through the tough time in her life, are surprised by the change in Angana today.

'I will go with her where ever she wishes to study for university,' said Shyam Baba reassuring me, when I professed my concern over sending her abroad to study.

Angana kept her sincerity and dedication. She worked with faith, hope and conviction to change her life for the better.

Miracles happen when we open ourselves to them and work with diligence and sincerity towards our goal. Angana visualized herself at NYU all the time while in high school and followed her dream with full belief.

Miracles happen when we allow them to take place
—MAA

❖

SUNNY BHAIYA AND NITIN'S ACCIDENT

Sunny Bhaiya, Nitin and Sumit (Nitin's brother), were driving back from Khatu to Delhi, in the early morning on 5 January 2012. The car met with an accident. Nitin was stuck behind the steering wheel. A man came from nowhere, wrenched opened the door and forced the seat back. Sunny Bhaiya and Sumit crawled out of the wreck and carefully pulled Nitin out. His chest and face were lacerated with glass splinters.

Baba told Sunny bhaiya, 'Nitin will be fine.'

But Nitin's condition was critical. Sunny Bhaiya ripped Nitin's shirt open and started taking the glass splinters out. He called for an ambulance which came very quickly.

Glass shards had pierced Sunny Bhaiya's eye.

'If the glass had pierced it a hair-width above the wound, you would have lost your eye,' the doctor who examined Sunny Bhaiya informed him.

Doctors attended to Sunny Bhaiya first as according to them Nitin didn't have any hope to live. Nitin had lost sensation in most of his body.

'Nitin are you alive?' Sunny Bhaiya asked.

'Umm,' Nitin faintly responded.

They moved him to Medanta hospital, one of the leading

hospitals of Delhi, with a critical care unit. The doctors examined him and gave up as his blood pressure plummeted, his respiratory reading was at 7 (which is lower than a person in coma).

News had been sent to the Khatu temple about the accident. The priest in the Khatu temple sent a small parcel with a devotee to the hospital for Nitin's welfare. The priest had instructed the devotee to keep the parcel under Nitin's pillow. As the devotee placed the parcel, Nitin's blood pressure shot to 120/80 and his respiratory reading went from 7 to 22 (within the normal range). However, he was still in critical danger due to the severe injuries and the doctors were unable to stop the internal bleeding.

Devotees organized special prayers and the internal bleeding stopped at almost within twenty-four hours after the accident. Before starting surgery, the doctors anticipated Nitin would need a brain operation.

In the meantime Nitin's uncle who is a doctor at AIIMS, came to Medanta hospital to talk to the doctors.

Baba told the uncle, through Sunny Bhaiya, 'The brain cannot be touched. Take this packet and go inside the operation theatre.'

'I will not be allowed to go inside the operation theatre.'

'Just walk in and no one will stop you,' Baba said.

'How will I go the operation theatre amongst brain specialists and other surgeons?'

He spoke professionally to the surgeons about the case and walked into the theatre with them. No one asked him to leave.

Once in the theatre, doctors decided to access the nerve through the cheekbone instead of the brain. Brain surgery was called off. The doctors operated on Nitin for thirteen hours.

Baba kept channelling through Sunny Bhaiya and narrating to all the family members and devotees what was happening. After the surgery the uncle came out and prostrated on the floor in front of Sunny Bhaiya and said, 'Jai ho Shyam Baba! It is a miracle that I have witnessed just now.'

The surgeon from Medanta came out and said, 'We believe in God and do not believe in supernatural powers. But something unworldly was looking out for Nitin, because his case was next to impossible.'

Never feel lonely or helpless. Remember Shyam Baba is always with you. Have trust and patience

—MAA

DEVKI JINDAL

One of Maa's devout devotees, Vinod Jindal, was very happy as his son, Sumit, and daughter-in-law Vanita were due to deliver their first child in 2011. On 7 March 2011, Vanita felt a severe pain in her stomach and on Sunny Bhaiya's advice, she went to the hospital for check-up. After the check-up, doctor said that this was a false pain and since the pain was unbearable, she gave her a painkiller.

But Baba insisted that Vanita should go to the hospital and said, 'The baby has no heartbeat and the blood has become water.'

Vanita went to her gynaecologist who confirmed that all was fine and prescribed painkillers. But Baba insisted that the baby was in distress and needed urgent attention.

The next day, around 9 p.m. in the evening, the couple got a call from Sunny Bhaiya. He told them, 'Take Vanita to the doctor immediately and do not take her to your doctor. Take her to another doctor—the baby's heartbeat is going and if needed get her operated to deliver the child.'

Vanita went to a gynaecologist, who was her maternal aunt. She told her about what Baba said. When the doctor checked the heart beat of the baby, they found that it had gone down.

Vanita went into labour and was admitted in the hospital and kept under observation the entire night. On examination she was found normotensive full-term pregnancy in early labour. Later, the doctor also found that her foetal heartbeat was variable with episodes of brady cardea. However, the labour failed to progress.

Emergency surgery was done and at the time of surgery, it was seen that that there was no amniotic fluid around the baby.

'It was a miracle that in spite of the absence of fluid, the baby was unharmed,' stated the doctor.

By Baba's blessings Vanita delivered her daughter, Devki (meaning belonging to God). Her name was given by Baba in fagun mela pilgrimage.

Living with gratitude makes you a more content person.
Contentment leads to inner peace and joy

—**MAA**

❖

KOMAL JAIN

During the pilgrimage in Khatu in November 2014, I was searching for more dimensions of Maa's blessings for this book and Nitin recommended I talk to Komal Jain, as she had, experienced a life-changing experience.

As soon as I returned to London, I telephoned Komal who was visiting her aunt in Delhi.

When I introduced myself to her she was equally excited to share her story with me. There was a great synergy as she was very open and willing to discuss her journey from troughs to peaks. She had a cheerful positive tone with innocence and humility in her voice.

I thought she was extremely matured for a woman of twenty-five years, to be able to talk about her most difficult fears and how she overcame them.

After I finished my interview with her, I felt both humbled and inspired at the same time. I felt so blessed to have taken on my project of discovering Maa's devotees and sharing in their experiences.

Komal was born with very low vision, myopia and

photophobia. She was dependent on others and could not bear sunlight. Her parents tried to get the best treatment available. They went to the best eye institutions in India. However, none of the doctors could understand what was wrong with her.

It was a depressing situation and very tough for her and her parents. As a result she suffered with very low confidence, fear and insecurity. Her aunt, Keerti Singh started teaching at Komal's school in order to help her. She used to hold Komal's hand and walk with her everywhere in the school.

Finally her aunt, a devotee of Shyam Baba, took Komal to Maa in 2003.

Baba said, 'I will help you. You will go to America and I will go with you.'

They were in disbelief. Komal was so dependent on her family that it was difficult to imagine her going anywhere on her own nearby, let alone to a foreign land.

Maa gave her a small palm-size container full of ghee to apply on her eyelids every day. Komal has been applying a dab of the ghee on her eyelids ever since, yet the ghee never runs out.

Slowly, Komal's eyes started to get better and she devoted herself to her studies. As her eyes improved, Komal's faith soared. She was determined to succeed and be an independent woman.

Meanwhile, Maa passed away. By now Komal's trust in Maa and Baba was so deep she knew they would continue to be with her. Her efforts were rewarded with amazing high school exam results. She topped in her entire county/district.

For Komal this was a reflection of her new confidence and security she had developed living with Maa and Baba by her side.

She was offered a place in the prestigious National Law School in Ahmedabad and did her LLB from there. She was sent to the US from the Law school for a competition where she came third. After she returned, she finished her LLM and is now teaching law students in Jaipur.

When I spoke to her, the most significant thing that came across was her faith in Maa and Baba. She met Maa only once but her faith and belief became so high that she still takes blessings from Maa's photo and is determined to overcome all hurdles with Maa's blessings.

Education is a very important tool for growth. The more knowledge we share the more it will increase

—**MAA**

MAA'S ASTRAL PRESENCE

To me Komal's story was a clear example of how Maa continues to help her devotees from an astral level. Her devotees still feel her presence and sometimes also get inner guidance and direction. Almost all the devotees I spoke to during my research stated how terribly they missed her presence on earth, yet most of them still connect with her through their meditation and through her photos.

Such is the magnanimity and warmth that even today, ten years after Maa left her physical body, her photos emanate energy and warmth that dispel doubts, grief and insecurity. They radiate divinity and hope and her smile instantly quietens the disturbed mind.

Maa is timeless and limitless.

Have faith, everything will be fine

—MAA

Chapter Seventeen

Shyam Baba's Description of Maa

I was at Maa's temple in December 2014 and during the prayers, Baba channelled through Sunny Bhaiya and blessed my intention of paying tribute to Maa's life.

Shyam Baba described Maa as follows:

Maa was like a Kalpa Tree, a tree that just gives bountifully. It has divine power and unending ability to give. She kept giving to people and they took from her in their own ways. Some plucked gently, some tried to shake the tree to get the fruits. But she kept giving fruits to everyone irrespective of their approach and attitude. She gracefully and magnanimously kept blessing all in every which way with her divine smile and humility.

Maa was a rare devotee and I have her in the highest esteem and respect. She is my Maa too. I have placed her on my head where she truly belongs. She did so much for everyone that even I feel indebted to her for her selfless devotion and surrender to me.

Maa's heart was like a lotus leaf. The lotus grows in mud and muck but still flourishes and flowers. Amongst all adversities, she held me with the highest purity and highest devotion. She spread infinite love and compassion with absolutely no expectation from anyone in return.

Her biggest strength was that although she was in this world, she never became part of it. She fulfilled all her roles most diligently, but never got into the attachment of the material world. Although she was human she remained part of me. She did not allow the density of this world to drown her.

A lotus leaf has water drops that shine. They are visible to only those who observe carefully and the leaf holds them quietly together. That is how Maa kept her joys and sorrows together in her heart. You would have had to enter her heart and see, if you really wished to know her. As she never expected anything from anyone, she happily kept giving with no ill feelings and grudges. She was always consistent in her demeanour with everyone and that was marked by love, kindness, forgiveness and compassion.

Maa was Annapurna, the goddess of food, as she provided food for so many kitchens of her devotees by her blessings. She was Laxmi, the goddess of wealth, as she created livelihoods for thousands of devotees and now they are leading such prosperous lives. She was Saraswati, the goddess of knowledge, for people who got a voice from her. She helped so many mute people to speak. Maa became Shiva for her devotees when there was the need to take the toxins and poison out of their lives. Maa played Vishnu's role by nurturing the needs of her big family and even bigger family of her devotees. Maa played Brahma's role by changing so many devotees' destiny. She performed so many miracles and curtailed suffering in her devotees' lives by often taking their troubles on herself.

Maa was divine, living a human life fulfilling all her duties of this world. She was a lady who performed both a man and woman's roles. She was complete, independent and whole.

You do your duties and fulfil your responsibilities with utmost sincerity and leave the rest for Baba to take care

—MAA

/

Final Reflections

During the process of writing this book I began to reflect and focus on the wisdom, experience and learning from Maa that guided me to become the person I am today. I realized that I had momentarily diverted my focus on her loss over her blessings which continued beyond her physical presence on this earth.

My learning is to celebrate what we have today and count our blessings, which we often tend to forget. I was holding on to the pain I experienced after she passed away, which took me away from living in the moment. I'm now learning to live with Maa as part of me in my heart. I know that I can always seek her guidance and love within me. I am discovering that answers come to me when I give myself enough time, space and stillness; to trust myself more and follow my inner guidance.

To err is human, and we are soul in a human body that

are meant to experience a variety of emotions to help us evolve. Emotions are meant to be felt and not suppressed. The suffering comes when we suppress them or get too attached and identify ourselves with them. Maa's acceptance and non-judgemental approach to people allowed them to express their feelings freely. I feel if we can allow ourselves to honour our feelings truthfully and not judge ourselves, we can help heal ourselves and help others around us.

Most of us have dominant and passive sides. Out of our seven main chakras (energy centres), some of us are more spiritually inclined (crown chakra), some are more intuitive (third eye chakra), some more expressive (throat chakra), some more loving (heart chakra), some are strong-willed (solar plexus chakra), some are great with relationships (sacral chakra) while some are more grounded (root chakra).

Maa was complete in every aspect. She was the most grounded and stable person I have met and the most spiritual and intuitive person I have known. She spoke truthfully and led her life with unparalleled willpower with a magnanimous heart. She lived a life of a yogi in this real world, fulfilling every role diligently. She demonstrated the integrity by handling hurdles with joy and loving both the dark and the bright side of each of us unconditionally.

During this process I did some introspection about how I could help balance my energy centres and increase my consciousness. Mindfulness, yoga, meditation, reading inspirational books, walks amid nature, massages, a healthy diet and most importantly, sharing a good hearty laugh with family and friends, I found as simple and effective tools. Life is simple and beautiful and if we can discover its simplicity we can all help make the world a more beautiful and loving place.

Thank you, Maa, for gracing us with the art of forgiveness, acceptance and surrender with unconditional love by living it as an example. You united all as one through the essence of faith and true love. We hope to continue to illuminate the light of unconditional love in us thereby enriching our life's journey to a more meaningful and fulfilling path, helping us nourish our mind, body and soul.

A life of love, compassion,
forgiveness and surrender leads to liberation

—**MAA**

Acknowledgements

I would begin by thanking my husband, Sudhir, for trusting my abilities. His constant support enabled me to fulfil my dream of paying a humble tribute to my idol, Maa.

I am blessed with Angana and Ayush, who are my inspiration and source of strength. Thank you for gracing me with the joys of motherhood.

I thank my parents, with whom I began my journey with Maa and for their continued support for me to be with Maa.

Special thanks to Simon Brown, my macrobiotic teacher, who helped me organize my thoughts and to weave them objectively.

My heartfelt thanks to Meenu, Nitin Bhaiya, all the Shyam Baba devotees and Maa's family who helped me collate information on Maa and Baba.

Above all and most importantly, this journey became possible with Sunny Bhaiya's faith in me. I would not have been me today without his care and support since Maa passed away.

I humbly dedicate this book to Maa and her cause towards humanity. The royalty from this book will go towards the reconstruction of Maa's dharamshaala—Vatsalya Bhavan—in Khatu, a project I have undertaken with Sunny Bhaiya, as a tribute to Maa's faith and true love.

Glossary

Aarti—a ritual performed in homes and temples in which incense and light is offered to a deity. Every deity has a special devotional song sung during this ritual.

Beta—an expression used with love, child-like.

Bhajan—devotional songs of praise of the gods and deities.

Bhakti—devotion.

Bhaiya—a title used as a mark of respect for a brother.

Chakra—energy centres in the soul. The name derives from the wheel but in the yogic context.

Chattar—is like an umbrella made of silver or gold. It denotes respect to the deity or ruler who looks after the people and their safety.

Churma—it is a popular Rajasthani delicacy. It is coarsely ground wheat crushed and cooked with ghee and sugar.

Darshan—an auspicious sight of a deity or a great saintly person.

Dharamshaala—pilgrims' rest-house.

Didi—a title given to a sister to be addressed with respect.

Dwadashi—in Sanskrit Dwadashi means the twelfth day of the lunar cycle.

Ekadashi—the eleventh day of each lunar month considered an auspicious day dedicated to Lord Vishnu. In Sanskrit, it means eleventh day.

Fagun mela—is a popular festival/fair associated with Shyam Baba temples all over the world (also known as Shyam Baba fagun mela or nishan yatra). It is believed Barbarik's sheesh (head) appeared on fagun ekadashi (eleventh day on the lunar cycle in spring).

Kalash—a metal pot with a large base and a small mouth, large enough to hold a coconut. It is viewed as an auspicious object.

Karma—the sum of a person's actions in this and previous states of existence, viewed as deciding their fate in future existences (in Hinduism and Buddhism).

Kalyug—era or age of vice (said to be starting 3000 B.C. and ongoing). It is the last of the four stages the world goes through as part of the cycle of eras described in the Sanskrit scriptures. It is associated with discord or quarrel.

Kirtan—praise and chanting as a devotional tradition.

Jaagran—all-night-long prayer.

Puja—prayer

Sheesh—head

Shyamjal—holy water from Shyam kund. Shyam kund is a pond in Khatu, near the temple. It has an unending water supply and has miraculous powers.

Vibhuti—holy powder.

About the Author

An economics graduate from the University of Delhi, with a diploma in systems analysis, **Sangeeta Maheshwari** has keen interests in holistic living and alternative therapies. She has studied and trained in macrobiotic lifestyle and Reiki, and has conducted workshops in London to increase the awareness of 'self' and how to overcome stress and anxiety. Through The Maheshwari A2Z Foundation, a charity she co-founded with her husband, she works for the empowerment of underprivileged children in India. Sangeeta is a global citizen and currently lives in London, England with her husband and two children.

For more information visit www.sangeetamaheshwari.com

Saints & Sinners Ball

Stacy M. Jones

ISBN: 978-0-578-49741-9
Imprint: Stacy M. Jones
First printing edition 2019

Any references to historical events, real people, or real places are used fictitiously. Names, characters, and places are products of the author's imagination.

Book design by Sharon Aponte, Chick & a Mouse Graphic Design.

For more information and to contact the author:
www.stacymjones.com

DEDICATION

For Kelley
25 years of amazing friendship

ACKNOWLEDGEMENTS

Saints & Sinners Ball would not have been created without a wonderful creative team working with me. A special thanks to Sharon Aponte with Chick & a Mouse Graphic Design for the great cover, and Dj Hendrickson for her invaluable editing and suggestions. And to all my readers and those who continue to support me on this journey – thank you. You make writing these stories a joy.

SAINTS & SINNERS BALL

Chapter One

The moment Harper Ryan crossed the bridge over the Mississippi River, connecting Tennessee to Arkansas, the stress left her shoulders. She had been driving for two days. The first night she made it from Manhattan to Bristol, Virginia. Today, she had been traversing the long length of Tennessee. She had flown to Nashville before but had never traveled the length of the state. It was long and boring. She had another two and a half hours to Little Rock – her final destination.

While Harper had learned to drive as most kids did around age sixteen, she never had much use for it in Manhattan. She had a driver or took a cab. On a rare occasion when Harper was younger, she had taken the subway. Her father, Maxwell Ryan, had chastised her for that decision so she never took the subway as an adult. If she was being honest with herself, Harper's father chastised her about nearly all of her decisions.

He'd been the one who had given her the brand-new Land Rover when he had sternly suggested she leave Manhattan. Without realizing it, he had handed Harper the keys to her freedom. He had told Harper she should leave to take some time to think about how she disgraced the family. Really, Harper finally felt like she had been let out of her cage. She had to admit though, driving this far all alone had been a challenge. She was readjusting to being behind the wheel, but she certainly didn't feel confident.

The Ryans were a wealthy upper eastside Manhattan family going back generations. They owned *Charlotte*, a national lifestyle magazine. Harper had been the editor-in-chief of her family's more than one-hundred-year-old publication until she was fired by her father for bringing scandal on their good name.

Truth was, it wasn't Harper's scandal. It was her husband, now ex-husband, Nick, who had the affair and gotten tied in with the mob. It was Harper who had cooperated with the FBI and kept her good name and her family's intact. What did she have to show for it? Not a damn thing. She lost nearly all her friends, her marriage, and her job.

Now here she was heading to live with her father's sister, her beloved Aunt Hattie. Given the early death of Harper's mother, Hattie was like a mom to her in many ways. They really only clashed on one main issue – Aunt Hattie was a psychic and fancied herself a witch. Not only fancied herself like that, but she owned a shop – Hattie's Cauldron: Potions and Pastries. The shop did quite well, which surprised Harper to no end.

Hattie was charismatic though. If Harper really had to admit it, Hattie did have a special kind of magic. She knew more than a few things that Harper had no idea how she knew. From what Harper could tell Hattie always kept it positive, too. There were no hexing or negative spells — just all love, light and positivity, which Harper was in desperate need of.

Hattie had tried to convince Harper more than once that she had magic in her, too. That those magic and psychic abilities were a trait that ran down the female side of the Ryan family line. Harper wasn't buying it. She was keeping her feet firmly grounded. Harper would try to be supportive of her aunt while she was at her house. But she sure the heck wasn't going to get involved in all that. Harper planned to get back to her roots and write and take some time to reevaluate her life plan.

A couple of weeks to forty, this definitely wasn't what she had envisioned for herself. Aunt Hattie kept telling her this was the time for reinvention — "Like a phoenix rising from the ashes," she said. Harper wished. She felt more like a half-dead pigeon tossed beneath a shrub in Central Park.

The rest of the drive passed quickly for Harper. She didn't need to stop, and before she knew it, she was navigating the streets into her aunt's neighborhood in the Heights. Memories of her time here as a little girl came flooding back. She loved to visit her aunt. The old house with its huge rooms and hardwood floors. Her aunt's knick-knacks and colorful rooms, it was wondrous to her as a child. At home in Manhattan, everything had been so constrained and sterile.

Harper pulled partway into the wide driveway that ran the length of the left side of the house. She hit the brakes a little too hard and lurched forward, snapping her seatbelt in place. She'd have to work on her driving. She popped the SUV into park and looked up at the old Victorian house. It looked exactly the same.

The house was painted a gray-blue with white trim. The front porch wrapped around the sides. Harper remembered spending so much time on that porch in her youth, laying on the swing reading, playing with the dogs, and just relaxing from the hot afternoon sun.

Harper took a step out of the SUV, planted her feet on southern ground, and breathed in the fresh air. The weather was mild. She pulled off her cardigan and adjusted her shirt underneath. Looking around, she didn't see her aunt, but she did see a man on a ladder on the side of the house.

"Excuse me," Harper called out, walking up the driveway toward him. He had tan cargo pants on and a blue flannel work shirt. A baseball cap covered his head and shielded part of his face from her view. She assumed he worked for her aunt, which was perfect because she didn't know how she could carry in all her stuff herself.

Approaching the ladder, she looked up and asked brazenly, "Do you think you can stop doing that and help me with my luggage?"

The man gave a hearty laugh. He didn't turn to look at her. He kept right on working on the window he was installing. Speaking over his shoulder, sarcastically he asked, "Do I look like a bellhop to you?"

Chapter Two

Harper stepped back, unsure of what to say. She looked up at him, wondering if he was joking, but more importantly, if he was going to stop what he was doing and assist her. He didn't. He just kept hammering the window frame. She tried to interrupt between each bang of the hammer but couldn't get the words out.

Finally, Harper cleared her throat and said sternly, "I could use your assistance. I'm Hattie's niece. I'm sure she would approve if you spent a few minutes helping me. We will compensate you for it."

The man stopped what he was doing and turned to look down at Harper. She wasn't sure if she was more struck by how annoyed he looked or how handsome he was.

He climbed down the ladder and firmly planted his feet on the ground. He turned to face her for the first time. They stood nearly eye-to-eye. Harper was about five-foot-seven, and he couldn't have been more than an inch taller. His dark smooth skin was complimented by dark brown soulful eyes. He appraised her, and it made Harper intensely uncomfortable. Although she was fully dressed, she felt naked under his gaze.

Finally, he asked curiously, "What makes you think I work for your aunt?"

"Well," Harper started and gestured up to the window, "you're clearly doing work. I know my aunt must need help around here. I just assumed you were her hired help."

"That was your first mistake. You assumed," he said with a smirk. "Hattie said you were a bit full of yourself."

Harper was taken aback. "I can assure you my aunt said no such thing," she barked, indignant to think this man knew anything about her.

The man just stood his ground, looking at her. He didn't flinch.

Harper took in his staunch demeanor and realized quickly she wasn't a match for him. She softened and asked sheepishly, "Did she really say that?"

The man tipped his head back and looked to the sky. He laughed again loudly. Looking back at her with a wide smile, he said, "No, of course not. I'm just getting a rise out of you. You must be Harper. I'm Jackson. I live across the street. I was just helping your aunt fix a few windows."

Harper nodded, looking up at his craftmanship. It was pretty good.

Jackson cautioned, "You probably shouldn't assume everyone is the hired help. This isn't Manhattan. Some of us are just neighborly."

Duly chastised, Harper conceded. "It's good of you to help her. Is she around?"

"She's at the shop. She left me the key to let you in." He pulled the key from his pocket and handed it to her.

Harper accepted it and tried to ignore the feeling that spread through her when his hand touched hers. She looked at him quizzically. "You must know my aunt well for her to have given you a key?"

Jackson nodded. "Your aunt and I became fast friends when I moved in a few months ago. I stop in to her shop usually once a day. She feeds me dinner sometimes, and I help around here with what I can. I'm fairly new in town. Your aunt has been a good friend to me."

Harper smiled. "She's like that." Harper turned and looked back at her SUV. "Well, I better start bringing in my stuff. Thanks for the key."

Harper walked back down the driveway, wondering how she was ever going to get all her stuff into the house by herself. She opened the back part of her SUV and looked at all her things. She wasn't sure if she was happy to be rid of so much stuff or found it pathetic that all she owned was reduced to what could fit into the SUV. She did have some larger furniture pieces she didn't want to part with in storage in Manhattan, but really, what she was looking at was all she had.

Harper was so lost in thought she didn't hear Jackson approach. He called to her, "I didn't say I wouldn't help you."

"Oh, I just assumed…" Harper trailed off.

"There you go assuming again," Jackson teased. His smile revealed perfectly straight white teeth with a slight gap between the front top two teeth that made his smile sexier in Harper's opinion.

"I appreciate that. I wasn't sure how I was going to get everything in myself."

Jackson looked at her boxes and designer suitcases. He started pulling items out. "Well, don't go thinking I'm nice or anything. Your aunt would hex me if I didn't offer to assist."

Harper pulled back and looked at him. A bit astounded that this sensible-seeming man could believe in all that, she asked, "Don't tell me you believe in all that magic nonsense?"

"Do I believe your aunt would actually hex me," Jackson asked rhetorically, "no, definitely not. She's too sweet for that. But I do think intuition and intent is a real thing. Who's to say someone can't be a bit psychic or put enough good energy into the world to make positive things happen?"

"I just think it's all a bit silly," Harper explained as she started pulling boxes out and setting them on the ground.

"Front or side door?" Jackson asked, looking up at the house. He had two boxes stacked on top of each other.

"Front. We can put them in the front hall and then get them upstairs."

Jackson nodded, and Harper trailed after him with boxes in hand.

As they climbed the front porch steps, she said, "What do you do for work?"

"I'm retired," Jackson said curtly.

"Retired?" Harped asked. "You look so young. Tech millionaire?"

"Not even close," Jackson said and then explained, "Army Colonel. I retired after thirty years a few months ago."

"Impressive," Harper said aloud, even though she hadn't meant to.

He raised his eyebrows at her. "Don't go being impressed. I don't need anyone falling in love with me."

Chapter Three

Harper just stood on the porch with boxes in hand and her mouth wide open. "I, uh…" Harper tried to respond and failed. He was infuriating.

Jackson laughed at her. He got the front door open and they entered. Hattie's two Golden Retrievers, Sparkle and Shine, came running up to them. Jackson navigated around them, setting the boxes down in the center hallway near the wide staircase that was in the middle of the home on the left.

He patted each of the dogs, scratching their heads and talking to them like they were old pals. He turned to Harper and said, "Chill out. I was kidding you. You're really easy to get a rise out of, you know? You're too serious."

"Most of the men I've known have been very serious. I'm not used to being teased like that."

Jackson watched her. "Just relax, and we'll get along fine."

They spent the next hour unpacking Harper's SUV and moving the boxes, suitcases and bags up to the second floor. Hattie had told Harper to take her old room. It had a lovely window seat on the front and the right side was rounded to accommodate the home's turret design. When Harper was little, Hattie had used the rounded space with its big wide windows as a reading nook. Harper hoped to do the same.

After the last of her stuff was in the room, Harper turned to Jackson. "I appreciate the help. Is there any way I can repay you?"

"No, I'm happy to help," he said. "Now I need to get back to fixing those windows. The Saints & Sinners Ball is here next week, and your aunt needs the place in shape."

"Saints & Sinners Ball?" Harper asked, unsure of what Jackson meant.

Jackson shrugged. "As I said, I'm new in town, too. From what I hear, it's the society event of the season. Your aunt hosted it last year and is doing it again this year. It's on Fat Tuesday. You know Mardi Gras. Hattie has big tents arriving in a few days for the backyard and the caterer. I'm surprised she didn't tell you about it."

"I'm not," Harper said and rolled her eyes. "I was coming here to escape events like that. Hattie knows that. I'm sure she knew if she told me, I would have delayed my arrival."

"Just give it a chance," Jackson encouraged. "Little Rock is different from Manhattan. The people, too." He headed towards her door but turned back. "Hattie told me a little about what you just went through. It's hard right now, I know. It gets easier, I promise."

Before Harper could respond, Jackson was gone. Harper looked around her old room. The furniture had been updated from the little girl princess bedding and décor to a more modern shabby chic. The room was large, taking up nearly the entire front of the home. The queen size bed had a natural wood headboard with two end tables flanking each side. There was a chest of drawers and a longer dresser with a mirror. The window seat was adorned with the same white, light lilac and gray pillows that were on the comforter and bed pillows. The light gray curtains were the perfect match for each of the windows. Harper was happy to see that her aunt had kept the reading nook. There were conformable oversized chairs and a table between them.

Harper closed her eyes and took a deep breath. The events of the last few months were finally catching up to her. So much had changed. She thought she was ready for this new life, but she felt a bit overwhelmed. *One step at a time*, she reminded herself.

She heard Jackson's hammering start back up. There was something oddly comforting knowing she wasn't alone. Not one for living in a mess, Harper got down to unpacking. She put clothes and shoes away and some personal items in the drawers. She tucked other items neatly in the closet and hung a few pictures she had brought from New York.

A couple of hours later, she stood back and appraised the neatly arranged room. Harper was exhausted but happy. She heard doors being opened and closed and her Aunt Hattie's voice downstairs.

Harper took a quick peek in the mirror, reapplied some lip gloss, straightened her honey-colored long hair and went to greet her aunt.

As Harper hit the landing in the middle of the staircase, she admired the bright blue and gold flower-designed stained-glass window and intricate detailing on the dark wood staircase. She turned and took the last several steps to the first floor of the home. Turning left, she headed to the back of the home to the kitchen. As she approached, Harper heard her aunt having a conversation with someone. But no one was responding. Her aunt would say a few words, pause, and then start speaking again.

Harper peeked her head around the corner into the kitchen. "Aunt Hattie, I'm here."

Hattie jumped at the sound of Harper's voice. She turned and opened her arms wide. Harper went and hugged her aunt. Hattie said, "Jackson called me and told me you were getting settled. You look lovely. Is your room okay?"

"Thank you. I feel a mess. The room is wonderful. I appreciate you letting me move in." Harper pulled back and looked around her aunt. She asked, "I thought I heard you talking to someone. Who's here?"

Hattie hesitated, seemed to fumble for a response. Finally, Hattie waved her hand. "You know me, just talking to myself. I'm an old woman, we do that." Hattie went back to the center island and pulled groceries out of the reusable bags.

Harper went over to help. She pulled oranges out of the bag and put them in the fridge along with some milk and cheese. Turning to Hattie, she joked, "Just don't tell me there's ghosts here. That would be more than I can take."

Chapter Four

Hattie was as sure as she was standing there that Harper was going to catch her talking to herself again, and there would be more questions she wasn't ready to answer. She wasn't really talking to herself though. Harper had been exactly right. The girl just didn't know it. Hattie was talking to her late husband, Clive Beauregard VI, simply known as Beau. His family was the original owners of the house – Beauregard Manor – as it was known in Little Rock.

The house, built right around 1900, was on an oversized plot of land at the corner of Hawthorne and Polk in the Heights neighborhood of Little Rock. The house's huge backyard backed right up to the St. Joseph's Catholic Parish. The parish grounds were massive. Visitors followed on Polk, which ran down the right side of Hattie's property line, to the entrance marked by a brick archway and a large wrought-iron gate that was usually open. Directly back was the large Catholic church with an elementary school to its right along with an administration building. On the left was the church rectory, the place where the parish priest resided. Behind that was just woods.

There was a narrow walkway flanked by trees that connected Hattie's backyard directly to the side of the lawn of the church rectory. Hattie was raised Catholic but lapsed over the years. She knew her Spiritualism beliefs were a clash, but the parish didn't seem to mind being that close to Hattie's home. The parish priest, who oversaw the entire property including the church, school and administration, was Fr. Patrick McNally. He was new and had just started over the previous summer.

Given the proximity to Hattie's yard, she had seen the priest a few times. They were not necessarily friendly but neighborly. Hattie assumed he knew about her beliefs, and she clearly knew and respected his. They seemed to keep a mutual respectable distance.

For as out there as some people thought Hattie was, she was still harboring one secret. And she wasn't sure that Harper was ready to hear about it. Hattie could speak to the dearly departed. She was a medium, but it wasn't a skill she ever used outside of her house. She had enough going on with the living. She had no time to be chatting up the dead, too. Except, that is, for her husband Beau, who popped in and out, and kept Hattie company. There were other spirits roaming around the old house, relatives of Beau's. Hattie knew she was going to have to explain eventually to Harper, but today wasn't that day.

As Hattie busied herself making a salad for the dinner, she heard Jackson knock twice on the back door and then enter, calling her name as he cut through the porch. "Am I too early?" he asked as he entered the kitchen.

Hattie turned to him. "Not at all. Could you grab those dishes on the island and set the table? Harper just went up to take a shower before dinner. How did it go earlier?"

Jackson grabbed the plates and silverware. As he was arranging them on the table, he explained, "She's wound a bit tight, but to be fair, I was giving her a hard time. She thought I was a handyman and demanded my help carrying her stuff."

Hattie drew back, a wide smile on her face. "She had people in Manhattan that did almost everything for her. She had a driver, an assistant, and a concierge at her building. She's probably gotten a bit spoiled. She'll relax eventually. What do you think though? She's pretty."

Jackson stopped setting the table and looked directly at Hattie. "She's very pretty, but that doesn't matter. This is not a setup. We are both recently divorced. I told you, I'm in no state for a relationship."

Hattie threw her hands in the air. "You only live once."

"You only live once for what?" Harper interrupted as she walked casually into the kitchen. She drew up short though when she saw Jackson. She reached up and touched her wet hair. She took a step back.

Hattie saw the look on Harper's face. "I forgot to tell you Jackson was coming to dinner, didn't I? I'm sorry. He's here most evenings."

"It's okay, I just didn't dry my hair or put on makeup," Harper said. "Let me go get myself more together."

"No need to on my account," Jackson offered.

"I guess I'm going to have to get used to you being around," Harper said dryly and sat down at the table.

Hattie brought the salad to the big farm table that took up one entire side wall of the kitchen. She had made a salad and hearty chicken soup with some fresh Italian bread on the side. After they had all served themselves, Hattie said, "We need to get to planning on the Saints & Sinners Ball. I will need both of you to help."

"I wish you had told me," Harper whined. "I'm really in no mood for big festive parties. I was hoping to fly under the radar here at least for a while."

Hattie felt for her. She really did, but she wasn't going to let Harper sulk and shrink into oblivion. Hattie touched Harper's arm. "Listen now, you went through some terrible things in New York. You need to regroup and get back out there. Besides, Fat Tuesday is March fifth this year and just ten days before your birthday. It's time to celebrate."

"Not much to celebrate," Harper said ruefully as she ripped off a piece of bread from the loaf.

"We can go together," Jackson offered with a teasing smile. "I've got women chasing me all over this city that I'm trying to avoid. Didn't you hear? I'm the new handsome bachelor in town."

"I'm sure you are," Harper said sarcastically and took a bite of bread, chewing deliberately while giving him a dirty look.

"Your New York attitude can help me fend them off." Jackson laughed.

Before Jackson or Harper could say another word, Hattie jumped in. "See? All settled. You'll go together to the ball." Taking a spoonful of soup and a bite of bread, she added, "We only have four days left until Tuesday. The tents are coming tomorrow, the decorator is coming the day after next and the caterer and others. I need coordination help, especially with the shop."

Turning to Harper, Hattie directed, "You can help here or you can always practice your magic and help out at the shop."

"No to the shop and your witchy ways," Harper grumbled. "I don't plan on going there anytime soon, but I'd be happy to help here."

Hattie smiled. She was not happy Harper was still down on the magic but pleased she'd be spending more time with Jackson. Hattie informed her, "You'll need a gown for the event. It's formal evening attire. I have a beautiful mask for you upstairs."

"Mask?" Harper asked confused.

"It's a masquerade ball," Hattie explained.

Harper smiled for the first time. She said excited, "You didn't say I can hide and pretend to be anyone I want."

"I guess that's true for everyone," Hattie agreed.

"You can pretend you're a sweet southern belle instead of a grouchy Yankee," Jackson offered, finishing off his soup.

Harper shot him a look, but he wasn't even looking at her. The effect of her annoyance fell flat.

Chapter Five

The days flew by in a scurry of activity. Harper barely saw her aunt. Hattie had been working long hours at the shop and then came home to continue preparations for the ball. Over the last few days, people had been dropping off items for the silent auction, and it was giving Harper a chance to meet a few people. What initially felt like being thrown to the wolves was proving to be a good way to jump into life in Little Rock.

Harper had been amazed at how little time it took her to feel settled into Hattie's house and her new city. She hated admitting he was right about anything, but what Jackson had said proved to be true. Little Rock was very different from Manhattan, and for that, Harper was thankful.

With the preparation out of the way, they eased right into the evening of the ball. Harper was standing in her room, putting the finishing touches on her makeup and curling the wisps of hair that framed her face. Her hair was pulled back in a stylish chignon.

Her gown was dark purple chiffon, strapless and floor-length that pulled in at her waist and showed the small curve of her hip. The gown had a sparkly beaded embellishment around her middle and a slit that went up high on her thigh. She'd never wear something that daring in Manhattan. The intricately-designed silver mask Hattie had bought her was perfect.

"You look amazing," Hattie commented as she stepped into Harper's room.

Harper turned to see her aunt. Hattie was wearing a lovely, floor-length gray chiffon gown that had a sheer sleeve. It was plain, but Hattie had dressed it up with a diamond necklace and bracelet. Hattie's short, stylish gray hair was the perfect cut for her. The whole look was understated but looked spectacular. Harper hugged her. "You look pretty amazing yourself."

"You're not angry because I told Jackson he could be your date?" Hattie wondered.

"At first," Harper admitted. "But he's been really helpful the last few days. I'm getting adjusted to his sense of humor, too."

"He doesn't mean any harm. I know that much. But I am having a bit of a rough time figuring him out," Hattie admitted as she checked herself one last time in the mirror. "He's a good man. I think just a bit closed off."

Harper nodded. "I'm just not used to anyone teasing me."

"How are you feeling?" Hattie inquired, changing the subject.

"I'm fine, why?"

Hattie rubbed a hand across her stomach. "Something isn't right about tonight, and I can't quite place it."

"Are you worried something will go wrong with the event?"

"No, nothing like that." Hattie hesitated and then went on. "I sense danger, but there's nothing rational to indicate that. I pulled a few Tarot cards, and I got death a few times. It doesn't make sense. Just keep your eyes open."

Harper reached out and squeezed her aunt's hand. "It will be okay."

Hattie leaned in and kissed Harper's cheek. "I'll see you outside. Don't forget to put your mask on. Jackson is already downstairs waiting for you."

Harper applied a little more lipstick and slipped on her heels. She put her mask on and tied it behind her head. It covered a good deal of her face and allowed Harper added anonymity, not that many people knew who she was anyway. But it was a freeing feeling.

She carefully walked down the stairs in her dress. Reaching the first floor, Harper saw Jackson waiting for her across the hall in the living room. He stood near the fireplace dressed in a tailored dark navy suit with a buttoned vest, jacket and tie. He had a crisp white shirt underneath and a striking copper metal Roman warrior mask. It had points at the top and looked medieval. Overall the look was striking, stylish and handsome.

As Harper entered the living room, Jackson didn't take his eyes off of her. Harper knew men well enough to know what the look meant, but all he squawked out was, "You clean up well."

Then he looked down at the floor and back up at Harper. He shrugged his shoulders and admitted, "I feel a bit foolish in this mask, but Hattie gave it to me and said it would be perfect. This isn't how I'm used to dressing."

"The mask is perfect for you. It's masculine and rugged, and a bit jagged on the ends like your personality," Harper offered with an overly sweet teasing smile. He could tease, so could she. It was true though. The mask fit him perfectly. She'd even go so far to admit he looked sexy, but she was never going to tell him that.

Instead, she admitted, "This isn't a dress my father would have allowed me to wear." She did a little spin and laughed, trying to break the tension. "I hope it looks okay."

"More than okay," he smiled. "You ready to do this? There are people out there already. If you want to bail and come back inside, I'll make an excuse for your exit."

"That's sweet of you, but I think I'll be okay."

The two headed for the front door, and just as they were crossing the threshold into the evening air, a slight chill ran down Harper's spine and a sense of dread took hold. She shivered. It was a fleeting feeling, passing as quickly as it came. Jackson raised his eyebrows at her, but she didn't have a response. He offered her his arm, and she took it. Harper hated admitting it, but she felt good on his arm, comforted almost.

The big white tents covered nearly all of Hattie's backyard. Harper saw a number of guests arriving, leaving their keys with the valet who would find places to park the cars in the local neighborhood and with businesses who had offered up their parking lots for the evening. Harper had been to more formal events and balls than she could count, but she had never attended a masquerade. Harper was enjoying seeing the colorful and intricately designed masks that the guests wore. Mardi Gras was apparently a much bigger deal in the south than she was used to in the northeast.

Jackson guided them into the tent, which was enclosed. While it was early March and the weather was warmer, it was still a bit chilly in the evenings. They weren't in the tent five minutes when a woman, probably in her fifties if Harper had to guess, approached. She had on a tight gaudy pink dress that was so tight her cleavage came spilling over the top and a feathered pink mask. It was such a sight Harper wasn't sure where to look.

"Jackson, you better save me a dance," the woman crooned. She reached out her hand and ran it down Jackson's chest. She shot Harper a nasty look as she touched him. Harper couldn't help but smile at the audacity and ridiculousness of the woman.

Jackson took a visible step back from her. "Belinda, sorry, no dancing this evening. I'm here with my date. This is Harper. She's new in town."

Harper started to say hello but was cut off.

Belinda said sharply, "I know she's Hattie's niece. We don't really need any more of her kind here."

"My kind?" Harper inquired angrily. Jackson reached down and squeezed her hand. Harper looked at him in annoyance. She knew he did it to silence her.

"Witches," Belinda hissed.

A sarcastic laugh escaped Harper's lips. She looked down her nose at the woman. "I assure you, I'm not a witch. But I don't think you should be here at my aunt's home insulting her."

Before the woman could say another word, Jackson pulled Harper away and to the other side of the tent. "Can't have you getting in catfights already. You haven't even been here a week."

"Well, she shouldn't insult my family." Harper regained her composure. She wasn't sure why she was so easily triggered. She'd never been in a fight in her life. She certainly wasn't going to start now.

Once she calmed down, Harper looked at Jackson with disgust. "She was awful. Tell me she isn't someone you've dated."

Jackson laughed. It was a full belly laugh, too. Loud enough for people around them to look. "Absolutely not. Her name is Belinda Danvers, and she's been in your aunt's shop a few times, always looking to hex some poor guy. She's tried to make a move on me before. That's why I asked you to be my date, I needed a good cover."

Harper opened her mouth to speak, but she didn't have a retort.

Jackson slid a finger under her chin and closed her mouth. He looked her right in the eyes. "I'm teasing you. Settle down." He grabbed her hand. "Come on, let's go mingle and meet some people. I heard everyone that's anyone will be here."

The pair spent the next couple hours meeting new people who welcomed them both to the city. Neither ate much and both sipped their drinks. The music was lively, the conversation was inviting, and Harper was starting to feel a bit at ease.

Chapter Six

"Hattie, you look lovely," Tucker Reese swooned as he pulled her into an embrace. He had on an ill-fitted suit and a black mask with tacky red beading.

She batted his fat hands away and moved them off her hips. "You old coot. Don't grope me. Where's your wife?" Hattie turned and looked around the tent searching for his wife, who wasn't anywhere to be seen.

Tucker knocked back his martini in one gulp and placed his glass on the tray of the server as they passed. "Lizzie wasn't feeling well tonight so she stayed home. I'm all on my own. Figured you'd keep me company." He reached his hands back to Hattie's middle, and she checked him with her hip. It nearly knocked him over. Tucker was clearly drunk.

Tucker was sixty-five, fat and bald. The sunspots on his hands and face hinted at far more time on the golf course than in a courtroom. He was the elected prosecuting attorney in Little Rock and ran the Pulaski County Prosecutor's office. His underlings did most of the work while he took the public credit. He was also a known womanizer, although Hattie wasn't sure what woman would be desperate enough.

"I thought I'd stop by your shop one of these days. I think my wife needs a little love potion, if you know what I mean." He laughed at his own innuendo while Hattie grimaced.

"Tell her to stop by herself, I'd be happy to help her," Hattie said. What she meant was she'd be happy to give Lizzie the spell to stop his philandering or one to give her the courage to leave him. She'd like to give Tucker a potion to make it shrivel and fall off, but she couldn't have that kind of karma on her soul, as satisfying as it would be.

"The mayor here yet?" Tucker asked. "We went duck hunting, and he owes me some money."

"Over there," Hattie pointed in the hopes he'd leave her side.

"Save me a dance," he slurred as he leaned in to kiss her.

She dodged out of his way and ground the heel of her shoe into the top of his foot as she moved past him. He yelped in pain. Hattie placed a hand on his arm and smiled sympathetically. "Oh, I'm so sorry, Tucker. I don't wear heels often, I got all tripped up."

That will teach him, Hattie thought as she moved farther into the tent, regaining her composure and making small talk with each of her guests. The tent was ablaze with white twinkle lights and candles on each table. The Mardi Gras decorations were tasteful and vibrant. The jazz band was playing, food was being served, and drinks were flowing. All seemed to be running smoothly.

Hattie kept an eye out for Harper and Jackson. The two seemed to be enjoying their time together. They both periodically checked in with the catering staff and gave Hattie a quick nod that all was okay. Then they would go back to laughing with each other and meeting the array of Little Rock society out for the evening.

Hattie mingled with the ladies from the Junior League and the Little Rock Garden Club. The Garden Club was responsible for the gigantic bronze bunny statue on Kavanaugh. It was right down from Hattie's shop. The jury was still out for Hattie on how she felt about it. She loved how whimsical it was, but if she looked too closely, there was something creepy in its eyes.

Hattie continued her rounds. She air-kissed cheeks, told ladies they looked lovely and made the appropriate small talk. She may be the city's resident witch, but she was still raised a New York society girl.

"Dan Barnes!" Hattie called out when she caught sight of him. Dan had been the editor-in-chief with the Little Rock Record but was now the editor-in-chief of *Rock City Life*, a monthly magazine and digital daily that covered food, culture, parties, people and more. Pretty much everything Little Rock high society had to offer. If you were fortunate enough to grace their pages, you were the "in" crowd.

Dan was one of Hattie's favorite people in Little Rock. He was no-nonsense and a good egg. If it didn't work out with Jackson, Dan was definitely a consideration for Harper. He was handsome, had a mess of dark hair and a sweet lopsided smile. He was far too married to his work though. He left the paper for work-life balance he claimed, but Dan worked just as hard at *Rock City Life*. He just got to eat good food and drink on the job now.

"Hattie, you weren't supposed to recognize me wearing my mask," Dan teased. He struck a pose with his hands on his hips and face turned to the sky. He laughed at himself before turning and giving Hattie a hug.

"You look handsome. Where's your date for the ball?"

"No date. No one loves me," he joked. Looking around, Dan added, "This is a great party. There's going to be awesome photos for the magazine next month. Before the night ends, make sure we get one of you."

"We can include my niece, Harper, too. Did I tell you she just moved here?" Hattie asked, looking around for Harper. When she couldn't spot her, she turned back to Dan. "You should connect with her. Harper was editor-in-chief of our family's lifestyle magazine *Charlotte* in New York. She'd be a great freelancer for you."

"I'm always looking for talent," Dan admitted. "I'm familiar with *Charlotte*. Who isn't? I don't like admitting it, but I could use some help with the direction of the magazine. I'm sure Harper's a wealth of information. I'd be happy to connect with her. Is she here now?"

"She was here with my neighbor Jackson, but I don't see either of them. Let me walk around and see if I can find her."

Hattie headed off towards the house, making her way across the dance floor. She stopped to speak to a few people she knew. Then she ran into a couple of her favorite clients. Nearly forty minutes later, Hattie was wrapping up a discussion about the benefits of valerian tea for sleep when a piercing scream startled her.

The scream grew louder. The band stopped playing, and everyone turned to see where the scream was coming from. Hattie would know that scream anywhere. It was Harper.

Chapter Seven

Hattie moved quickly through the opening in the tent and bumped right into Jackson. Together they walked around to the backside of the tent where the scream had come from. They got to the top of the narrow path that connected Hattie's property to the Catholic parish, and what they saw stopped them cold. They both pulled off their masks to take a clearer look.

Harper was standing midway in the path and was looking into the trees. All that was visible to Hattie was the bottom half of what appeared to be a man, just his legs below the knee and feet in dress shoes were sticking out. With that, Hattie and Jackson took off moving quickly towards her.

Jackson reached Harper before Hattie did. He took Harper by the arm and spun her away from the man. He held back Hattie, too. He moved swiftly but efficiently. Jackson bent over the man who was lying face up in the grass. Hattie could see that the man's eyes were open beneath the mask he was still wearing, but they were not focused on anything. There was a distinct bullet hole in the man's forehead. There was no question he was dead. Jackson checked the man's pulse to be absolutely certain and stepped back to them.

"We need to call the police. Do we know who he is?"

Hattie wouldn't need the man's mask removed to know his identity. She had just spoken to him earlier in the evening. It was Prosecuting Attorney Tucker Reese.

Jackson pulled his cellphone from his pants pocket and called 911. He explained the situation and promised to let no one near the scene. Hattie turned back to see guests forming in a group at the top of the path. She waved the few of them away that started to walk towards them.

She turned to Harper. "Are you okay? Hurt anywhere?"

"I'm all right. Just shaken," Harper explained. Then she started, "I was waiting for Jackson, and I heard arguing…"

Harper was cut off by a man approaching from the opposite end of the path. Hattie turned to see Fr. Patrick McNally walking towards them.

"What happened here?" Fr. McNally inquired, looking at Hattie and Harper and then down to the dead man. He looked back to Hattie for an explanation.

Fr. McNally was young for a parish priest. He was in his early fifties, and when he wasn't working, dressed in casual clothes rather than the black pants and shirt and white collar many older priests wore. Hattie took in his jeans and red pullover sweater. His pants were muddy and so were his hands. His dark hair was messy and out of place. Hattie was immediately suspicious.

"Where did you come from?" Hattie asked curtly.

Fr. McNally stumbled over his words, "I was in my residence, and I heard screaming. I came out to see what was happening. I saw the three of you here."

"Why are you all muddy?" Hattie eyed him suspiciously.

He looked down at his pants and his hands. Fr. McNally must have realized Hattie's suspicions because he answered quickly. "It's not what you think. I was in the basement going through some old boxes. I had just come up when I heard the screaming."

Hattie put a protective arm around Harper. While his explanation was reasonable, she knew in her gut something was off. She turned to Jackson. "I'm taking Harper in the house. Keep him here."

Harper started to speak, but Hattie shook her head no. Harper got still again. Her eyes were wide, and she was trembling. As Hattie walked Harper past the crowd, she could hear the sirens off in the distance. Hattie turned to her guests. "You should go back into the tent. A man was killed. The police will want to speak with all of us."

Hattie heard the gasps of the women and the hushed words of the men, asking each other who it was that was killed. But they all did as Hattie asked and turned around and went back into the tent.

As Hattie was walking Harper back to the house, Dan approached. He pulled off his mask and asked, "Do you need help?"

Hattie touched his arm. "Walk with me into the house, please."

The three of them made their way around the tent into the front yard. As they headed up the front walkway, several Little Rock police cars pulled into the driveway. As cops got out and approached, Hattie explained that Harper had found the body, and they were going into the house to wait. Hattie explained where they could find the body. She added that Jackson, her neighbor, had called 911 and was standing guard.

Hattie looked at the detective, "You're going to want to get this one right. The dead man is Tucker Reese. Jackson is also keeping an eye on Fr. McNally, the parish priest. He approached us when we found the body. He seems out of sorts."

One of the detectives, a tall black man who had massive arms and a chest that strained the material of his shirt, stepped forward. He offered his hand to Hattie. "I'm Detective Tyson Granger. The other detectives will head down to where the body is, but I'll speak to you both now."

Hattie nodded in understanding and the four of them went into Hattie's house through the front door. She motioned for them to head into the large living room on the right off the hallway.

Hattie turned to Dan and told him to light the fireplace while she motioned for Det. Granger and Harper to take a seat.

Once seated, Harper reached up and untied her mask. "I forgot I still had this on," Harper explained to no one in particular. Sparkle and Shine came over to Harper and rubbed up against her legs. She gave each of them a pet behind the ears.

Det. Granger turned to Hattie and Dan, "I'd like to speak to Harper alone first, so if we can have some privacy, that will be appreciated."

Hattie didn't want to leave Harper. After the murder of her friend in New York, and now this, Hattie felt horrible for her. Harper was strong, but there was only so much one person can take. At least she had the dogs for comfort and protection.

Seeming to sense her hesitation, Det. Granger assured, "I'll go slow, and if Harper needs a break, we can stop."

Harper spoke up, "I'll be fine. It's okay, Aunt Hattie, really."

Hattie and Dan left them and walked into the back of the house to the kitchen. Sitting at the kitchen table, Dan asked, "Was it really Tucker Reese?"

"If I didn't see the bullet hole in his head myself, I would have thought he was passed out drunk."

Chapter Eight

"As I said my name is Det. Tyson Granger. I just need to hear what happened," he said, sitting forward in his chair with his hands resting on his knees.

Harper leaned back and closed her eyes. She took a deep breath. "I just moved here last week from New York," she started. "I didn't know many people at the party. My aunt's neighbor, Jackson, is new to town, too. We had been walking around meeting people together when he had a call he needed to take. While I was waiting, I walked towards the woods at the very back of the yard, and that's when I heard people arguing."

Granger interrupted. "Could you hear what they were saying?"

"No, it was just muffled words, but I could tell from the tone it was harsh and angry. I followed to where the voices were coming from, and that's when I saw two men through the trees. I was on the edge of the lawn, not to the clearing yet, but I could see through the trees. I just thought it was two people arguing so I turned away. But then I heard a noise. It was like something falling. I turned back, and they were gone."

Granger moved farther to the edge of his seat. "I'm not sure I understand. What do you mean like something falling?"

"It's hard to explain." Harper sighed. "It was like leaves crunching and twigs snapping. Maybe it was when the man fell or maybe the other man ran through the trees. I don't know, but I couldn't have had my back to them for more than a few minutes. I was just standing there looking up at Jackson. I was thinking he looked annoyed, and I wondered what was wrong."

"Could you see either of the men from where you were standing?" Granger inquired.

"The man who wasn't shot, yes, but not really. I could see him, but he had a mask that fully covered his face. It was red and gold and had horns like the devil. Actually, the whole mask looked a bit like the devil. I couldn't make out anything else about him. That mask was all I could see."

"You ended up finding the body, correct?" Granger confirmed. "When did you realize something was wrong?"

Harper's voice grew quiet. "I heard that noise and when I turned back, there was no one there. People don't disappear that fast so I got curious. I walked along the tree line to the edge of the clearing. That's when I could see someone's feet sticking out. The rest of him was in the more wooded part. I assumed maybe he was drunk and fell. I was going to see if he needed help. But when I got there…"

"Did you realize right away that he was deceased?"

Harper nodded. "His eyes were open, he wasn't moving. I could see the bullet hole. There was blood. I couldn't seem to move after that. I wanted to run, but I couldn't move my feet. All I could do was scream." Harper started to softly cry.

Granger reached over and rubbed her arm. "You didn't see anyone else? The other person in the mask wasn't around?"

"No, there was no one. If he was in the woods, I didn't see him. I'm sure it was a man."

"How do you know that?"

"His height. The way he carried himself. His voice." Harper paused and then said forcefully, "It was definitely a man."

"You didn't know the deceased?" Granger questioned.

"I just moved here," Harper reiterated. "I barely know anyone. He wasn't someone I had been introduced to or had met this evening."

Granger pulled out a pen and notepad from the folder he had in his hands and jotted down some notes. He looked back up at Harper, "Is there anything else you can think of that might be important? Even the smallest detail."

Harper thought for a moment but nothing was coming to her. "Not right now," she said finally, and then asked. "Can I get a drink of water?"

"Sure, I think we are all set. I'll stop by when I have more questions."

They both got up, and as Harper turned to leave, Granger asked, "What made you leave New York to come to Little Rock?"

Harper felt no need to lie. He could easily find out on his own. "My ex-husband got tied in with the mob, had an affair, and one of his friends was murdered. I testified against him. After that, I don't think many people wanted me to stay in the city. I was trying to avoid more scandal."

Granger looked at her with a mix of surprise and admiration. "You testified against your own husband?"

"The FBI asked for my help," Harper explained. "I helped. He clearly wasn't the man I thought he was when we were married. Sometimes you just have to do what's right. After I helped, I then had to testify."

Granger raised his eyebrows. "You helped the FBI?"

"I'm tougher than I look, Detective," Harper noted. Then thoughtfully, as much to herself as to him, she said firmly, "I think I'm tougher than I even realize sometimes."

Harper looked around the detective as a uniformed cop entered the room. Det. Granger turned his attention to the cop. He was young, looked barely out of college. He excused himself for interrupting. "There have been five more burglaries tonight. We just got the call on the radio. The homeowners are here at the party. All of them. They were just notified. I know you've been pulled off that case for this one, but Det. Thompson said you'd want to know."

"Thanks, I do," Det. Granger said sternly. He took an audible breath and ran a hand down his face. The cop turned and walked out.

"Burglaries?" Harper asked concerned.

Det. Granger turned his attention back to her. "It's nothing to worry about. We've had several house burglaries on nights like this. When there are big events in town that have wealthy guests in attendance, thieves know it's a good night to hit those houses. Of course, we encourage house alarms and such, but it happens in every city."

"Did he say there were five tonight?" Harper inquired, adjusting her gown. It felt light and airy when she put it on early in the evening. Now it felt heavy, weighing her down.

"Yes, five houses got hit. If it's like the others, the thieves will have taken mostly expensive jewelry. Easy grabs," Granger explained.

"Oh, that's terrible." Harper grimaced. "I don't understand how people can be so terrible. All the people were here at the ball?"

Det. Granger nodded but remained tightlipped and didn't offer her any more information. He looked worried, but maintained his composure. He shook Harper's hand and said he would be in touch. Det. Granger headed towards the front door just as Jackson walked in.

Chapter Nine

Harper met Jackson in the hallway as she followed Granger to the door. The detective stopped and asked Jackson to meet him in the morning at the police station to give a formal statement. Jackson shook the man's hand and said he'd be there first thing.

After the door closed, Harper turned to Jackson and sighed loudly. He looked at Harper with concern. "You turned out to be an exciting first date," Jackson said, offering a sympathetic smile.

"Yeah most women aren't usually finding dead bodies," Harper countered. "When you were out there did you hear if the police know any more?"

Before Jackson could answer, Hattie appeared down the hall at the threshold of the kitchen. She waved both of them back. As Harper and Jackson entered the room, Harper drew up short. She hadn't known the man that had walked into the house with them, and right now outside of Hattie and Jackson, she wasn't trusting anyone. Apparently, Jackson felt the same.

"Who are you?" Jackson asked with a hint of annoyance in his voice.

Dan stood and started to speak, but Hattie cut him off. "This is Dan Barnes. He's the editor-in-chief for *Rock City Life*. I was speaking to him right before Harper screamed."

"Right before, as in you were standing with him?" Jackson asked. He stood with part of his body shielding Harper. She peered over his shoulder at Dan, sizing him up.

"Well no, I guess not right before," Hattie offered. She turned to Dan, "What would you say, like thirty to forty minutes before?"

"About that," Dan agreed. Looking at Jackson he inquired, "Why does it matter?"

"Because we don't know who killed the man, everyone's a suspect," Jackson said definitively.

"Jackson," Hattie admonished. She sat down at the table, pulling Dan by the arm back down to his seat. "I've known Dan for close to ten years. I can assure you he didn't kill Tucker Reese. I had just been speaking to him about the magazine and recommending Harper for some freelance work. I was in search of the two of you when I heard Harper scream."

Dan looked past Jackson and right at Harper. "I swear to you I was in the tent. I used to be the editor-in-chief at the local paper, and now I run *Rock City Life*. I was here working tonight. Besides, I wouldn't kill anyone."

Harper moved around Jackson. She went to the table and shook the man's hand. No alarm bells went off for her, but then again, she had trusted her husband right up until the end. Harper said resigned, "I wish we were meeting under better circumstances. Given what happened, you can imagine we are both a bit shaken."

Jackson still wasn't moving. He had his hands on his hips and was staring down Dan. He gruffed, "As far as I'm concerned, anyone not standing in front of me in the moments leading up to Harper finding the body is suspect."

Hattie shot him a look of exasperation. "You'll have to excuse him. He's retired military and not the trusting type."

"I get it," Dan conceded. He turned to Jackson. "I'm a friend, really. I want the cops to solve this as much as you do. I don't know too many people that liked Tucker Reese, but something like this can tarnish a city."

Jackson didn't move or say anything. He just stood there and watched them. It was endearing to Harper the way he was protective of them already, even if she felt it was misplaced.

Hattie got up and gave her a hug. "Let me make you some tea."

"What's happening outside? What will the police do now?" Harper asked no one in particular.

Jackson's voice was cold and direct. "They have everyone in the tent. They called the medical examiner and crime scene techs. They will question everyone they can, and go over the scene looking for evidence. Hopefully with enough witnesses, they can solve this quickly."

"I don't know how. He was wearing a full-face mask." Harper wrapped her arms around herself for warmth.

Jackson walked into the living room and pulled a small throw blanket off the couch and brought it to her, draping it over her bare shoulders. "What kind of mask was he wearing?"

"It looked like the devil. It had horns at the top and was red and gold. I couldn't see any of his face showing. I didn't see the color of his suit, but it was dark. I couldn't make out much else."

"Nothing else to identify him, then?" Jackson asked. He stepped back from Harper and leaned against the wall, crossing his arms over his chest.

Harper shook her head no. She asked Jackson, "Who were you talking to? You took that call, and that's when I walked to the edge of the property to give you space. I saw two men through the trees and heard them arguing, but didn't think anything of it. I turned back around and you looked so angry. I got distracted watching you."

Jackson pinched the bridge of his nose. "It was personal."

"I see," Harper said.

"It's not like that," Jackson conceded. "It was my ex-wife. She calls sometimes. She's been calling all day so I finally just answered so she'd stop."

Harper didn't press further. She wouldn't want to have to talk about Nick. Looking around at each of them, she asked, "Did anyone else see the man in the devil mask at the party?"

Before anyone could answer, a voice came from right behind Harper. "That's the question of the hour," said Matthew Inslee as he walked into the kitchen from the back porch. He startled everyone, but Harper practically jumped out of her skin. Sparkle and Shine put themselves between Harper and the man and started barking loudly at him.

Chapter Ten

Jackson immediately squared off with the man. "What are you doing in Hattie's house?"

"Settle down," Inslee said over the barking. He flashed his badge. "I'm with the Prosecutor's Office. Stop these damn dogs."

Hattie shooed them out of the kitchen.

Inslee explained, "I'll be heading up the criminal case once there is an arrest. Det. Granger said I would find Ms. Harper Ryan in here."

"You don't just go sneaking around like that," Jackson cautioned. "We are all a bit on edge."

Inslee ignored Jackson's rebuke. He moved to Harper and offered her his hand. She took it. "Granger said you'd be in here. He didn't say you were this attractive though."

Hattie got up and crossed the room to him. She said dryly, "What an odd thing to say to a murder witness. Jackson's right. You should have knocked or announced yourself. I can only imagine you were listening in on our conversation. What can we do for you, Mr. Inslee?"

"The infamous Hattie Ryan Beauregard. I heard you were…" Inslee paused and then with an exaggeration in his voice added, "perceptive."

"That's one word for it," Hattie smirked. "Why don't you take a seat, Harper was just going upstairs to get changed. She's a bit cold."

Hattie walked to Harper and whispered to Jackson, "Go up with her and wait a bit before you come down."

Harper wasn't sure what her aunt was up to, but she didn't like the look of Inslee. His dark slicked back hair and closely shaved beard were far too perfect. His movie star good looks weren't as becoming as the man thought. He came off arrogant and brash. Hattie had been right though. She was freezing now and uncomfortable in the gown.

Jackson guided her up the stairs, and then walked with her to her bedroom. He stopped at the threshold. Harper turned to see what he was doing. "You were just in here a few days ago. Come in. Take a seat. I'll be just a minute."

Jackson didn't look comfortable being there, but he sat in a chair in the reading nook. Harper watched him from the corner of her eye as she pulled a pair of jeans from her closet and a long-sleeve shirt. She went to the hallway bathroom and quickly changed. She took a quick look in the mirror. Her face was red and blotchy and her mascara had run from crying. She washed her face, and then applied just a small amount of makeup to look presentable. By the time she got back, Jackson had taken off his suit jacket, vest and tie. He undid the top button of his shirt.

"More comfortable?" she asked quietly as she hung up her dress.

"Definitely." Jackson yawned and rubbed at his eyes.

Harper sat down in the chair opposite him. She took a deep breath, and then unable to stop herself, she started to cry. She covered her face with her hands and sobbed. Jackson didn't say anything. Once she calmed down, he got up and grabbed a box of tissues that were on her dresser and handed them to her. "It's normal after trauma," he reassured. "It's good to get it out."

She blew her nose and wiped her eyes. "You don't really know me that well. This is a lot for me. I had a completely different life in Manhattan until a few months ago. It's been upside down ever since."

He smiled at her. "Harper, I get it more than you know. Getting divorced and retiring from the Army, I don't feel quite like myself either. I got up nearly every day and put on a uniform. I had structure to my days. I had a defined mission." He looked out the door for several seconds and then back at her. "Now, I don't know what I have anymore."

Harper nodded in understanding. "Maybe we can call a truce and not be so sarcastic with each other. I don't have any friends here, and I could probably use one."

She stuck her hand out to him. "Friends?"

"Friends," he agreed and clasped her hand. Then Jackson said, "To answer your question from earlier, no I didn't see a man in that kind of mask. I wasn't really looking for him though so I could have missed him. Nothing seemed off at the party. Everyone seemed to be having a great time."

They both sat back in their chairs. Harper was trying to remember if she saw the man earlier in the evening, but nothing was clicking. Their silence was interrupted by Hattie.

She yelled from downstairs, "Harper, could you come down, please."

Harper and Jackson both got up and walked down the stairs. As they hit the first floor, Hattie explained, "I spoke briefly to Mr. Inslee about the party and guests that were in attendance. I got rid of him for the evening. Told him it was better that you meet him at his office tomorrow. We scheduled for ten, after Jackson meets with Det. Granger. Dan has left as well."

Looking directly at Jackson, she added, "It would be great if you could go with Harper tomorrow since you were looking right at her while it was happening. I also think Inslee has other intentions on his mind, if you know what I mean."

"I'd be happy to go," Jackson offered. "He seemed slick."

"That's a good word for him," Hattie agreed, squeezing his hand. "That's why I wanted to be rid of him this evening. Told him Harper wasn't in the best shape to give another statement." She reached out with her other hand and squeezed Harper's.

Hattie added ruefully, "This definitely wasn't how I planned tonight to go. Some of the guests have headed home. The police are still processing the scene. I also heard there have been several burglaries of guests here. There are more cops talking to those people. I asked the caterer to bring in some food. I know you probably aren't hungry, Harper, but you need to eat."

Harper was starving actually. She hadn't eaten since earlier that afternoon. At now close to eleven, her stomach was growling. She appreciated Hattie's quick thinking. While Harper knew she'd have to show Hattie and Jackson she didn't need quite this much babying, she was going to accept it tonight.

Chapter Eleven

At nine-thirty the next morning, Harper walked out the side porch door of Hattie's house and met Jackson in the driveway. He was just getting back from his meeting with Det. Granger. Together, they walked to the backyard to see if the crime scene techs were still working. The yellow crime scene tape was set up around the perimeter where the body was found, but all was quiet. After mutual agreement that Jackson knew the city a bit better, they climbed into his truck and headed on their way to Harper's meeting at the prosecutor's office.

Jackson navigated the city streets with ease. About twenty minutes later, they were pulling into a parking spot a few blocks from the courthouse. As Jackson put the truck in park, he looked at Harper. "You nervous?"

"I wouldn't say nervous, I just want to get it over with," Harper conceded. "I just went through this a few months ago, talking to cops and prosecutors. I don't want this to be normal in my life."

Jackson nodded in understanding. The pair got out of the truck and walked the few blocks. They made it through court security and up to the fourth floor of the Pulaski County Courthouse. Tucker Reese's name was still etched on the door. Bill Myers was his assistant and would be taking over until a special election could be held.

As Jackson pulled open the heavy wood door that led into the prosecutor's office, they nearly walked right into Fr. McNally, who was dressed in traditional priest clothing and collar. He was shaking Inslee's hand and thanking him. For what, they didn't hear. Fr. McNally gave them both a curt nod and left. Jackson looked at Harper with eyebrows raised. She just shrugged.

As the two entered the office, Harper picked up the dirty look Inslee directed at Jackson, who was still watching the priest walk away. It was clear Inslee didn't like that Jackson had tagged along.

Reaching out his hand to Harper, Inslee said, "You both know Fr. McNally, I presume." Then he paused and added, "Well you may not know him well since you're both new in the city from what I hear. Anyway, he's not a suspect as much as your aunt would like him to be."

"Pretty quick to clear someone, don't you think?" Jackson inquired, turning his attention back to the prosecutor. "Maybe he had a solid alibi, I don't know, but his actions were a bit off last night. Hattie wasn't the only one who thought so."

"Well we can't have a woman like Hattie tarnishing someone's good name," Inslee exclaimed resolutely. "Now," he said turning to Harper, "let's head into my office."

Turning to Jackson, Inslee said curtly, "You'll wait here."

Harper looked back to Jackson and smiled just to let him know she'd be okay. Once inside Inslee's office, he guided her to a round table in the corner. He took the seat next to her rather than opposite. Inslee patted her knee and said, "Hopefully, we can have a good chat."

Harper pushed his hand off her leg. "It won't be that good if you keep insulting my aunt."

Inslee pulled back in feigned innocence. "I merely meant that with her certain brand of spirituality that she'd be at odds with the Catholic church so you can understand how she'd be suspicious of Fr. McNally when there's no cause. The man spent two years in Brazil working with at-risk youth before coming to us last summer."

Harper folder her arms and interjected angrily, "Hattie was suspicious of Fr. McNally because he was acting suspiciously. He came out of nowhere and was covered in dirt, almost like he'd been struggling with someone.

"Besides," Harper added indignantly, "both Hattie and I were raised Catholic. She has no hard feelings towards the Catholic religion or anyone. I think it's you with the problem."

Inslee got up and closed his office door. He stood at the entrance. With condescension in his voice he explained, "Harper, you're really getting this all wrong. I can tell you're like me. You don't believe in psychics and witches and all that. I've never thought Hattie's shop was good for our city. I'm surprised they haven't run her out of the Heights by now. I'm just saying, I can't allow her to tarnish a good man's name. And this isn't really how you want to start out your life here."

Harper stood. "I'm here to talk about what I saw last night. If that's not why I'm here, I have nothing else to discuss with you. If you're looking for what I saw and what I know about the murder of your boss, then let's get on with it." Harper started toward the door.

Inslee eyed her, but she wasn't going to let this man make her uncomfortable. Harper had dealt with men far more privileged and slicker than Inslee all her life.

Inslee touched Harper on the arm as she reached past him to open the door. Inslee relented, "Please sit down. I need to hear what you saw. We can leave your aunt out of the discussion."

Harper reluctantly sat back down at the table, and over the next hour, reiterated the story she had told Det. Granger the night before. When Harper was done, Inslee asked her the same kinds of questions over and over again about who she knew in the city, specifically if she knew Tucker Reese before that night. Harper explained that Hattie and Jackson were the only people she knew, and no, she had never met Tucker Reese. No matter how Inslee asked the questions, Harper's answers were the same because truth only had one version.

"There's really no way you could identify the killer, then?" Inslee asked in conclusion, disappointment evident in his voice.

"No, I'm sorry," Harper said, feeling somewhat defeated. "There's not anything I can remember right now that would help with that."

The meeting ended on that note, and Harper got up to leave. Before she left the office, Inslee surprised her when he said, "I made some calls about you to some contacts I have in New York. You were a pretty big deal up there."

Harper just looked at him and didn't confirm or deny.

Inslee went on, "If you want to succeed here in Little Rock, you're going to have to make sure you get in with the right group of people. I can help you. Make sure you have the right connections. After this case is over, I'll take you to dinner."

It wasn't a question. Harper felt her temper rising again. She hated presumptive men. Before turning her back on Inslee and leaving his office, Harper said, "I know how to make my way with the people I want to surround myself with. I survived in Manhattan. I don't think a small city like Little Rock will be a problem for me."

Chapter Twelve

"We've got trouble brewing, I can feel it in my bones," Hattie cautioned her assistant Beatrix, who was a new addition to the shop. Hattie had known she was going to need extra time to teach Harper the way of the Ryan women and how to use her gifts properly. To have that time available, she'd need someone to help her – someone who knew what they were doing.

Beatrix was twenty and originally from New Orleans. She was a sturdy girl, thick-hipped, broad-shouldered with full round face. She had long hair that had been dyed a shocking red, a drastic change from her natural chestnut mane. She was attractive and wholesome but quietly powerful. Beatrix was the kind of girl that could be the best friend you ever had or your worst enemy if she was crossed. Hattie loved that about her. In a lot of ways, she reminded Hattie of herself when she was younger.

Beatrix had worked in her mother's Voodoo shop in the French Quarter in New Orleans. She had her own magical skill set that complemented Hattie's needs perfectly. While Hattie was not a practitioner of Voodoo, the magical arts she practiced were not all that different. Beatrix was still an apprentice, but in other ways, she was far beyond her years.

The two worked together easily and naturally at Hattie's Cauldron: Potions and Pastries, which was wedged between a boutique dress store and a high-end hair salon on Kavanaugh Boulevard, smack in the middle of Hattie's Heights neighborhood. The shop had floor to ceiling shelves of loose tea and herbs in jars on the wall behind the display case that held freshly made pastries with a coffee station at the end. Ensuring that the shop was more than just a place to make a purchase, Hattie had couches and tables strategically placed to let customers get comfortable and take some time to relax. There were also tables with candles and essential oils for sale.

Beatrix was listening to Hattie while she refilled glass bowls of various gemstones that were great for meditation, among other uses. The bowls were lined up next to each other on three shelves that covered the back wall of the shop. Along with each gemstone, there was a small card in front that explained the stone's purpose and how best to use it.

Along the back wall was also a red velvet-draped doorway that led to where the real magic happened. Behind the drape, in addition to the industrial kitchen in the far back, Hattie had a comfortable room that held most of her supplies for the occasional potion she created. Most required herbs and essential oils from the front of the shop and additional supplies Hattie kept in the back.

There was also a small room with a couch, a comfortable chair and a table where Hattie did her special readings. She occasionally used her Celtic Tarot cards that had been passed down through the generations, but mostly, Hattie could take the hands of her clients or an object or photo and tap into the situation or person.

"Did you hear me?" Hattie called over her shoulder to Beatrix. They were the only two in the shop before the midmorning coffee rush.

"Yes, I did," Beatrix responded, still dropping new gemstones in the bowls. She had tackled the pink quartz and then moved on to the emerald stones. "I've been feeling it for a few days, too, but wasn't sure where the feeling was coming from. I thought maybe because my mom was angry that I didn't make it home for Mardi Gras. With school, there was no way."

Beatrix had even skipped the Saints & Sinners Ball to work on a paper she had for her psychology class. She was a second-year student at the University of Arkansas in Little Rock.

"I felt it before the ball," Hattie admitted. She ran a hand down her bright purple caftan and adjusted the belt that showed off her ample curves. "It's more than just Tucker Reese's murder. There's the jewelry thefts of our guests last night. All the good, positive energy this neighborhood normally has is off. I've never felt this way in Little Rock, but after speaking with Matthew Inslee, I'm afraid that man is going to be trouble for us."

"Does he have any real power?" Beatrix asked. She wrapped up refilling the gemstones and made her way behind the counter where Hattie was standing. She started making a fresh pot of coffee.

"He's a prosecutor so he has a good deal of power in the courtroom. Not sure about his connections on running us out of here."

"Is that what you're worried about?" Beatrix asked with a worried look on her face. She brushed her red hair away from her eyes.

"For the first time, yes, I am," Hattie admitted, arranging pastries in the display case. They always had a bit of a rush in the early afternoon right after lunch, and today, Hattie wasn't quite prepared.

"Maybe we should do a protection spell tonight," Beatrix offered. "We could do one here at the shop and one at your house. My mom has a really powerful one I can ask her about."

Hattie thought for a moment. "Yes, let's do that. I just don't trust the man at all."

The two were interrupted by a voice coming from the front door. "It's never good when Hattie Beauregard doesn't trust someone. Who is it now, Hattie?"

Hattie turned to see who had overheard their conversation.

Chapter Thirteen

"Oh Lottie, you're here already!" Hattie exclaimed. She was relieved it hadn't been someone else given what she and Beatrix had been discussing. Lottie was one of her best customers.

"I was just getting some snacks and coffee ready for you ladies. I didn't hear you come in."

Lottie was a petite woman, short gray hair and always wore bright red lipstick. Most women her age wouldn't have been able to pull it off, but Lottie did with ease. She was a retired high school history teacher and close to Hattie's sixty-seven years. Her husband had passed a few years prior. Lottie often regaled Hattie with the history of witches in the United States and Europe.

Lottie had a coffee klatch of ladies that she met with regularly at Hattie's. They came to the shop to get their supplies of loose teas and discuss the local

Heights gossip. They were women in the know about everyone and everything.

"The rest of the girls will be right along." Lottie sat in her usual spot at the large rectangle table in the middle of the room. She turned back to Hattie and asked again, "So, who don't you trust?"

"I'm sure you heard that Tucker Reese was murdered at the Saints & Sinners Ball. Matthew Inslee is interviewing my niece today. She found Tucker's body. Inslee just makes my bones ache," Hattie explained as she fixed the woman's favorite blueberry tea. As the water was warming in the pot, Hattie sat down at the table with Lottie. "Do you know much about him?"

"I taught him tenth grade American history," Lottie said. She waved her hand in the air as if brushing away a bad smell. "He was a terrible student. A bully and a know-it-all, who really didn't know much."

A few more of the ladies came in and joined Lottie at the table. They placed their coffee, tea and pastry orders with Beatrix who went to fix everything. When it was ready, Hattie helped her carry it all over to the table. As Hattie was setting down a small pot of tea, one of the women she didn't know well said, "I heard Inslee has been unhappy with his job lately. He's thinking about leaving for a criminal defense firm. I heard he wants more spotlight and more money."

Hattie sighed. "Sounds like him. He's probably happy to get the Reese case then."

Another woman, Judy, chimed in. She drawled, "Y'all, I don't like to speak ill of the dead," she paused for dramatic effect while the other women nodded their heads along, "but I heard that Lizzie, Tucker's wife, was looking for a good divorce attorney because she was going to leave Tucker and take him for all he's worth."

"Well can you blame her?" Lottie asked rhetorically. "The man couldn't keep it in his pants. He was drunk going way back. Judy, you went to school with Lizzie, didn't you?"

"I did, and she came from such a good family. Her daddy was so upset when she married Tucker. It was her momma who calmed Lizzie's daddy down and let the marriage go forward. She assured him that Lizzie could straighten Tucker out. She said he'd get over his wild ways once he was married." Judy shook her head in disgust. "It's been nothing but trouble for Lizzie since."

"He had a girlfriend, right?" Lottie asked.

Judy nodded. "Some awful woman named Roxy. She was brash and tacky. I heard they split up though."

Lottie leaned across the table and waved the other women in. She said barely above a whisper, "Do y'all think maybe Lizzie bumped him off?"

"Oh Lordy!" Judy exclaimed and clutched at her pearls. "What a scandal that would be!"

Hattie and Lottie exchanged a look.

"Stranger things have happened." Lottie continued, "Maybe she hired someone. Or what about Lizzie's brother. He's always been in trouble. I heard he was in prison recently."

"Drew wouldn't hurt a fly," Judy assured. "He was in for insurance fraud not anything violent."

"Well maybe he didn't pull the trigger, but having been in jail he certainly has connections to find someone who would," Lottie offered. "Besides, how much does Lizzie stand to inherit with Tucker dead? She could never say no to her brother from what I hear."

Hattie could tell all this got Judy thinking about her old friend.

Judy conceded, "Several million at least. Tucker had other businesses, and his family had oil money." She looked around to each of the women and asked in a whisper, "You really think Drew would have had him killed?"

The woman all looked to one another, their eyes wide. A murmur of speculation went around the table. Then when they grew quiet, Judy asked, "Hattie, are you able with your cards to see who killed him?"

"Oh, I wish it worked like that," Hattie responded. She took a seat next to Judy and explained. "I can get insight into state of mind. I can see deception, death and even danger. I can't really see murder though."

Judy patted her hand. "Too bad you aren't one of those mediums who can talk to the dead. You could just give Tucker a holler and asked him directly who killed him."

Hattie gave a weak smile. If only they knew, and if only it was that simple. She changed the subject quickly. "Did you hear about the burglaries last night? It was guests at the party. Apparently, there were five houses hit. This makes at least eleven in the last few months."

"I don't know what's happening in this city," Lottie lamented. "But then again, these women are practically advertising their millions in jewels, and then don't properly lock up their homes. They think it's still the 1950s."

"My friends were robbed a few weeks back," Judy confided. "They had been at a charity ball for the hospital. The thieves took more than two million in jewelry – diamond bracelets, necklaces, emerald pieces they had, all of it."

"Did they have an alarm?" Lottie asked as she sipped more tea.

"No," Judy said. "They live right here, on Country Club Road. They never thought this would happen. Luckily they have insurance to cover their loss."

"They take anything else?" Lottie asked.

"That's the funny thing," Judy admitted, looking perplexed. "No, everything else was fine. They went right for the jewelry. None of the electronics. Even their gun cabinet went untouched."

"Hopefully, the cops will catch them soon," Hattie interjected. "They are probably selling them on the black market or whatever it is jewelry thieves do."

The women around the table agreed and went back to talking about the latest gossip from the neighborhood.

Chapter Fourteen

"Would you wait up!" Jackson called after Harper who had stormed out of Inslee's office. As Harper had passed by Jackson, who was sitting in the hallway outside, she had given him a look like she wanted to throttle someone. Then Harper bolted down the stairs and out of the courthouse. Harper was several feet ahead of Jackson walking back to his truck. It was really more of a sprint, and Jackson could barely keep up with her.

Harper turned abruptly and shouted to Jackson. "That man makes my skin crawl! I couldn't stand looking at him for another second."

"What's happened?" Jackson asked as he finally caught up to her, a little out of breath.

Harper paced on the sidewalk. Her face was flushed and her hair had started to come out of the neatly arranged ponytail Harper had styled that morning. She looked to Jackson and said exasperated,

"I'm not this fragile woman you all think I am. Let's take care of Harper. We need to baby Harper. I'm a grown woman who worked with the FBI to take down my husband and a crime boss. I don't need Inslee or anyone else to tell me how to get on and survive in Little Rock. I made it in New York City for heaven's sake. I was the editor-in-chief of a prestigious magazine. I think I can handle it here."

Jackson looked at her a bit dumbfounded. He reached for her and then took his hand back. He started to speak and then stopped himself. He watched her closely.

"Well," she demanded. "Don't you have anything to say? Are you just going to stand there and look at me like I've lost my mind?"

"No, I just…"

"Forget it, let's go. I need lunch." Then Harper turned and headed the few blocks down to Jackson's truck.

Once they were both in the truck, Jackson looked at Harper and asked, "Do you want to talk about it now or at lunch?"

"Lunch," Harper fumed. She sat there with her arms folded and stared straight ahead. She was hoping Jackson wouldn't play the *what do you want to eat* game. She hoped he'd just make the decision.

Harper wasn't disappointed. Jackson kept quiet. He didn't press her to talk as he drove out of downtown and up Cantrell Road back into their Heights neighborhood. Jackson's truck came to a stop on North Van Buren right in front of Cheers, a local restaurant. The patio was empty. Jackson looked at Harper and raised his eyebrows in a question. Harper got out of the truck as a reply.

Together they walked the few steps to Cheers and took a seat on the patio. The weather was warming up, and it was nice enough to sit outside. While a lot of people might be chilly, for Harper the sixty-degree weather felt like spring.

They placed their orders and sipped their drinks. Finally, Jackson asked cautiously, "You ready to talk about it?"

"Thanks for not pushing me before," Harper said and meant it. She had needed time to think and process what she was feeling.

Jackson smiled at her in response and waited for her to continue.

"I don't trust Inslee," Harper admitted. "He seems out to get Hattie. He was saying how she was unfairly trying to railroad Fr. McNally."

Jackson agreed. "I didn't like that friendly handshake they shared as we were walking into the prosecutor's office. If Fr. McNally didn't do anything wrong, he didn't do anything. I just don't know how you determine that only twelve hours after the crime was committed."

The waitress came and dropped off Harper's chicken salad and Jackson's burger. Harper forked her salad, taking a bite of chicken. "I know this didn't technically happen on Hattie's property, but I feel like we need to protect her. From what, I'm not sure, but I want to find out who did this."

Jackson was mid-bite of his burger. He looked at Harper as he chewed. He took a drink and washed it down. "What do you mean 'find out'? You can't interfere in a police investigation."

"I just want to dig around a little, nothing dangerous," Harper assured him. Then she got serious. "I don't know what Hattie told you, but what I said outside of the courthouse is true. I don't need either of you to baby me."

Jackson put his fork down. He looked at Harper and caught her eye. His gaze was intense and sincere. "Harper, I'm not babying you. You found a dead body last night. Anyone would be concerned about you. If someone wasn't worried about you, they aren't the kind of people you should keep in your life."

Harper sighed. She sat back in her chair and rubbed her temples. "Since I arrived here in Little Rock, it feels like everyone is walking on eggshells around me. I'm not going to crack. Yeah, everything with my ex was terrible, but I got through it."

"I don't know how you got through it. Your aunt, especially, knows how strong you are. I see that, too. You have nothing to prove."

Harper didn't say anything for a few moments. She just watched him. She'd never met anyone like him before. Jackson didn't seem to judge her for anything. She believed what he said. There was a familiarity about him she enjoyed. She hadn't even known him a week, and she was comfortable with him already. That rarely, almost never, happened for her.

She took a drink of sweet tea. She looked over the top of her glass. "So, will you help me?"

"Help you do what exactly?" Jackson eyed her cautiously.

Harper shrugged. "I don't know yet. I want to dig around a little and see what we can find out."

Jackson wiped his mouth with his napkin and laid it back in his lap. "Do you really want to tangle with Det. Granger? He doesn't look like someone whose toes I want to step on."

Harper laughed. "Jackson, you're a retired Army Colonel, and you're afraid of a detective?"

"I'm not afraid," Jackson said, his eyes leveling hers. "We are both new in town. I don't think our first order of business should be making the cops angry."

"I'll give you that," Harper agreed. "We need a local to help us navigate. I don't want to worry Hattie. Do you have any friends?"

"I'm lookin' at her," Jackson quipped with a big smile.

"Gosh, you're useless," Harper laughed. "I think I might know of someone who can help us." She pulled out her phone and placed the call. Much to Jackson's dismay, Harper asked the person on the other end of the phone to meet.

Chapter Fifteen

Dan Barnes' office at *Rock City Life* was a nondescript brick building in downtown Little Rock. It was on the second floor over a deli at the corner of E. Markham and Scott Streets in an open loft space. He had the only enclosed office. The rest of the room was open desks and work tables. Harper had been expecting a downtown building like her own in New York, but comparing *Charlotte* to *Rock City Life* probably wasn't fair. She liked the building though. It had good character.

Harper and Jackson walked back to Dan's office on the far-right side of the open space. He noticed them and got up from the desk and walked to greet them. Harper extended her hand to Dan as she crossed the threshold into his office. "Thanks for agreeing to see us, Dan. We appreciate it."

Dan shook Harper's hand. "I was surprised you called. I didn't think we got off on the best foot last night."

"You're not the only one," Jackson grumbled, coming into the office behind Harper. His hands were shoved into his pockets.

Harper shot him a look and silently mouthed the words, "Be nice."

Jackson shrugged.

Dan asked Jackson, "What did you say? I didn't catch that, sorry."

Jackson cleared his throat. "Nothing, I was just agreeing with you that we didn't meet under the best circumstances last night. It's nice of you to meet with us."

Harper knew Jackson was adamantly against meeting with Dan. Back at Cheers, once Jackson realized who she was calling, he kept mouthing the word no and motioning for her to hang up. Instead of being annoyed with him, Harper found it a bit comical. She wasn't exactly sure what Jackson had against Dan, but Harper had gotten a good vibe. Plus, who better to know everyone's secrets than the editor-in-chief of the city's most in-the-know magazine.

Dan headed back to his desk and moved a pile of papers off to the side and started cleaning up a bit. Harper assumed his desk was probably perpetually cluttered. Dan motioned for Jackson and Harper to sit. Dan started to sit behind his desk. But he was barely down in his chair when he got up again and came around the desk to close his office door. As Dan started back towards his chair, he asked, "What can I help you with?"

Harper looked to Jackson, but he waved at her to get on with it. She explained, "I'm hoping we can keep this conversation between us. Jackson and I are both new in the city, but we have some concerns about the murder of Tucker Reese, most particularly how it might affect Hattie."

Dan interrupted. "How would this affect Hattie?"

"I met with Matthew Inslee this morning. He was meeting with Fr. McNally as I arrived. Inslee's already cleared him. He assured me Fr. McNally didn't do anything wrong. I don't know how that's possible. Inslee also made some comments about not liking having Hattie in the city and about her shop. I'm worried given how close the murder was to Hattie's property, Inslee might see it as a chance to make trouble."

"What do you think I can do about it?" Dan asked sharply, taken aback.

Harper shifted in her seat and explained, "It's not that I think you can help with that, but I want to see what I can dig up. The more I can find, the more I can protect Hattie."

"It's been less than twenty-four hours. Shouldn't you let the cops do their jobs?"

Jackson, obviously feeling vindicated, grinned. "That's exactly what I said."

Annoyed, Harper injected. "We can just call it women's intuition, but something is off. I can feel it. That priest is being let off way too easily. This is a high-profile case, so everyone should be suspect until they are cleared – thoroughly cleared. Inslee gave me no real indication why the priest was cleared – other than Hattie shouldn't have suspected him in the first place. I was there, and he was acting suspiciously."

"You would have made a good reporter," Dan said, pointing a finger at her, clearly pleased at her insight. "You've got a nose for news. I'll make you a deal. If I help you, will you help me?"

Jackson rolled his eyes, and Harper casually reached an arm over and pinched his side. He jerked in his seat. Harper knew she was taking liberties with Jackson he probably didn't allow others.

"What can I help you with?" Harper asked cautiously.

"I was looking into *Charlotte*," Dan started. He pulled a few copies of the magazine from the pile on his desk and laid them in front of her.

Harper felt a twinge of regret seeing the magazine she had given so many years of her life to. She had been very proud of her work. Leaving the way she had, Harper felt like she was missing a sense of closure. Maybe in some ways, Harper was still mourning the life she had.

Dan continued and snapped Harper out of her train of thought. "You turned the sales for the magazine around in the time you were there. Not that it was failing, but you made some solid changes to up its readership in a time when magazine sales were tanking. I want you to help me here as a consultant. I can't pay you much, but I have some budget."

Harper was flattered. Dan saw more in her efforts with *Charlotte* than even her father had. Harper hadn't thought she'd find work this quickly when she arrived in Little Rock, but this seemed like a golden opportunity. It would put Harper in the direct path with movers and shakers in the city. Without missing a beat, Harper agreed.

"I'll take you up on the offer. Send me over a contract of what you have in mind. In the meantime, Jackson and I are going to talk through the case. We will figure out what specific information you might be able to help us with. Sound good?"

Dan smiled big. He stood up and shook her hand. "Sounds like a terrific plan. I'll get something over to you by tomorrow."

Harper got up to leave. She looked down at Jackson who had his legs kicked out, his hands folded over his stomach and a look on his face like he wanted to be anywhere else in the world.

Chapter Sixteen

After Lottie, Judy and the other ladies left the shop, Hattie had asked Beatrix to cover the store for her while she ran home for a bit. Hattie couldn't leave too long in case someone wanted a psychic reading or a special potion Beatrix didn't know how to whip together yet. But with Beatrix there, it would give Hattie at least an hour or so.

Hattie entered the house from the back porch. She set her purse down on the kitchen counter and went into her living room. "Beau!" she called out loudly and waited. She hadn't seen him since the day Harper had arrived in Little Rock. It wasn't like him to be so quiet in the house, but Hattie assumed he was giving Harper a chance to get settled.

Heading out of the living room into the hall and up the stairs, she reached the second-floor landing and called out to him again. Hattie listened for any creak or sign. Nothing. She went room by room looking for Beau or the other spirits of ancestors that sometimes inhabited the house. There was nothing but eerie quiet.

Hattie went into her large bedroom that was in the back of the house. Her four-poster bed was neatly made. Some of Beau's favorite clothes still hung in the closet three years after his death. Hattie had donated some items, but she kept his favorites. She sat in the comfortable reading chair in the corner of her bedroom and called out to him again. Normally Beau readily appeared. Some days, Hattie couldn't get rid of him.

"Beau, I really need you," Hattie pleaded. She had no control over her mediumship abilities. It was nothing she ever nurtured and toyed with. She had read that if she practiced, she'd have more control. But it wasn't something Hattie wanted to dive into just yet.

Frustrated, Hattie got up and looked out the window that overlooked the backyard. The tent company had come that morning and removed the tents, and the caterer had cleaned up their mess. She looked out farther to where the crime scene tape made a weak blockade closing off the clearing between the trees. It was then Hattie saw a man. He was standing with his back towards her. He had on a suit and his hands were folded behind his back as if assessing the scene. Hattie wondered which detective he was. She was sure she hadn't met him the night before.

Almost as if he knew he was being watched, he turned slowly and looked directly up to the window where Hattie was peering out. It took Hattie's eyes a minute to adjust, but then she realized with heart-stopping reality that he wasn't a detective after all.

The black mask with the tacky red beads adorned his face. Blood dripped down the left side of his face and the bullet hole in his forehead was apparent. His mouth set in a grim line. He watched Hattie as she watched him. Then she screamed. His mouth turned up into a cold, evil smirk. Tucker knew Hattie could see him.

She stepped back from the window and let the curtains close. Turning quickly, Hattie was startled once again. Beau's ghostly form was standing in the hallway.

"Hattie, what's the matter? You look like you've seen a ghost," he laughed. It was a running joke between them, but Hattie's heart was pounding in her ears. Hattie wasn't sure why she was surprised she could see Tucker, she'd seen other spirits on the property. He was vile in life. She had never wanted to encounter him in death.

"Seriously, Hattie, what's wrong?" Beau moved towards her. He was a big guy in life, not overweight just tall and broad-shouldered. Sometimes Beau came to Hattie as he did in the last years of his life, like Hattie was now — wrinkled and aged. Other times, Beau came to her as he did now, the way he looked in his youth when they had just been married. He reached for Hattie, but his energy just passed through her arm.

"Where have you been? I haven't seen you since Harper arrived."

"I've popped in and out. I didn't want to startle Harper or have you need to explain why you were talking to yourself so I've kept my distance," Beau said, still with a worried expression on his face.

Hattie sat down in the chair. "There was a murder here last night at the Saints & Sinners Ball. Tucker Reese, the elected prosecuting attorney, was shot in the clearing between our house and the parish. Harper found the body."

Beau knelt down in front of her, making direct eye contact with Hattie. "I'm so sorry. I didn't know. I was at the ball for a little while, but you all seemed to be having so much fun, I left you to it."

"You were there?" Hattie asked.

"Yes, but not for long. Minutes maybe. It's hard to judge time on this side."

Excited, Hattie asked, "Did you see a man in a red and gold devil mask? It covered his whole face and had horns coming out the top."

Beau stood and seemed to think for a moment. "I think I did. Briefly though. It was right around the time I was leaving. I thought it odd he had a full mask on when everyone else's just covered their eyes."

"That was the killer," Hattie confided. "That's all Harper saw of him. What else can you tell me?"

"My dear, I wish I could tell you who it was. I can't, but let me think about what I can remember," Beau said. He walked to the window and looked out. With his back turned, Beau detailed, "He had on gloves. I remember that. I would say that it was definitely a man. I didn't see the back of him just the front, and the horns were blocking his hair. If I recall, he was also somewhat taller than I would assume for a woman. Not close to my height but average man if I had to venture a guess."

He turned back to Hattie, "Does any of that help?"

"It's more than we had before. Did you see who he was talking to?"

"No. I was there to see Harper. I was looking for her. She looked lovely."

Hattie smiled. "She really has grown into a wonderful woman."

"She has," Beau agreed. He went back to Hattie and wrapped his ghostly arms around her. He nuzzled her neck, which just felt cold and tingly against Hattie's skin.

"No one has ever been more beautiful than you, my sweet Hattie."

Hattie blushed. The fact that Beau could still make her blush this many years on made Hattie smile. They had a great love in life. It seems it was continuing on even after death. Her gift had one good benefit. She let herself enjoy the feel of his energy for a moment. Then Hattie was brought back to reality.

Hattie asked, "Did you see Tucker Reese outside? I just saw him when I was looking out the window."

"I didn't, but I'll keep watch."

Just then, Hattie heard Jackson's truck pull up. "I should go. Harper and Jackson are home. Please stay close."

Chapter Seventeen

Hattie hit the bottom step with her dogs in tow just as Harper and Jackson walked into the kitchen from the back porch. Hattie tried to regain her composure, but she was still shaken from having seen Tucker in the backyard. Maybe Hattie could just simply ask who killed him. Surely, Tucker would know with whom he was speaking to right before he was shot or at least Hattie hoped so. But that meant having to talk to him, and that's something Hattie was hoping to avoid.

She moved down the hallway, calling out to Harper, trying to make her voice sound calm and even. "That took a while. How'd it go with Matthew Inslee?"

Harper popped her head out of the fridge. "He's arrogant and a bunch of other things I shouldn't say aloud."

"Yes, we know that, Harper, but how did it go?" Hattie stressed.

Harper pulled out the pitcher of sweet tea and held it up to Jackson who was sitting at the kitchen table. "Want some?" He said yes, and Harper poured three glasses. Handing one to Hattie, she said frustrated, "Fr. McNally was there as we walked in. Inslee cleared him already. The meeting went downhill from there. It was pointless."

Hattie set the glass of tea down on the counter and wrung her hands. She knew Inslee wasn't going to take her suspicions of the priest seriously. People rarely did when the clergy was accused of any wrongdoing. Hattie knew she was going to have to do something about it.

"What did Inslee say about me?" Hattie asked, leveling a look at Harper.

Harper looked to Jackson. Hattie interrupted, drawing Harper's attention back to her. "We do not keep secrets in this house, Harper. If he had something to say, tell me. I can't do anything about it otherwise."

Harper sighed but relented. "Inslee basically said that of course you'd accuse a priest given you're a witch. Then he wondered why people in the Heights hadn't run you and your shop out of town yet."

Hattie shook her head, disgusted. She walked over to the table with Jackson. She sat and turned to Harper. "What are we going to do about this?"

Jackson spoke up. "What do you mean? There's nothing we can do. The police are investigating. I tried telling Harper that already."

Hattie turned to her niece. "You want to look into things, don't you?"

Harper shrugged and sat at the table. "I want to nose around and see what I can find. There's no way Fr. McNally was cleared that easily."

"I think that's a great idea," Hattie said, smacking her hand down on the table. Turning to Jackson, she instructed, "You can help her."

Jackson let out a surprised laugh. "I love how you two just boss me around."

Hattie raised her eyebrows at him.

Jackson held up his hands in surrender. "I already tried arguing with Harper and lost. I'm already helping. We just came from Dan's office." Then with a mischievous grin, Jackson added, "He has a crush on Harper so he's willing to help us."

Smacking at him playfully with her hand, Harper howled, "He most certainly does not have a crush on me!"

"Calm down," Jackson chided her. "Yes, he does. That's why he was so eager to help you. Sure, you did great work at the magazine, and he wants to benefit from that, but he also wants to spend time with you."

Harper started to argue, but Hattie put her hand on hers. She agreed with Jackson. "Harper, I think Dan does have a little crush, and that's okay. Let him. He's a nice guy."

Looking between Harper and Jackson, Hattie asked, "What's the plan then?"

"I thought Jackson and I could make a plan of action. Any ideas where we should start?"

"I think you should talk to my friend Lottie and her friend Judy. They knew Tucker and his wife Lizzie very well. You should probably talk to Lizzie, too. From what I heard today she was thinking of divorcing him. Now that's just gossip, which runs fast and loose in the Heights."

"Did you hear that?" Harper interrupted. "I thought I heard a car door slam."

Jackson stood and looked out the side kitchen window that gave him a view of the driveway.
"You did. The cops are here in full force."

They all jumped at the sound of heavy banging on the front door. Hattie went to answer the door with Jackson and Harper in tow.

She was met by Det. Granger. He thrust paperwork towards Hattie. She peered down at it, but it didn't make sense at first glance. Hattie looked up at him for an answer.

Det. Granger didn't make eye contact with her. He mumbled, "We have a warrant to search your home. Given the proximity of the murder and the burglaries of your guests…"

"This is asinine!" Harper yelled, interrupting him. "You have no reason to suspect Hattie or me for that matter of anything."

Hattie waved Harper off and said resolute, "This is Inslee's doing. I know you're just doing your job, Det. Granger. Just try not to trash my house, please. It's very old. Things are fragile."

Det. Granger finally looked up at her and made eye contact. "We won't take long, but I have to ask you all to clear out while we search. Is there a basement or attic?"

"There's no basement, but there is an attic, not that anyone has been up there in ages. But you're free to search it." Turning back to Harper and Jackson, Hattie said, "I have to get back to the shop. Could you both stay over at your house, Jackson, and then you can lock up for me when they are done? I'm going to be late tonight. Beatrix and I have a little project we have to work on at nightfall."

Chapter Eighteen

"Who's Beatrix?" Harper asked curiously as Jackson unlocked the front door and stepped inside the enclosed front porch that ran the length of the home. Harper didn't say it out loud, but she was happy she was going to get a chance to check out Jackson's place. She was curious about the man. He didn't say much about his life. Harper wanted to know more.

"Beatrix is the assistant your aunt hired to help in the shop when she found out you were moving here," Jackson explained, distracted as he grabbed his mail and stepped into the foyer.

Jackson offered Harper the five-cent tour, and she jumped at the chance. Then Harper worried she seemed too eager. But if she came across that way, Jackson didn't give any sign of noticing. He lived in a rehabbed Craftsman with hardwoods, crown moldings and the unique built-ins the style was known for. The front door opened to a small foyer that had a staircase to the second floor and hallway that ran back to the kitchen. Off to the left was the living room, which flowed back into a dining room. A door on the right of the dining room took them to the kitchen. The dining room also had French doors that led to a back deck.

Upstairs there were four bedrooms off the main hallway plus a bathroom. It was similar to Hattie's house upstairs but smaller and fewer bedrooms. His bedroom had a nice dark wood dresser set plus a big bed with the same dark wood headboard. Jackson's bed was made neatly. He even had decorative throw pillows Harper assumed came with the comforter set, which was a simple navy blue. Harper was both intrigued and amused that a bachelor would not only have throw pillows but have them on a neatly made bed. Military values Harper guessed.

They walked back downstairs, and Harper took a seat on the brown leather sofa. Jackson offered her a drink, and she declined. He sat in a reclining chair in the corner of the room.

Once they were seated and comfortable, Jackson admitted, "We probably should have seen this coming."

"What do you mean?" Harper asked, kicking off her shoes and tucking her feet under her.

"This is Inslee's doing. If the cops really suspected your aunt of any wrongdoing, they would have searched her place last night not given her an entire night and half day to hide evidence. He's just doing this as a show of force."

"What do you really think is his issue with her?" Harper wondered. Although Harper had grown up with her aunt, and Hattie was the person she trusted most in the world, she still felt like Jackson might have an advantage having spent more recent time in close proximity to her.

"It could be anything. If I had to guess – fear."

"Fear of what though because Hattie thinks she's psychic and a witch?"

Jackson didn't say anything for a few seconds. Then he leaned forward in his chair and looked over at Harper. "You really don't think she's psychic?"

"It's not that I don't believe Hattie is a psychic or witch, it's that I don't believe those are real things. I don't believe in that at all."

"I see," Jackson said thoughtfully. "So, because you don't believe in them, it must not be real, right?"

Harper sighed loudly. "Are you telling me you really believe?"

"Yes," Jackson said emphatically. "At the very least, I believe that your aunt is gifted, and who am I to question that gift. You should step back and at least give your aunt the benefit of the doubt. Otherwise, it's kind of disrespectful to someone who cares about you a great deal."

Then Jackson added quickly, "You can't explain everything in the world, Harper. You're better off looking at things with an open mind."

Harper thought for several moments. She felt scolded like she was a child, but Jackson did have a point. "Got it," was all she conceded.

Harper knew deep down that Hattie was gifted. For that matter, Hattie's father's sisters had been gifted as well as women on the Ryan side generations before. It's not like Hattie was the first in the family.

Harper knew the stories since childhood. She just still had a hard time believing.

Jackson was watching her. Harper smirked. "Since you lectured me instead of just answering my question, do you think that's why Inslee's afraid of Hattie?"

"I don't know," Jackson admitted. "It's something though. He seems to have taken an immediate dislike to Hattie, and he's running with it."

Harper got up and walked to the window. She called over her shoulder, "They are still over there. Think they will be long?"

"You not comfortable here?"

Harper laughed. "No, nothing like that. I like your house. It's cozy. I just wondered how long they'd be." Harper felt nervous and a bit excitedly anxious. She wasn't sure why.

Harper looked over at Jackson sitting in his chair. She asked, "What did you study in college?"

"Criminal justice."

"Oh, so that helps us out," Harper teased. "When you were in the Army, did you go to Iraq?"

Jackson nodded, but didn't elaborate.

She continued, "Afghanistan?"

Jackson nodded again. He raised his eyebrows at her. "What is this? Twenty questions?"

She shrugged. "Just trying to get to know you better. You're all…" Harper stopped. She wasn't sure what word she was trying to find. Secretive wasn't right. Then Harper remembered what Hattie had said, so she finished her thought, "Closed off."

"I've been accused of that before. I could say the same about you." And that was all Jackson gave her.

He got up and walked to the kitchen, leaving Harper to stand alone in the living room.

A few minutes later, Jackson came back with two glasses of tea. He handed Harper one. "I'm thirsty so you're drinking, too."

As Harper took the glass from him, their fingers brushed. They lingered for a moment before Jackson pulled his hand back. Neither one of them sat back down. They both just stood there in the middle of his living room appraising each other.

Jackson's eyes never left Harper's as he took a sip. He said, "This isn't nearly as good as Hattie's, but it will do."

Wanting desperately to get back to the conversation before Jackson interrupted, Harper said softly, "I know this probably hasn't been your experience, but I'm someone you can trust. I'm not going to hurt you or take anything from you. You're just someone I'd like to get to know better."

"Same," Jackson replied, short on words but his gaze never wavered.

Harper was hoping for more of a response, but that would have to do. They were arm's length apart. The air was thick between them. She took a sip, and then without thinking about it, licked her bottom lip. When Harper looked up, Jackson was watching her intently, focused in on her mouth. Harper suddenly wondered what it would be like to kiss him. His lips were full, inviting. She felt foolish for thinking such a thing, although, from the look on his face, his thoughts didn't seem to be far off.

Harper wasn't used to this kind of chemistry with a man. She wanted to explore it. She wanted to flirt with him and say something interesting, but her mind was blank. Finally, she broke the tension in the only way she knew how. "Who do you think killed Tucker Reese?"

Chapter Nineteen

After several seconds of awkward silence, Jackson moved away from Harper and sat down in his chair again. "Who do I think killed Tucker Reese?" Jackson said as much to himself as to her. "I don't really know. I can tell you who I think would be on my list of suspects though."

"Before you do that," Harper interrupted, still standing in the middle of the room, "do you have a dry erase board or paper or something we can make a visual murder board?"

"A murder board?" Jackson looked at her bemused. "You do this often?"

"No, I saw it on a cop TV show though," Harper explained excitedly. "They write it all down so they can stand back and look at it. They get other clues and ideas."

Harper started feeling that old rush of adrenaline she used to feel when she began plotting out the next magazine. She'd gather her team around for a brainstorming session. Any idea, no matter how silly it seemed, went on the board. They would sort through later to see what was relevant and what stuck. Harper was of the *get it out, then get it good* mentality. It was the way she wrote, too. Harper realized she missed working and wanted to be a part of any team. Specifically, Harper liked the idea of being on Jackson's team. One thing for sure, she missed feeling useful.

Without saying anything, Jackson got up and walked upstairs. He came back down a few minutes later with a few markers and some large poster-sized sticky notes. "Will this do?"

"Perfect," Harper beamed.

Jackson rolled his eyes at her. "You are way too excited about this. So where do we start, Ms. Detective?"

"Not sure." Harper took a red marker in her hand and looked at the blank page of paper. "Let's start with what we know for sure. The facts."

Harper and Jackson spent the next hour going over every detail they knew to be true, including time and date of death, details about the party, the sparse details they knew about the devil-masked man, and even who they saw while the murder was taking place so they could rule out who couldn't have been the killer. They talked about the murder weapon, and obviously, Jackson knew much more about guns than Harper ever cared to know.

As Jackson talked about something that he was so clearly knowledgeable about, he relaxed. His face was animated. He gestured with his hands when he spoke. Harper liked watching him, learning from him.

Harper was used to being the one in charge. Getting to step back was refreshing for her.

Jackson suddenly stopped talking. With his head cocked to the side, looking at Harper with curiosity, he asked, "What are you smiling about?"

Harper was caught off guard. She hadn't realized she was actually smiling while listening to him. "Nothing, I…" Harper stammered and then stopped. She didn't have an excuse. She fidgeted with the marker. Harper suddenly felt like a kid with her first crush.

Jackson just looked at her, a confused expression on his face.

Harper tried to regain her normal composure. She decided honesty was probably best. "You just look handsome when you're talking about something you're really interested in. Your face kind of lights up. I like it."

"Oh, well, thanks…" Jackson sputtered, running a hand down his face. He laughed. "Now you got me all distracted. Let's get back to work."

Harper offered, "Maybe his wife or girlfriend killed him. I heard he wasn't always faithful. Isn't that what they always say? It's someone they know."

"That's what they say, but I think nearly everyone at the party, except us, knew him. But you're right, the wife and girlfriend should be high on the suspect list."

Jackson got up and pulled off two pieces of paper. With his own marker, he made another list. Jackson turned to Harper who was watching him and explained, "This is our to-do list. And that can be our suspect list."

"You're getting into this now," Harper teased.

Jackson ignored her and continued, "There are two suspects who stand out the most to me that need to be explored – the wife and the priest."

"I agree with what we know right now," Harper said. "I wonder if Tucker was working on any big cases. Maybe someone who wanted retaliation?"

"That's a possibility, too," Jackson agreed. He stopped writing. "Was Inslee at the party?"

Harper thought for a moment. "I don't know. I hadn't met him before he came into Hattie's house after. If he was there, I wasn't introduced to him. He sure acted like he wasn't."

"That's what I mean. He was dressed in a suit, not formal attire. But for some reason, I remember his name on the guest list."

Harper grabbed her cellphone and called Dan. He answered almost immediately. She asked if he had seen Inslee at the party. After hanging up, Harper explained to Jackson, "Dan said Inslee was there early, talking to a group of women from the Junior League, but didn't see him later."

Jackson said sarcastically, "Danny boy sure answered your call quickly."

Harper ignored him. She sat down on the couch going over the events of the evening. She asked, "Don't you think that if Inslee was there when I found Tucker's body, he would have come running over? Maybe he left before it happened."

"Maybe, but if he was there and didn't tell us, that strikes me as suspicious."

"What motive would Inslee have to kill his boss?" Harper asked.

Jackson shrugged. "I don't know yet. Motive is the next list."

Car doors slamming interrupted their work. Harper and Jackson moved toward the front door and stepped out onto the enclosed front porch. They had a direct line of sight to Hattie's front yard. The cops were leaving. Harper noted, "I should probably go and lock up the house."

"You coming back?" Jackson asked.

"Haven't you had enough of me for one day?" Harper queried, a teasing smile on her face.

"We have work to do," Jackson replied matter of fact. Harper saw the corners of his mouth turn up into an almost smile. He added, "I thought maybe we'd order pizza for dinner."

"Arkansas pizza is not going to entice a New Yorker," Harper groaned. "Is it dreadful?"

"You're not going to get New York pizza down here in the south. That's one adjustment you'll have to make, princess. I found a place that's decent. Try it."

"Fine, fine," Harper relented. "You order, and I'll go lock up. There's money in my wallet."

"I don't want your money," Jackson said absentmindedly as he walked back into the living room.

About twenty minutes later, they were enjoying pizza at Jackson's kitchen table. Harper thought it wasn't bad. Definitely not what she had in Manhattan, but she'd adjust. After dinner, they spent the rest of the evening making a plan to find Tucker Reese's killer.

Chapter Twenty

It was just after seven in the evening. Hattie closed up shop as she always did at six. Beatrix was walking around the shop, using white sage to purify the space as she went. This was a normal end of the day task. Clear out and purify the energy of the day so tomorrow they could start anew.

But tonight, they were doing something else – a protection spell. Hattie was at the rectangle table in the middle of the room. The lights in the shop were off and the shades drawn. The pair were working by candlelight. Hattie had a black candle lit on the table and her supplies in front of her. Beatrix brought over the sage and picked up each of the four tiger's eye stones that Hattie had on the table and passed them through the sage smoke.

Hattie, with Beatrix by her side, then drew a circle of black salt on the table. Then Hattie picked up each of the tiger's eye stones and placed them for north, south, east and west. She placed her cauldron in the middle of the circle, and Beatrix saged a circle of smoke around that. With each step Hattie was focused on her intent for protection.

Then one by one Hattie added a bit of olive oil, rosemary and one star anise to the cauldron. She lit a candle under it and let it burn. Hattie and Beatrix held hands and chanted words of protection asking the elements of the earth to feed their spell and place a ring of protection around the shop. Their voices were strong and intent even stronger. Once they were satisfied with their work, Hattie took each of the tiger's eye stones and placed them in the four outermost corners of the shop. Then she sprinkled a row of black salt across the doorway and window sills. She came back to Beatrix, and they said a few more words of protection and snuffed out the candle to close the spell.

"How do you feel?" Hattie asked.

"Good, the energy was strong. I can tell you're as powerful as my mother. Are you going to do the same spell at your house?"

"I am," Hattie said. "I'm going to try to get Harper to help me out. I don't know that she will. Harper's gifted. She just doesn't recognize it."

"She'll get there. I have a feeling," Beatrix said seriously. "You should invite Harper to the shop, not to help with the magic or readings, but tell her you need someone to wait on customers who need coffee and tea. Maybe if Harper's here and sees it's not so unusual, she might feel better."

Hattie looked at the girl, a bit surprised. "That's very perceptive of you. How did you think of that?"

Beatrix started cleaning up the spell remnants. "You grew up with this from your aunts you said. I grew up with it from my mom. It's something we always knew. You said Harper grew up very different. We only know from our perspective until we are exposed to something different."

Hattie laughed. "Are you sure you're twenty?"

Beatrix stopped and seemed to think for a minute. Then she shrugged. "My mom always said I was an old soul."

Hattie gave her a pat on the shoulder. "Well, old soul, this tired old lady is heading home. I think I'll take your advice. Thanks for staying late to help me."

With that Hattie and Beatrix left the shop. Hattie took a deep breath of fresh air. It was dark but usually Hattie didn't mind walking through her neighborhood at night. Since the murder, the air had felt different. Hattie wouldn't say she felt unsafe, it was just different. She quickened her pace.

Hattie distracted herself wondering if Harper was still with Jackson. She could tell they were growing on each other. In fact, if Hattie were to guess, she thought Jackson might even be a bit jealous about Dan. Jackson had a bit of competition whether he had admitted his attraction to Harper to himself or not.

Hattie made it to her house safely, and once inside, she turned on a few lights and began pulling leftovers from the Saints & Sinners Ball out of the fridge. Sparkle and Shine danced around her feet, snapping at crumbs Hattie dropped from above. As Hattie was fixing herself a plate to be heated, the dogs started to growl. She looked down at them confused and then a shiver ran down her spine.

Hattie felt him before she saw or heard him. She turned and came face to face with Tucker's spirit. Hattie started to speak, but the words caught in her throat.

Tucker smirked. "I knew you could see me earlier today. Everyone said you had witchy skills, Hattie. I never really believed them. I thought it was a con, something to entertain the old ladies and give the young ones some hope for love. You're the real deal, lady, and you're going to help me."

"How can I help you?" Hattie asked cautiously, patting the dogs, letting them know she was okay. Hattie wanted to yell for her husband Beau, but she didn't want to give away that her deceased husband was in the home before she had to.

Tucker walked to the corner of the kitchen. He looked out the window. "You're going to help find who killed me."

Confused, Hattie asked, "You don't know who killed you?"

Tucker turned back to her, his expression seemed lost as if trying to recall a memory. "No," he said sadly. "I don't even remember being killed. I was standing there one minute, then standing over my dead body the next."

"You were talking to someone when you were killed. Harper saw you," Hattie explained. She walked up to Tucker. "Who were you talking to?"

He looked past her, looking around her kitchen. His eyes never landing on a spot. Hattie could almost see the wheels turning in this brain.

Finally, Tucker whispered, "I don't remember."

Frustrated, Hattie demanded, "What's the last thing you do remember?"

"I don't know," he said dejected.

"Think harder," Hattie pressed him. "Do you remember the party?"

"I was talking to a guy from the public defender's office," Tucker recalled. "Then there was someone waving to me from outside the tent. He waved for me to come to him. I followed him to the back of the property and down that clearing between the trees." Tucker paused.

He said annoyed, "I remember being angry, but I don't remember anything else. My mind is just blank." Tucker added, "I don't remember what happened, but then I was standing over my body. That girl, your niece, was screaming. I got out of there, but now that I think of it, I don't remember where I went."

Hattie didn't really understand how death worked. She and Beau didn't talk much about it. It had been at least five months after Beau died before he came to her. It was the longest five months of her life. Now Beau came in and out, but she was never really sure where he went when he was not with her. Beau said it would be hard for the living to understand, and Hattie didn't press him.

Tucker reached out his hand to touch Hattie on the arm, but it passed right through her. With concern on his face, he asked, "Why can't I touch you?"

"You're dead, Tucker, a ghost, a spirit," Hattie explained more impatiently than she meant. She softened her tone. "You can't touch the living. It takes a lot of energy and focus, more than you'll have right now."

"You'll help me, won't you? No one else can see me," Tucker pleaded. "I have to know who killed me."

"Tucker, I'm not sure I know how to help you," Hattie admitted. "Harper and Jackson did say they were going to look into things, but who knows what they will find."

Tucker's eye got wide. "But someone other than the cops is looking to find my killer, right?"

"Yes, my niece."

"Good I don't trust the cops."

Chapter Twenty-One

After Hattie assured Tucker that she'd help him if he promised to behave himself and not try to talk to her when her niece was around, he finally left. Hattie picked at her food, threw her dishes in the dishwasher and went to the second floor. She took a long hot shower, letting the water beat over her back and shoulders, trying to forget the stress of the day. After toweling her short hair nearly dry, Hattie pulled on a cotton nightgown and crawled into bed.

Hattie turned the television on, just for the noise, but wasn't really paying attention. She wanted to call out to Beau, but she was tired. Hattie wouldn't know what to say to him. She wasn't sure he'd be all that supportive of her helping to track down a killer.

At close to nine, she heard Harper come in. Hattie heard her moving things around the kitchen and then walk up the stairs. "You're home late," Hattie called out to her.

Harper poked her head into Hattie's room and teased, "I haven't had a curfew since I was sixteen. I didn't know you were waiting up for me."

Hattie gave a weak smile. "I wasn't. I just came up to bed, watching a little television before I call it a night. Come over and sit with me." Hattie patted the bed next to her. Harper slipped off her shoes and climbed up on Hattie's bed. Harper laid down next to her aunt and then rolled on her side, brushing her hair out of her face. "What was your project?" Harper asked curiously.

"Do you really want to know?" Hattie asked skeptically. Harper said yes, and Hattie continued, "I thought it best given Inslee's attitude towards me to do a little protection spell around the shop. My assistant Beatrix helped me."

"Are you going to do one here at the house, too?"

"I am," Hattie answered. Hesitantly she asked, "Would you like to help me? I know you don't believe in all that, but I could use the help. If no, it's okay, I can ask Beatrix."

Harper seemed to think about it. Then she gently declined, "I think you should probably have Beatrix help. I'm not really into it, and don't think I'd be helpful. I'd like to meet Beatrix though. Jackson said she was nice and a great help to you."

Hattie didn't argue with Harper the way she would have before. She said simply, "Beatrix is a lovely girl. She's young, away from home for the first time, but wise beyond her years. I can ask her if she's available tomorrow night."

"Sounds good," Harper said. She yawned and started to get up to leave.

Hattie tugged the back of Harper's shirt. "You can tell an old lady to mind her own business, but were you with Jackson this whole time?"

Harper laid back down, resting her head on the pillow. "Yeah, we were talking about the murder. I think we have some ideas of things to explore."

Harper spent the next twenty minutes going over the details and ideas she and Jackson had come up with. Hattie knew their plan now, and it seemed to be a solid one. Harper concluded by saying, "You need to stay out of it though. Let us look into it. Inslee is gunning for you. Don't give him an excuse to do something crazy. Jackson said the cops searching here was just to show force."

"It's not surprising," Hattie said resolutely. "Inslee doesn't scare me. But I'll let you and Jackson take the lead. You'll ask for help when you need it."

Hattie wanted to know what else occurred while they were at his house all evening. Anyone could see the chemistry between them, even if they were blind to it. Hattie had the feeling that the more time they spent together the less they'd be able to deny the attraction. Hattie just wasn't sure they'd be willing to do anything about it. Hattie thought Jackson was a good match for Harper. He was strong, independent but would both encourage and tame, when needed, her strong-willed nature. Plus, Jackson could take care of Harper when needed as well.

"What are you thinking?" Harper asked, bringing Hattie's thoughts back to the present.

"Oh, just if I were younger and single, I'd have been happy to spend an evening alone with Jackson." Hattie smiled and peeked over at Harper out of the corner of her eye. Harper was smiling, too.

"He's a handsome man," Harper admitted, her voice soft and dreamy. "I don't think he's ready for anything beyond friendship."

"Are you ready for more than friendship?" Hattie asked, a bit surprised at what Harper just admitted.

"I don't know," Harper said, sounding unsure of herself. She sat up in bed, crossed her legs under her and looked at her aunt. "When I left New York, I thought it was going to take me months, years even, to get over Nick and my marriage. Given everything that's been going on, I've barely thought of him. It's like I just slipped into this entire new life and forgot about my past."

Harper took an audible breath and breathed it out slowly. "I guess maybe it will all hit me at some point, but right now, it feels like I'm just ready to move forward."

"Nick wasn't the great love of your life," Hattie said gently but firmly. "He was probably brought into your life to teach you some lessons, and now you're ready for whatever comes next. Time doesn't indicate depth of love, remember that."

"What do you mean?"

"I just mean that it wouldn't be unusual to have a deeper connection with someone you just met. Just because you knew Nick longer, doesn't mean he means more to you."

Harper nodded, but didn't offer her thoughts on the matter. She kissed Hattie on the cheek and said goodnight. Hattie rolled over and fell into a dreamless sleep.

Chapter Twenty-Two

"I wouldn't have taken you for someone who snored."

Harper blinked once, then twice and fully opened her eyes. Jackson was standing over Harper's bed with a cup of coffee in his outstretched hand.

"What are you doing in my bedroom?" she asked, her voice groggy from sleep. She sat up, stretched her arms and looked around her room. There was the bra she wore the night before hooked by its strap on the desk chair. Panties were tossed on the floor as were her jeans. Harper wasn't a slob by any stretch, but by the time she got home and was ready for bed, she was exhausted. Harper had slipped off her clothes and put on pajamas. She was grateful now she hadn't gone to bed in the buff.

Looking at the bra, Harper realized although she had a very thin tee-shirt on, she didn't have on a bra. She was staring at the one hanging on the desk when

Jackson snapped her out of it. "It's a bra. You know I've seen one before."

"Well you haven't seen mine," Harper responded, annoyed at his presence. She grabbed the coffee out of his hand and took a satisfying sip. "Why are you here? It's only seven."

Jackson walked across the room and sat in a chair facing the bed. He kicked his legs out in front of him and seemed quite comfortable invading her space. "We have work to do. Get up, lazy."

"Aren't you going to be a gentleman and let me get myself together…alone," Harper snarled.

"You're fine. You don't have anything I haven't seen before," Jackson said, eyeing her over his coffee cup. "Hattie is already at the shop. She let me in and told me to come up and wake you. Lottie and Judy are going to meet us there early so we can ask them some questions."

"That's all well and good, but seriously, Jackson, I'm barely dressed. Get out."

"No," he teased. "You were flirting with me last night. I want to see what I'm working with here. You're all buttoned up usually." Jackson barely got the words out before he cracked up laughing at himself.

Harper was ready to throttle him.

Jackson got up and walked to the door. Before he left, he turned to Harper and said flirtatiously, "You're cute in the morning with no makeup on and messy hair. Maybe one day you'll be asking me to stay instead of kicking me out of your room." Jackson winked at her, then turned and left. He didn't even wait for her response.

Harper sat there with her mouth open. She wasn't sure if he was serious or just teasing her, but he infuriated her. Harper sat in bed, with the covers up to her waist in case he came back, savoring the last of her coffee. At least he made it the way she liked it. After realizing Jackson probably wasn't coming back, Harper headed for the shower and was ready in under thirty minutes.

"Finally, the princess is ready," Jackson chided her when Harper greeted him in the kitchen.

"Why do you keep calling me princess?"

"Because it clearly annoys you. Every time I do, you crinkle up your nose at me," Jackson admitted. "It's cute, like a little rabbit."

Harper grimaced at him, and they headed to Hattie's shop. Harper couldn't remember the last time she'd been there. She had to have been fifteen, maybe sixteen years old. Harper had visited Hattie since then but always skipped going to the shop. Harper felt like going there admitted her aunt's gift might be legitimate. Jackson was right though, Harper needed to give Hattie the benefit of the doubt and respect it even if she didn't understand it.

Entering the shop, Harper thought she'd be overwhelmed by the smell of incense, but in reality, she was greeted with a wave of strong-smelling coffee and chocolate. It felt warm and wonderful. The tables and chairs looked comfortable and inviting. Nothing about the shop screamed dark witchy magic, not that it ever did if Harper's memory served her. Over the years, Harper must have created an image of the shop in her head that was far removed from reality. She felt silly now. Harper had loved being in the shop as a kid.

Jackson walked over to a table where two older women sat. They were drinking cups of tea and eating scones. He stuck out his hand, "I think we've met before or at least seen each other here in the shop. I'm Jackson. Thanks for meeting with us."

Lottie smiled up at him and shook his hand. "Anything for Hattie. I'm Lottie and this is Judy."

Jackson and Harper took a seat at the table. Jackson explained, "I think it's probably a bit odd that we'd be looking into who killed Tucker Reese, but we don't trust Matthew Inslee. The moment he got the cops to search Hattie's house brought it home for me that maybe he wasn't so inclined to find the truth."

Lottie waved him off. "We don't need an explanation. Everyone in this town, for the most part, knows that Matthew Inslee always has an agenda, and it's a self-serving one at that. What would you like to know?"

Harper and Jackson had talked about a plan of action on the walk over to the shop. Neither wanted to come right out and accuse Tucker's widow, Lizzie. But ruling her in or out at the start was important. "For us, everyone is a suspect until they aren't. I know Lizzie was your friend, Judy, so we want to clear her as soon as possible and find the killer especially if Inslee decides to turn his attention to her. I wonder if you think Lizzie is capable of killing her husband?"

"Lordy no," Judy said. "I just can't imagine she'd do it. That said, the more I thought after we talked the other day, her brother, Drew, is a scoundrel. I remember even as children he was always getting in trouble."

Chapter Twenty-Three

"Tell me about Lizzie if you can," Jackson directed to Judy. He was jotting down some notes as Judy talked. Hattie came over and put down coffee in front of Jackson and Harper. Then she slid a chocolate croissant in front of Harper and a raspberry cheese Danish in front of Jackson. She mouthed, "your favorites," to Harper as she walked back behind the counter. Harper gave Hattie a grateful smile.

Judy leaned into the table and spoke to them. Her voice was low and even. "I've known Lizzie practically my whole life. I heard through friends that she had gotten tired of Tucker tomcatting around. She was going to divorce him and go after his money."

"Lizzie was angry with him and ready to be done with their marriage?" Jackson confirmed.

"Wouldn't you be if your spouse was cheating on you?" Judy asked and looked to each of them for confirmation.

While they both said they understood, Harper noticed that Jackson had winced at the question.

"It wasn't a judgment. I just wanted to make sure that was her mental state."

Harper wondered, "Did he know she was searching for an attorney or that she had made this decision?"

"From what my friends have said, yes he did. Tucker and Lizzie had a huge fight last week, and that was part of why she wasn't at the Saints & Sinners Ball. Tucker told her that she could get the best attorney she could find, but that Lizzie could leave the marriage with what she brought into it," Judy explained and then added with emphasis, "and that was practically nothing."

From behind the counter, Hattie asked, "Judy, we know it wasn't Lizzie that shot Tucker. Harper said it was a man so do you know where Drew is?"

"He's here in Little Rock," Judy informed them. Her face was starting to get red and she was fidgeting in her seat. "You don't think Lizzie had anything to do with it, do you?"

Harper looked to Jackson. He patted Judy on the hand and assured her, "We can't get ahead of ourselves. But it looks like right now we can't rule her out. Do you know much about her brother?"

Judy took another sip of her tea and asked Hattie for more. "You better bring me another scone. This is too much for me."

Then turning her attention back to Jackson, Judy said, "Drew was always in trouble. Even when we were children, he was getting yelled at by teachers. I can't think of a day he wasn't in detention. As we grew older, his misbehavior became more serious. I think we were in our twenties the first time he got in trouble with the law. I can't remember why now, but later, he got more sophisticated and then went to prison for insurance fraud. But he never physically hurt anyone."

"That's good. This might not even be anything, but it warrants checking," Harper reassured.

"Do you know where he's living?" Jackson asked.

"Sure," Judy replied. "He's been staying with Lizzie and Tucker since he got out of prison. He's been trying to get back on his feet, but it's hard for a felon to find decent work."

The front door of the shop opened, drawing Harper's attention away from Judy. No one came through the door. It was Matthew Inslee, and he was oddly just standing at the threshold, door open, but not stepping into the shop.

"Can I help you, Mr. Inslee?" Hattie asked. When he didn't say anything, she raised her eyebrows at the man. "Are you here perhaps to tell me that nothing was found in that ridiculous search of my house?"

Inslee started to speak, but his voice caught in his throat. "No," he squeaked, "nothing was found." Then with his voice strong, Inslee said, "I need to speak with Harper."

"She's right here. You can meet in the backroom," Hattie offered. She looked down at Harper, who had her eyes fixed on Inslee.

"No, that's okay," Inslee stammered. "Out here on the sidewalk will be just fine."

"Are you afraid to come into the shop, Matthew?" Lottie asked from her seat. "It's not so scary. We promise not to turn you into a toad."

Harper got up and shrugged at Inslee's odd behavior. She came to the door and followed him outside. "What can I do for you?"

Once the shop door closed, Inslee demanded, "I need to know the details of the conversation you heard between Tucker and the man who killed him."

"I told you before, I didn't hear what they were saying."

"I don't believe you," Inslee challenged.

"Whether you believe me or not has no bearing on the truth. And the truth is as I said, I didn't hear what they were talking about. I heard men's voices, raised and the tone was angry, but I couldn't make out words," Harper countered matter of fact.

Inslee had his hands on his hips, his eyes searching Harper's face. "We have a witness that saw Tucker and the man speaking for several minutes. Curiously they also saw you not too far from the clearing. I find it odd that you couldn't hear them."

"Did you happen to factor in that it was a party with close to two hundred people? There was a band playing as well. Standing feet from the person next to you it was hard to make out what they were saying. You should know, you were there."

Inslee didn't address his presence at the ball and seemed to ignore all logic. "I think you're protecting your aunt."

"Protecting her from what?" Harper barked.

"Everyone in this city knows about your aunt's witchy ways. I think she had something to do with this. Maybe even with all those jewelry heists. Hattie knew exactly who would be at her party. Someone saw her speaking to Tucker early in the evening. Hattie had her voice raised with him. She stomped on his foot. Then Tucker's dead. Curious, don't you think?"

Harper would have laughed if the accusation wasn't so serious. "I don't know about my aunt's interaction with Tucker earlier that evening, but I can assure you Hattie's not a murderer, and she's no thief. Hattie is well into her sixties. How exactly is she burglarizing homes while also being there at the party the whole time? Nothing you're saying is making sense. As I said before, it was a man who shot Tucker."

"Couldn't she have sent one of her minions to do her dirty work?"

Harper did laugh at that. "Hattie's not the wicked witch. I assure you there are no flying monkeys bumping off the townspeople who make her angry."

Inslee glared down at Harper, but she wasn't breaking. This was the most ridiculous thing she'd ever heard. Harper pointed a finger at him, nearly bumping his chest. Her voice low and even, Harper cautioned, "Mr. Inslee, you may have a problem with my aunt's spirituality and the way she practices that, but Hattie is no threat to this community. You may be a prosecutor in small-town Little Rock, but Hattie has the weight of the Ryan family empire in New York behind her."

Harper took a breath and continued, "Trust me, you want a fight, we will give you one. I can guarantee you it won't be one you'll win. I suggest you let this silly fixation with my aunt go and do your job to find the killer. Because if I have to do your job for you, trust me, every news outlet in America is going to know of your incompetence."

With that Harper left Inslee standing in the street. She flung open the door to the shop, looked at Jackson and demanded, "Let's go talk to Lizzie. We have a murder to solve."

Chapter Twenty-Four

"Oh my, someone's got her temper up," Judy said, polishing off the last of her scone. Turning to Hattie who was standing behind the counter, she asked curiously, "What do you think that was about?"

"Harper remembered who she is," Hattie declared evenly. She stared out the door where Harper had just barged in and demanded Jackson's attention. Jackson had obliged Harper without hesitation or saying a word. He had taken a last sip of coffee and followed Harper out.

Lottie broke Hattie's train of thought. "Why do you suppose Inslee didn't come inside?"

"Beatrix and I did a spell last night on the shop to protect us from him. He told Harper my shop should be closed," Hattie explained. Then she added with a hint of sarcasm, "That or he's afraid of me. You know how scary we witches are."

The ladies finished up the last of their snacks and tea and headed out. The shop was quiet while Hattie worked. She was putting together a prosperity spell kit for a client. Beatrix came in around ten, and Hattie explained what had happened with Inslee. The young girl was pleased their spell had worked.

The rest of the morning was fairly quiet. Hattie finished the spell kit while Beatrix waited on customers, mostly locals who were there for refills of loose tea. A couple bought stones and candles for meditation. At nearly eleven, Hattie heard Beatrix calling for her from the front of the shop.

When she walked out, Hattie was met with a woman she'd never seen before. The woman was well into her fifties, had dark, obviously dyed hair cut into a short bob that ended at her chin. Her face was red and puffy from crying. She was thin and average height. Hattie didn't find her particularly attractive, but she could see how men could.

"Can I help you?" Hattie asked, handing the woman a tissue.

The woman started to cry again. Hattie guided her to the back of the shop and into the room where she did readings. It was a comfortable space. The woman sat down on the couch while Hattie took the chair in the corner. If there hadn't been a large quartz stone sitting next to a deck of old Celtic tarot cards on the coffee table, the room could have been mistaken for a therapist's office.

"Now," Hattie started, her tone soft and soothing, "why don't you tell me what's wrong."

The woman stopped crying. She looked up at Hattie through bloodshot eyes and exclaimed, "I'm Tucker Reese's girlfriend. Well was, he's dead." Then she muttered more to herself, "I can't really get used to that. I was just with him the other night. Now, he's gone." She began to sob again.

Hattie knew Tucker had girlfriends on the side. That wasn't a secret to anyone in town. "How can I help you?"

"I'm Roxy, by the way. I just needed someone to talk to. I think I might know who killed Tucker." The woman sat back on the couch and took a deep breath.

"Shouldn't you go to the police with this information? I'm not sure how I can help?"

Roxy rubbed her temples and whined, "I can't right now. I need you to do that thing you do, talk to his ghost or whatever, and tell me if I'm correct. I don't want to accuse the wrong person."

"It doesn't really work that way. I'm not a medium so I don't talk to or see the dead," Hattie lied.

"You really haven't seen Tucker or talked to him since he died?"

Hattie ignored the question and countered, "Why don't you just tell me what you know, and then we can look at the situation with my cards and see what I can get."

"How much is it? I don't have a lot of money." Roxy paused, and then started crying again. "Actually, now that Tucker's dead, all his money goes to that cold fish Lizzie. He was paying my rent and for my car. I don't know what I'm going to do now."

Hattie didn't mean to, but she rolled her eyes. All the spell work in the world couldn't help women like Roxy who made poor decision after poor decision. Hattie waved her hand. "No charge. Why do you think you know who killed Tucker?"

"Because Tucker told me he was worried," Roxy explained. She sat more upright on the couch and crossed her legs. She looked at Hattie and explained as calmly as Hattie thought she could. "Tucker had been looking into something that the cops didn't even know about. He had stumbled onto something at the St. Joseph's Catholic Parish. Tucker said there was something funny about the new priest. Tucker said he was up to no good. But he didn't tell the cops because he said he hadn't figured it out completely yet."

The priest. Hattie knew there was something with Fr. McNally and now Roxy confirmed it. "Do you know if anyone else knew what Tucker was looking into?"

"I don't know. He didn't tell me that. Tucker had been watching the priest for a while. Tucker was obsessed."

"Is that all Tucker said?"

"Yeah, and now Tucker's dead," Roxy said. Then she looked worried. "Do you think I'm in danger?"

"I don't know," Hattie responded honestly. She was trying to think about what else she should ask. She also wondered how much Inslee knew and was now protecting the priest. Hattie pressed, "Anything else? Even the smallest details could help."

Roxy thought for a few moments and added, "Tucker met with a few people at night in parking lots. He never told me who, but he'd call and tell me he had another meeting. Tucker said he was getting close, very close. He said it was going to be a scandal that would rock the city, maybe even the entire nation. As soon as I heard Tucker was dead, I knew this was the cause."

Hattie asked the woman if she'd be willing to talk to Harper and Jackson. Roxy agreed, but she didn't want to go to the cops. Hattie assured her that was fine, for now at least.

Then Hattie did a reading on the situation. All she could confirm was that yes there were secrets surrounding the parish – deception, destruction and death. Hattie did another reading for Roxy about where things were headed for her now that Tucker wasn't going to be able to support her. Hattie couldn't get a read on the woman's life. The cards just kept coming back the same as before – deception, destruction and death. She tried twice more and the cards were the same.

"What's the matter?" Roxy asked with concern in her voice.

"I don't know," Hattie replied puzzled. "The cards are just showing the same. Come back in a couple of days when the energy is cleared and we can try again."

Roxy agreed and then left as abruptly as she had come into Hattie's shop.

Chapter Twenty-Five

Jackson and Harper were in his truck driving through the streets of Little Rock headed to visit Lizzie Reese. According to Judy, Tucker Reese had bought a five-thousand-square-foot, six-bedroom home in West Little Rock nearly eight years ago. His widow would inherit that now.

They were nearly there, and Harper wished they had thought to stop and pick something up to bring to the house. Even though Harper knew they were only going to question Lizzie, that was no reason to show up empty-handed. She was raised with manners. Turning to Jackson, Harper said hesitantly, "Could we circle back and stop at the market? I want to pick up a Bundt cake or something."

Jackson gave her a sideways glance. "You want to bring a homicide suspect a cake? I don't think that's an interrogation technique."

"We aren't barbarians," Harper said dramatically. "We have no idea if Lizzie had anything to do with Tucker's death, and she's a widow. She's in mourning. We can't barge in there like the cops. We need to finesse this."

"Who am I to deny a lady a cake," Jackson said sarcastically. He turned the truck around and went to Kroger on Chenal.

Twenty minutes later, Jackson and Harper were standing in front of the massive double wooden doors that were the grand entrance to the home. They rang the bell and waited. A few minutes later the door was answered by a disheveled-looking man who didn't seem to belong in a home this size or with this much opulence. He looked like he hadn't showered, his eyes were bloodshot, and he reeked of alcohol. Harper guessed it was Drew, Lizzie's brother.

"Can I help you?" he barked not making eye contact with either of them.

"We're looking for Lizzie Reese. Is she home?" Harper asked politely, the cake in her hands.

"Yeah, yeah," the man said and ran a hand through his unwashed blond locks. For a man in his early sixties, he was trim and had a full head of white-blond hair. He stepped out of the way and motioned for them to come in.

If the sheer size of the house didn't give away how much money Tucker Reese had, the interior surely did. No expense had been too much. The marble flooring in the wide-open foyer ran up the grand staircase to the second floor. The home clearly had been designed with every luxury and detail in mind. Lizzie had elegant taste.

"Who's here, Andrew?" a woman called from the formal living room, which was off to the left of the foyer.

"It's some people, Lizzie," Drew said. He looked at Harper. "They brought a store-bought cake."

Harper felt small and ill-prepared for the meeting. The reality was, Harper might very well have the same amount of money, if not more than the Reeses, given her sizable trust fund, but at the moment, she felt cheap.

"Stopping by was spur of the moment," Harper said as a way of explanation for the cake, which was actually a lovely flower-designed round vanilla cake.

"Dear, I can't hear you," Lizzie called from the living room. "Please come in. I'm just resting given the circumstance."

Drew turned and started to walk toward the living room. Harper and Jackson followed. The living room had light gray oversized furniture and a huge fireplace. Lizzie was sitting at the far end of the room in a chaise with a blanket covering her legs. She set down her book when they came in. Lizzie looked them over head to foot and asked, "Are you with the police department or the press?"

Before they could answer, Lizzie looked at her brother and turned her nose up in disgust. "You look like a dirty mess. I've told you before, you can't run around my house like that. Go shower and pull yourself together, and take the cake with you. Put it with the others."

Drew took the cake from Harper's hands and left the room.

"Now as I started to say, cops or press?"

Harper took a step forward toward the woman. "Neither, I'm Harper and this is Jackson. I'm Hattie Beauregard's niece. We came to pay our respects. We are very sorry for your loss."

"Oh, you're the girl that found Tucker," Lizzie said, connecting the dots. "I know your aunt. She's a lovely woman. I've been to her shop several times. She has some wonderful teas."

Lizzie didn't get up, but instead gestured with her hands towards the small couch near her chaise. "Why don't you both sit down. I'm so sorry about my brother. He has no manners. It's like we didn't grow up in the same family."

Turning to Jackson, Lizzie commented, "You're quite handsome, but I'm sure many women tell you that. Are you Hattie's neighbor? The one that's an Army Colonel?"

Jackson nodded. "Retired. I just moved here a few months back. And thank you for the compliment."

Before there was any time for awkward silence or Harper had a chance to ask a question, Lizzie clasped her hands together and leveled a look on them. "I didn't kill my husband if that's what you're curious about. The cops were already here. Reporters were already here. If I were going to kill Tucker, and trust me he deserved it, it wouldn't have been such a spectacle. Unlike Tucker who was all flash and no grace, I'd have the good sense not to make a public debacle of his death. I was here with a good friend that night. The police have already checked."

Harper was completely taken aback by the woman's words, but she related to them from her own recent circumstance. It was Jackson though who recovered before Harper did. He asked, "Do you know who'd want to kill your husband?"

"We never had children," Lizzie began. "I wasn't able to, and so for most of our marriage, we have lived a life of luxury. I focused on my charity work, and Tucker on building an empire. He's also cheated since before we were married. Of course, I didn't find that out until later. I think the better question is who didn't want him dead."

Pointing at them, she added, "I have my suspects though."

"And who might that be?" Jackson inquired. He sat forward on the seat, giving Lizzie his full attention.

Lizzie held up two fingers. "There's his mistress Roxy. Tucker just ended the affair last week. She was getting too expensive. I don't know what he ever saw in her anyway. But Roxy, and oh what a name, was quite angry when the affair ended as you can imagine. Now whether she'd kill him or had him killed, I don't know, but I'd be looking at her first if I had anything to say with what the police are doing."

Lizzie then said, "And there is all that mess with his secret investigation. Tucker didn't go into detail with me, but he was gone a lot. He was holed up in his office at all hours. Tucker muttered to himself more than usual. He was spooked. Caught up in something."

Harper looked to Jackson and then back at Lizzie. "Do you have any idea what that might be?" Harper asked.

"All I know is it had something do with the St. Joseph's Catholic Parish, but I don't know anything else. My husband did not talk to me about his investigations, and that one was very hush hush as you can imagine."

Lizzie looked over Jackson and whispered, "Could you get up and see if my brother is in the hallway listening in?"

Jackson got up and went out into the hall. He came back shaking his head. "All clear."

Lizzie lowered her voice. She waved them closer to her. Then Lizzie said, "I think my brother is up to no good like usual. Tucker and my brother never got along. Tucker wanted him out of this house. With Tucker gone, I can't have that kind of chaos now. I also have no idea where Andrew was the night Tucker was murdered because he wasn't here at home."

"You said up to no good. Any idea what?" Harper asked gently.

"None. If I knew for sure, I'd have him out of here," Lizzie replied firmly.

Harper nodded in understanding, but she really didn't know what else to say. Harper wasn't quite understanding what Lizzie meant, but it seemed like a family feud. Harper asked, "Did you tell the police about your suspects?"

"Yes, of course, I did," Lizzie said. "I was ready to divorce my husband. He was never faithful, but we made it work through the years. I got tired of competing for his attention. I want to live out my old age in peace. I was ready for the fight. I would have taken satisfaction in beating him in court or having him settle to keep his indiscretions off the public record. There's no victory in his death."

Harper thanked her for being so forthcoming with information. As they got up to leave, Lizzie dropped another bomb. "I don't know if I'd consider him a suspect, but my husband had a very contentious relationship with Dan Barnes, the editor-in-chief of *Rock City Life*. Mr. Barnes had threatened to expose something my husband was recently working on. Maybe it was that Catholic parish mess. I know they had words recently. If it was more than that, I don't know. But I'd keep my eye on him."

Chapter Twenty-Six

Harper looked back at the home as they closed the door. She felt an overwhelming sense of sadness for Lizzie. She related to the woman. Harper was days to forty, would never have children, and she had been in a marriage where her partner didn't remain faithful. That can take a toll on a person.

Harper in many ways imagined this is what her own life might have turned out like had she not left Nick when she did. Some women stay. That was never a choice for Harper. Once she found out about the affair, Harper made a plan to leave. There was no question in her mind.

Harper could feel Jackson's eyes on her. She turned to him, and he admitted, "That went nothing like I thought it would."

Harper couldn't find the right words to say so they walked in silence back to his truck.

Standing in the driveway, Jackson asked, "What did you think?"

Harper kicked at a stone in front of her foot. "I don't think Lizzie had her husband killed. I think she's right that if she did it, it wouldn't have gone down the way it did. Her suspect list seemed on target though. Well, except for Dan."

Jackson leveled a look at her and raised his eyebrows. "We are going to have to get into that at some point, but I'll save you the fight right now. You know, I was surprised. I didn't think Lizzie would be so…" Jackson paused.

"Strong?" Harper offered.

"Yeah, Lizzie doesn't seem like someone who would just keep living with a man who was cheating on her. I wanted to ask her why she stayed so long but didn't feel it was my place."

Harper looked back up at the house and back to Jackson. "That could have been my life."

"What do you mean?"

"My husband and I both came from money. No kids. We could have easily bought this house. My penthouse was twice the cost of this in Manhattan. But the moment I found out he cheated and was involved in criminal activity, I knew I was filing for divorce."

Jackson looked at her. He rocked back and forth on the balls of his feet. Finally, he admitted, "My ex-wife had an affair while I was overseas in Afghanistan. She told me in a letter. I was at war. What was I supposed to do about it? When I got back home, I left her. I'm not someone who could stay either."

Harper had suspected the end of Jackson's marriage wasn't his fault. But never in a million years would Harper have guessed that his wife cheated while he was at war, literally fighting for his life. She didn't even know his ex, but Harper started to hate her on a very visceral level. Harper reached out to him and put her hand on his arm. "I'm sorry. No one deserves to go through that."

Before Jackson could respond, the two of them were met with a police car pulling up the driveway. Harper looked to Jackson, and then watched the approaching car, trying desperately to come up with a good reason for being at Lizzie's house.

The car came to a stop right next to Jackson's truck. Det. Granger stepped out. He didn't look angry so much as confused. He hitched his jaw at them and asked, "What are you two doing here?"

Harper swallowed hard. "I came to pay my respects. I didn't want to come alone so Jackson came with me."

Det. Granger and Jackson shook hands. He gave Harper's shoulder a squeeze. "I only partially believe that. Why are you really here?"

When the two didn't say anything, Granger ventured, "Let me guess, Matthew Inslee has made you suspicious that we won't do our jobs and you decided to check things out for yourself?"

"Something like that," Jackson responded, not giving too much away.

Det. Granger looked up at the house and stared there for a few seconds too long. Harper followed his gaze. They had an audience. Drew was standing in a second-floor window glaring out at them, hostility written all over his face.

"Lizzie gave us her suspect list and then told us her brother Drew was up to no good, but she said she didn't know what," Harper offered. She was hoping that if Granger knew they weren't trying to hide anything that he'd go easy on them.

"Lizzie never said anything like that to me," Granger said dryly. Then he added, "I know Inslee has been giving you and your aunt a hard time. I didn't feel we had any reason to search Hattie's home, but Inslee pushed through the warrant for the search. I had to oblige him, but we found nothing just like I thought. I don't see things as he does."

"Why are you telling me this?" Harper asked cautiously.

"Because," Granger started, "I need you to trust me to do my job. I've already gone to my captain with my concerns about Inslee getting a warrant for your aunt's house. I just came from a closed-door meeting with Bill Myers at the prosecutor's office. I saw Inslee on the way out, and he says you threatened him. You apparently told him if he continued to mess with you and your aunt, let me quote here, 'he'd feel the full weight of the Ryan empire crashing down on him.'"

Jackson watched her with a look of both admiration and surprise. Harper just shrugged. "I don't think those were my exact words, but Inslee got the gist. We may not have connections here in Little Rock. We may not be part of the good old boys' club and the power brokers in this city, but in Manhattan our name means something. We have the money, resources and power to back it up. I simply made Inslee aware that if he was trying to scare us, it wasn't going to work."

"He got the message," Granger retorted, "but it also made him angrier. He's not someone to threaten. Inslee tried to get a warrant for your aunt's shop. He was denied that for now. He's not someone you want to keep going after."

Harper didn't say anything. She continued to stand her ground, not giving an inch. Jackson's eyes were fixated on her. She could mentally hear the questions he had.

Granger continued, "I can't control Inslee, but I can promise you I'm doing my job. And part of doing my job is making sure you aren't getting hurt in the process."

"I hear you, Detective," Harper humored him. "I'm not going to feel safe until the killer is caught."

Granger folded his arms over his large chest. "That's my point. I want whoever it is caught, too. I also want you out of my investigation. You have no idea what you're going to uncover."

"You'll be the first I call," Harper said and turned to leave.

"I'm serious, Harper. I can arrest you for obstruction of justice," Granger threatened.

"Trust me," Harper assured him calling over her shoulder, "I'm not going to do anything that will warrant that. Please by all means find the killer as fast as you can. If I happen to hear of anything, because it drops in my lap, I'll call you."

With that Harper left the two of them standing there. She got in Jackson's truck and waited.

She watched as Granger turned to Jackson and told him to keep an eye on her and not let her do anything stupid. Jackson gave a half-hearted nod and joined her in the truck while Granger walked into Lizzie's house.

Chapter Twenty-Seven

Hattie was a bit flustered after Roxy came to the shop, but she had to pull it together because she had more clients scheduled for readings. It took a lot of sage and some quiet meditation to calm Hattie's energy down and put focus where it needed to be.

As soon as she wrapped the last of her readings, Hattie practically ran out of the shop. On her way home, she even brushed off one of her neighbors who wanted to have a chat about some kids in the neighborhood who had been causing a ruckus on their skateboards. Hattie didn't care.

Banging open the back door, Hattie yelled, "Tucker! Tucker, are you here?"

Hattie waited a few more seconds. She yelled again. Then she ran to the backyard. It was a nice enough day. The sun was shining, and it was starting to feel like spring.

"Tucker!" Hattie called in a tense whisper. She didn't need her neighbors hearing her call the name of the dead man. Hattie waited and was about to go back inside when she saw the priest watching her from his side of the clearing.

"Do you need something, Fr. McNally?" Hattie called out, walking towards him. He shook his head no and quickly turned and walked the distance back to one of the parish buildings.

"He keeps coming to look at the spot," Tucker explained, appearing behind Hattie.

Hattie jumped not from fear but because he startled her. She turned to face him. "You're here. We need to talk, but inside so I don't look like I'm out here like some crazy person talking to myself."

Tucker followed her inside. Hattie sat at her kitchen table. It was then she noticed that Tucker looked different. The blood was gone from his face and the bullet hole was no longer apparent in his forehead. He also had different clothes on. Gone was the suit and tie. Tucker was now wearing a comfortable looking navy-blue sweater and jeans with simple loafers on his feet.

Hattie must have looked confused, because Tucker explained, "Apparently once you get adjusted on this side, you can change up how you appear. The longer I'm here, the more I learn. While I can't really feel my clothes, this just seems more comfortable. It's a mental thing. And who wants blood dripping down their face for eternity?"

The explanation seemed plausible to Hattie, but she didn't care about that right now. She said, "You said Fr. McNally is out there a lot. What is he doing?"

Tucker's ghostly form paced back and forth in her kitchen. He went to the window and looked out to the backyard. "I don't know. The priest just goes to the spot and looks around, almost as if he's looking for something. At first, I thought maybe he went to pray, but he wasn't praying. He's searching, but for what I don't know. I assume he hasn't found it, he keeps going back."

"Did you hear me calling for you?"

"That's why I came. Did you find out who killed me?" Tucker asked curiously.

"I had a woman named Roxy come to my shop today. Ring any bells?"

Tucker seemed lost in thought. Hattie wasn't sure if he was really searching his memory for her or if he was trying to concoct a lie. Finally, Tucker said excitedly, "I remember. I had an affair with her. I broke it off before I died." He stopped talking and seemed to think some more.

"Time is funny over here," Tucker added wistfully, "you don't really have a sense of it. Thinking about your life, time is hard, too. I'm not sure when I ended it with Roxy, but it was days or weeks before I died. Why did she come see you?"

"She told me she thinks she knows who killed you, or at least what your death might be connected to."

Tucker interrupted. "Roxy's not the sharpest knife in the drawer, if you know what I mean. I wasn't exactly spending time with her for the intellectual stimulation."

Hattie held her hand up. "I get the picture. Hear me out. Roxy said that you had been looking into the Catholic parish. She said you had suspicions about the priest. Roxy seemed to think this was what got you killed."

Tucker moved back from Hattie with an unsure look on his face. He looked right and left as if trying to knock something loose in his brain. Tucker said with skepticism in his voice, "I sort of remember something like that, but the details are fuzzy. Why would I ever tell Roxy something that important?"

"She seemed pretty broken up about your death. Maybe you're not remembering how close you were to her?"

"Hattie, my dear," Tucker stated condescendingly. "I had affairs. A woman here or there to keep my life interesting. I don't remember confiding in any of them. If I told Roxy something, I had a very specific reason. I either wanted information I thought she had or I was using her for something."

"That's fair, but she did know things. Can't you remember any more detail?" Hattie got up and made some tea. She felt bad for Tucker. Beau had been like this when he first crossed over. He had trouble remembering the details of his life. There were some memories that were crystal clear and others that seemed lost for eternity. There was no rhyme or reason to how the information came to him. It definitely didn't come in order of importance. Eventually, Beau's memory came back.

Tucker seemed lost in thought as Hattie brought her tea back to the table. After a time, he got a knowing look on his face. Tucker said excited, "I remember. I saw the priest one night, hanging around Murray Park. I was coming back from fishing. I waited around. Eventually, some other guy showed up. Fr. McNally handed the guy money and took something in a suitcase from him. I got suspicious after that. I remember I found out some things about him that weren't adding up, but I can't remember what that was now."

Tucker looked out the window and turned back to Hattie and added sadly, "I don't think I ever fully figured it out. Do you really think that's what got me killed?"

"I have no idea, but hopefully we can help you find out."

Hattie stood from the table abruptly and looked out the side window that overlooked the driveway. Turning back to Tucker, she said with urgency, "You should go. Harper is back. They went to meet with Lizzie." Hattie regretted saying the last part as soon as it was out of her mouth.

"If that's the case, I'm not going anywhere," Tucker said defiantly.

Chapter Twenty-Eight

Hattie pleaded with Tucker to leave, promising him she'd tell him everything later, but he wouldn't budge. In fact, he only got closer. Tucker planted his ghostly body right next to Hattie at the kitchen table, which is where Jackson and Harper found her when they entered the kitchen.

"I think we got some leads," Harper offered as they came in. Jackson sat at the table across from Hattie while Harper pulled out some sweet tea from the fridge. She poured Jackson a glass and handed it to him. Harper sipped hers, leaning against the counter looking at the table.

Hattie tried to smile, but her hands were shaking. At least she knew now that Harper couldn't see Tucker. With a shaky voice, Hattie asked, "You said you got some leads. What looks promising?"

"We weren't there that long and Lizzie basically gave us her entire suspect list, which is in-line with what we thought with a few added surprises," Jackson offered, taking a sip of tea.

Jackson put the glass down and clasped his hands in front of him on the table. "She suspected a mistress named Roxy and the priest. She also let it slip that she had no idea where Drew was that night. Lizzie said he was up to no good."

Then Jackson looked to Harper with a smug smile and added, "Lizzie also said we should look into Dan Barnes."

"What could Dan…" Hattie started to speak, but she was interrupted. She looked sharply to her side as she heard Tucker speak loudly.

Tucker slapped what would have been his knee and exclaimed, "I should have known Drew would have done me in! He never liked me. I was putting a stop to him sponging off our money."

Harper and Jackson were looking strangely at Hattie. Harper asked, "You okay? You started to ask what Dan could have had to do with this, but then you stopped."

Flustered, Hattie tried to regain her composure. She never had to do this before, talk to the dead and living at the same time. It was maddening. "I lost my train of thought, sorry," Hattie faked. "Hearing about Dan is surprising. The rest of the list makes perfect sense. Roxy paid me a visit today."

Harper's face registered surprise. "What did she want?"

"Probably money," Tucker chimed in.

Hattie did her best to ignore him. She had just told him why Roxy was there. "Roxy said she had some information about who might have killed Tucker. She thinks it's the parish, well the priest. Apparently, Tucker was looking into some suspicious activity of Fr. McNally."

Hattie spent the next few minutes updating Jackson and Harper on everything she had learned, including what Tucker remembered, leaving out how exactly she had gleaned that information.

"We are definitely going to have to follow up on that," Jackson said, looking over at Harper.

"Without question," Harper readily agreed. "I also think we need to follow up on the others as well. I'm going to do some research on Drew's background and his connections."

"He didn't know anyone but criminals," Tucker offered, waving a hand at Hattie who was still ignoring him.

Hattie finally looked at him, with a frustrated look on her face.

"What? I can save them some time," Tucker added.

Hattie quickly looked back at Harper, who was looking at her aunt with curiosity and also concern. "You sure you're all right?"

"Just tired," Hattie offered.

"Did you see Matthew Inslee at the party?" Jackson asked. "I remember his name on the guest list, and Dan saw him but he didn't say anything about being there when he showed up after the murder."

"He was there for a time," Hattie started, "I remember him, but no idea where he went until he showed up here. If I recall, Inslee dressed differently than when I saw him earlier in the night."

"It's funny you say that. Harper and I were wondering the same thing," said Jackson.

"I didn't see him there that night," Tucker interrupted. He was trying to get Hattie's attention again, but she refused to turn in his direction. Tucker shouted, "If one of my prosecutors were there, I find it odd he wouldn't have told me or came over the say hello!"

Turning to Jackson, Hattie offered, "I can get you the guest list so you can follow up with people to see if Inslee was seen later in the evening, if you're comfortable doing that."

Jackson agreed he'd take the guest list and run down any leads. Hattie was going to go back and talk to Roxy. As they were finalizing a plan, Harper's cellphone rang. She held it up for them. It was Dan Barnes. "You should answer that," Hattie told her.

Harper answered and spoke to Dan briefly and then hung up. "He wants to meet this evening. I said I'd meet him for dinner. He wants me to go over the magazine contract. I can also ask him some questions."

"Do you need me to go with you?" Jackson asked eagerly.

"I can handle it alone. I know what Lizzie said, but I don't think we have any reason not to trust Dan right now."

Jackson got up and walked to Harper. "I really don't think that's a good idea. I know you and Hattie think this guy is fine, but there's something he's hiding."

"Oh boy, he's got a crush on her," Tucker added, laughing.

Hattie shot Tucker a quick look to pipe down. "Harper, I trust Dan, but I think Jackson is right. If someone close to Tucker is suspecting him, you need to be cautious. Where are you meeting him?"

"We were going to meet at his office, but then he suggested dinner. He suggested Heights Taco & Tamale. I assume that's close?" Harper had a worried look on her face. Hattie didn't mean to cause any more stress on her, but caution was warranted.

"It's right around the corner. You can probably just walk to your date," Jackson interjected sarcastically.

Chapter Twenty-Nine

Harper knew Jackson was angry with her. She suspected he was just jealous. While Harper understood that Dan Barnes may very well be a suspect, she hadn't heard any valid reason yet to give in to that suspicion. But it amused her to no end that Jackson was jealous. Dan was smart, attractive in a bookish sort of way, and had gushed over her work. Another time, maybe, Harper could see herself dating him.

Harper wore her honey-blonde hair down in soft waves, applied a touch more makeup than she wore during the day and had even put on a simple knee-length green dress and heels. When she came down the stairs, Jackson was still there chatting with Hattie. He gave her a once over.

"You catch more flies with honey," Harper said to counter his look.

"Make sure you don't catch anything else," Jackson bantered back.

Hattie looked between them and laughed. Harper could tell her aunt was amused by the two of them. She suspected Hattie really enjoyed having both of them around. Harper was worried about Hattie's strange behavior that afternoon. It was almost as if she were interacting with someone that wasn't there. Harper knew how silly that seemed, but something was off.

As Harper walked into the restaurant, she felt a bit overdressed. She saw Dan sitting at one of the tables in the middle of the room and walked over. Dan got up and gave Harper a quick hug, which she thought was strange. Harper tried not to hug back like a New Yorker, all stiff and board-like. She didn't usually hug strangers though. Harper wondered if Jackson had been right and this was more of a date than she assumed.

"You look great," Dan said a little too eagerly. "I ordered some chips and cheese dip to start, but if you'd like something else, feel free. Everything here is delicious."

Harper took a moment to view the menu and made her selection. When the waiter came back, they both ordered. As a glass of water was set down in front of her, Harper asked, "Do you have the contract?"

Dan dug through his bag and produced a short two-page contract. Harper read it over. The pay was reasonable and the work was as they discussed. Harper pulled a pen out of her purse, signed it and gave it back to Dan with only one request. "Make a copy for me."

Dan agreed. "I'm really glad you're coming aboard to help. The magazine is in rough shape. It was mostly just events and parties and social occasions when I took it over, but that isn't keeping advertisers. I've been trying to change up what we cover. I was hoping to take more of a turn and branch out, but I wasn't sure what would work."

Over the next hour, Harper and Dan ate their dinner and had a lively, animated conversation about the magazine business. Harper gave Dan some great suggestions including upping the online content, pulling in more business features on people in the community and new businesses, and adding features about restaurants and food trucks, given how much of a foodie town Little Rock is.

Dan was taking notes as she spoke. For Harper, it felt great to get back in the swing of work. Losing *Charlotte* was a serious blow. Being able to use those skills to help revitalize *Rock City Life* was a challenge she was both interested in and ready for. The only catch was Dan's connection to Tucker. She wanted to address that with him head-on.

As dinner came to a close, Harper looked at Dan across the table and said with concern in her voice, "I really hope we can have a great working partnership. We seem to have similar ideas, and I think we can really give the magazine a new life, but there's one thing I have to know."

Dan looked at her with his eyes wide in anticipation. She continued, "I've heard some rumors that you didn't get along with Tucker Reese. Was there something that happened between you?"

Dan took a deep visible breath. He let it out slowly as he leaned back in his chair. "I didn't get along with Tucker," he admitted. "Even when I was the editor of the newspaper, Tucker was all bluster.

He wasn't one to give interviews. He kept his attorneys from giving the newspaper and the public the information they had a right to know. I fought Tucker and his office a lot. That's not really a secret to anyone. It was my job."

"I heard you might have argued with Tucker over a secret investigation into Fr. McNally. Is that true?" Harper asked directly.

What Dan had described was common in just about every community across America. Harper knew that much. People loved the media when they were running the story they wanted. Anything to the contrary, they were seen as the enemy. Harper also knew in her gut there was more to this story. Harper watched Dan fidget in his seat.

"Look, Dan," Harper continued. "I'm a New Yorker so I'm a straight-shooter. I thought you were, too. So, what's the story?"

Dan hesitated for a second and then admitted, "Tucker was working on something big in the months leading up to his death. I had gotten an anonymous news tip that Tucker was working on a case connected to the parish that would create a massive scandal. I tried to get information from Tucker a few times. He threatened me physically and legally if I told a soul. I told him I'd keep it quiet, but still, he shared nothing. We argued several times. I pushed hard, threatened him in return."

Dan stopped speaking for a moment. He seemed to regroup. "It's my job as a journalist. Nothing more, nothing less. I respected Tucker's need to keep it quiet while he investigated, but my worry was that he'd sweep it under the rug like they have done with other cases with well-known people in this city."

Harper looked at him across the table. She wasn't sure how hard to push. Harper asked gently, "What did you do about it?"

Dan threw his hands up. "Nothing. I didn't do a thing. Now he's dead, and we'll never know."

"You didn't kill him or have anything to do with his death?" Harper took a sip of her water and watched him over her glass.

"Is that what you think?" Dan snapped with shock in his voice. "How was I going to break a story from a dead man? That makes no sense."

"You didn't answer the question," Harper pushed, and she waited. She felt so far out of her depth asking these questions, but once Harper committed to taking on something, she wasn't backing down.

"No, of course not. I didn't kill Tucker," Dan denied. Then with an edge of sadness in his voice, he added, "I thought we could be friends, Harper. I thought we would work great together. And tell me if I'm wrong, but I thought there was an attraction here. I can't work with someone who thinks I'm a killer."

Harper hated that she felt bad for him. Dan seemed like a nice guy. Nothing jumped out to her that Dan could be a killer, but after her marriage, blind trust was nearly impossible.

"I'm sorry," Harper said sympathetically and meant it. "I had to ask. I hope you can understand that, and now that I know, I hope we can move past it."

"Did that guy Jackson think it was me? He didn't seem to like me very much."

Harper smiled. "Jackson is definitely suspicious of you. But no, it came from other sources."

"I know even if I ask, you're not going to tell me who, right?"

"You know I can't, and if you were in my shoes, you wouldn't either."

Chapter Thirty

Before Harper left the restaurant, Dan had asked if she wanted to work on a story related to Tucker's death. Harper wasn't sure that was a good idea. She gave a non-committal answer and left. On the walk back to Hattie's house, Harper's cellphone rang. It was a number she didn't recognize so she let it go to voicemail. It rang again and again. Whoever was calling was persistent.

Finally, on the fourth attempt, Harper answered and immediately wished she hadn't. It was a call from the prison where her ex-husband Nick was serving a two-year sentence. Before she realized it, the caller connected her to Nick.

"Harper, are you there?" Nick said on the other end. His voice was strange. Not like it had been when they were married. It took her a few seconds to realize it really was him.

"Why are you calling me?" Harper barked.

"Baby, don't be like that," Nick crooned. "I know what I did was horrible and you probably can't ever forgive me. We were married for all those years. I have something to tell you."

Harper wanted to hang up the phone. The last weeks with Nick flashed before her eyes. The meetings with the FBI, dealing with Carmine DeLuca, and Lola, Carmine's daughter. "You have two minutes. And then don't ever call me again."

His voice happy and excited, Nick blurted out, "I'm getting out soon. They are cutting my time for good behavior. I ratted out some guy in here so they are transferring me to county lockup. I should be out in six months. When I'm out, I want to come see you. I heard you aren't in Manhattan. Where are you?"

Harper had known when he was sentenced that Nick would eventually get out of prison, but she thought that would be in years and not months. She stood firm, "I'm not seeing you under any circumstance." Then Harper hung up without saying another word.

Harper walked the rest of the way to her aunt's house. She felt distracted, her mind a swirl of memories, some that once had been good but now tainted. She was numb from Nick's call. Harper never wanted to see him again, but she was worried he'd figure out she was at Hattie's. Nick had never visited Little Rock with Harper, but he knew how much Hattie meant to her.

Harper was so lost in thought that as she approached Hattie's house, she was nearly hit by a car speeding down the road. It passed through the open gates that marked the entrance to the parish. Harper couldn't see who was in the car, but it piqued her curiosity. Instead of going into her aunt's house, she went to the side lawn that connected to the backyard. When Harper reached the clearing, she hesitated to see if she heard voices. She didn't, just heard the car running. Harper crept quietly down the clearing to the edge of the parish property.

Peeking through the bare tree branches, Harper watched as a man got out of the car. He opened the back door and helped what appeared to be a girl get out of the car. She looked big, with a round swollen belly, probably eight or even nine months pregnant. Harper watched as the priest came out. Fr. McNally looked around as he walked to the car. Harper quickly stepped back into the trees to make sure she was out of sight. He didn't seem to see her.

Fr. McNally handed a thick envelope to the man. He looked inside and then put it in the car. The priest escorted the girl with the man into a small brick building that was set back behind the house that Fr. McNally had said was his residence. The three entered the simple square space that was probably no bigger than a large shed. It had no windows so Harper wasn't able to see what was happening. They were in there for a long time. Harper wasn't sure what she was witnessing. Worried she was going to get caught, she turned and ran up the path to the house before they came out.

Once inside the back porch, Harper called for her aunt. Both Jackson and Hattie came running into the kitchen. Harper was surprised to see Jackson there, but pleased that he was.

A bit out of breath from excitement and fear, Harper asked, "What's that building behind where Fr. McNally lives?"

"It's their storm shelter," Hattie explained. "It was built in the sixties as a nuclear fallout shelter. There's a bunker underground. You can access the stairs that take you down into the bunker from that building. The bunker is huge. It runs under nearly their entire property. It's used as a tornado shelter now for the local neighborhood. Why?"

Harper finally caught her breath. "When I was walking back from dinner, a car came speeding down the road. It nearly hit me. I was curious so I went down to the clearing. I saw Fr. McNally and a man bring a very pregnant girl down there. Fr. McNally also handed him a thick envelope."

Jackson looked to Hattie. His face a mix of shock and concern. "How old would you say she is?"

"I couldn't really see her face. I'm not sure."

"We should call the police," Jackson advised, pulling out his phone.

Hattie laid a hand on his arm to stop him. She countered, "We have no idea what's going on. They could just be giving the poor girl a place to stay. There are beds down there, entire rooms. There are bathrooms and showers. It has full electric and plumbing."

Harper protested, "Something's not right, Aunt Hattie. You tell me to use my intuition, and I'm telling you, it's not right."

"Calm down," Hattie assured her, patting Harper on the shoulder. Hattie's voice steady and sure, she added, "Listen here, you call the police now, they could say anything. They don't know we saw anything. We need to wait and find out more."

Jackson agreed. "I think Hattie's right."

"You may be right," Harper said looking at Hattie, "but it doesn't mean I have to like it."

Chapter Thirty-One

Hattie was dreaming that a dark force was covering her face trying to suffocate her. She thrashed around and used her hands to push it off of her. She couldn't make out exactly what it was, but it was too strong. She was growing weaker. It was consuming her. Right before it fully took over, a dog's loud, incessant barking jolted her awake, saving Hattie from the nightmare.

Hattie sat right up in bed, her back drenched in sweat. She blinked rapidly, trying to adjust her eyes to the darkness. The dogs barking wasn't her dream. It was real and happening that second. It alerted Hattie that something was very wrong. Sparkle and Shine were docile and quiet each night. Hattie's bare feet hit the floor, and she was on the move. Harper's door was still closed, and Hattie called her name. She didn't wait to see if it woke her. Hattie bounded down the stairs, moving faster than most people thought an old lady could move. The dogs grew louder.

Hattie hit the landing and opened the small hall closet. She pulled out an old wooden baseball bat that had been her husband's, and she advanced towards the kitchen. The dogs were standing at the kitchen door that opened to the porch and were barking like mad.

Hattie approached the door. As she did, Harper called her name as she came rushing to Hattie's side. "What's going on?" Harper whispered.

"I don't know, but I think someone is out there," Hattie indicated as she reached down and calmed the dogs. They continued to bark.

"Let me go see," Harper offered. She moved in front of her aunt and shooed the dogs to the side. Hattie pulled on the back of her shirt to stop her. Harper waved her off. She said with annoyance in her voice, "We can't stand here all night. If it's someone, maybe I'll scare him off."

Hattie watched as Harper unlatched the door and stepped onto the enclosed back porch. Hattie stepped out behind her and immediately saw a dark-hooded man in the window of the door that led outside. He locked eyes with Hattie. Both of them froze. Then he took off. Before Hattie could stop her, Harper took two fast steps and unlocked the porch door, flung it open and bounded down the steps after him.

Hattie stood there paralyzed not sure what to do, concerned for Harper's safety. That's when she saw Jackson run in the same direction as Harper and the man. She also saw the note attached to the door.

It was direct and to the point. *Stop or die.*

Hattie immediately rushed back inside and called the police. The 911 operator said they were sending a car immediately. They asked Hattie if she wanted them to stay on the line. She didn't. She went and stood at the back door.

Several minutes later a half-dressed Harper and Jackson came walking towards the porch from the backyard. They both looked cold and angry. "He got away," Harper scowled as they walked up the steps.

Once inside, Hattie locked the door behind them.

Harper explained, "The man took off into the backyard. I was closing in on him, but instead of running toward the road or cutting through the clearing, he ran straight for the woods. I was so close I nearly grabbed him, but he gained ground and darted right into the woods, cutting between the trees."

"I lost him, too," Jackson grunted.

Harper reached for his arm. "I didn't think you'd catch him. He was so far ahead."

"I stopped to put sneakers on before leaving the house," Jackson cursed, clearly frustrated with himself.

Harper lifted her bare foot to the side so Jackson could see the cuts and scrapes on her sole. "If you hadn't you wouldn't have been able to chase him at all. I got all cut up."

Jackson winced. "Let's get you fixed up."

Hattie got some antibiotic cream and some bandages. While Jackson was helping Harper clean and bandage her cuts, Hattie got the note and told them about it.

"Someone was trying to scare us," Harper said.

"Is that handwritten?" Jackson asked, holding out his hand to take the note from Hattie. He examined it. It was in simple block lettering, black ink on a plain white piece of paper.

Hattie heard the cop car pull up in the driveway and walked to the back porch to let them in. She called out, "Come this way. This is the door they were trying to open."

The cops came in and spent time inspecting the door. The younger of the two looked to Hattie and asked, "Where did you find the note?"

"It was tucked into the window on the door. He was clearly trying to turn the handle when we came down. I think the dogs slowed him down and then we scared him off. Harper and Jackson chased him into the woods."

The cops explained that Det. Granger was on his way so they'd hold off asking any more questions. When Det. Granger arrived a few minutes later, the cops got him up to speed.

Granger looked to Harper who was sitting on the kitchen chair her feet wrapped in bandages. "What did I tell you about wanting to protect you?"

"It's just a few cuts from the sticks in the woods. I started to chase him back there but was barefoot. I'm fine," Harper assured him.

Det. Granger hitched his jaw in Jackson's direction. "How'd you end up in the middle of this? I thought you lived across the street."

"I do," Jackson confirmed. "I had fallen asleep in the living room and woke up to dogs barking. That never happens in this neighborhood so I looked out the window and saw a guy standing on the side of Hattie's house. I threw on sneakers and ran out of the house. By then, he had already taken off, and Harper was chasing him. He ran into the woods behind the house. I never caught up to him."

Turning back to Harper and then to Jackson, "Can either of you give me a description?"

"He was Caucasian, medium build, but he had a cap on and a hood over it," Harper explained first. "I couldn't really see his facial features enough to describe him. It was so dark I don't know if it was someone I recognized or not."

Jackson added, "He ran pretty fast. He was definitely taller than I am by a few inches. He wasn't a big guy though. He had something in his hand as he was running. A screwdriver, maybe."

"I didn't even notice that," Harper admitted, looking at Jackson. "Is that what he was using to break in?"

"He could have been," Det. Grander said seriously. He took the note from Hattie and read it over. Pointing at Harper, he warned, "You need to drop this and let me do my job. You should heed this warning."

Det. Granger went to the door and checked it out. He told them he was going out back to walk the area and check out the woods. Nearly twenty minutes later, Granger came back in. "I'm going to follow up with you folks tomorrow. There's no one out there now and nothing I can see."

Holding up the note, Granger added, "I'm going to keep this. Lock up. I'll look more into this in the morning."

Jackson insisted on spending the rest of the night there. Hattie was glad. He went home and locked his house quickly. When Jackson got back to Hattie's, the three of them headed up the stairs with the two dogs close behind. Hattie showed Jackson the spare room he could have.

From her doorway, Harper called out, "I should have said it before, but those boxers look good on you. Didn't know you had such muscular, sexy legs." Then she giggled and closed the door.

Chapter Thirty-Two

Hattie barely fell back to sleep, and it was time to get up again. She made eggs and bacon for Harper and Jackson for breakfast, and then headed into her shop. Jackson had told them he had some things to take care of so he'd be unavailable for a while. Before he left, Jackson promised he'd spend some time following up with the guest list to see where Inslee was during the Saints & Sinners Ball. Harper seemed distracted and a bit moody. She told Hattie she might stop by the shop, but she wanted to shower, rebandage her feet and then had a few calls to make.

Hattie worked all morning and before she knew it, it was nearly noon. She hadn't heard anything from Det. Granger. She was contemplating giving him a call when Beatrix arrived for her afternoon shift.

Hattie looked up from behind the counter where she was bagging some loose tea. "We nearly had a break-in last night. Let's do that protection spell on the house tonight if you're available."

"Is everything okay?" Beatrix asked, a bit startled.

"Everything is fine. The police are looking into it. I'd just rather get the spell done sooner than later," Hattie assured her.

Beatrix agreed and went about fixing some fresh coffee for the afternoon. Then she busied herself by taking fresh pastries from the back and arranging them in the display case. Hattie was glad as they had been getting busier each afternoon. Hattie wondered if people were coming into the shop simply because they knew it was at her house where the murder took place. People could have a morbid fascination.

Hattie had two quick back-to-back readings that each took thirty minutes. When she came out from the backroom, Hattie was pleasantly surprised to see Harper sitting at a table with her laptop. Hattie went over and wrapped her arms around Harper's shoulders. Harper gave a bit of a jump from being startled. Hattie said happily, "I'm so glad you're here."

Harper smiled at her aunt. "I came to see if you needed help, but Beatrix has everything under control. I thought I'd do a little digging into Fr. McNally. What do you know about him?"

"Not much really. It seems, if I'm remembering correctly, he started over the summer. I think I heard he had been at a Catholic mission in Rio de Janeiro before coming here. You know they move priests around sometimes."

"Matthew Inslee had said something to that effect. Had Fr. McNally ever been here before? He seems pretty connected to the community for only being here such a short time," Harper speculated.

Hattie watched as Harper brought up a search page and typed in the priest's name.

"I don't think he's been here before. I'm pretty sure I would have heard that. Last summer, I think it was July, they had a big welcome event at the parish."

"Well, I don't know what it is, but there's something shady with him." Harper went to work searching different sites and digging for more background information on Fr. McNally.

"Fr. McNally has been going back to the spot where Tucker was killed," Hattie explained, sitting across from Harper. She couldn't say Tucker told her so she said, "I've noticed him a few times. It seems he's searching for something."

"That's interesting," Harper said, not looking up. Her head buried in her laptop.

Hattie was going to leave her to work. As she stood, Harper popped her head up. "I forgot to tell you last night, Nick called me."

Hattie sat right back down. This wasn't good at all. "What on earth did he want?"

"It seems Nick snitched on another prisoner, and for that, he's getting transferred. He's getting out early on good behavior or at least that's what he said." Harper took a sip of the coffee she had in front of her. Taking a big bite of her muffin, she added, "He wants to know where I am so he can visit. I hung up on him."

"Do you want me to pull some cards, and see if I can figure out what he really wants?" Hattie offered.

Harper shrugged. "Can't hurt. Let's do it after I see what I get here." With that Harper went back to work.

Hattie joined Beatrix behind the counter. She whispered to the girl, "At least she's in the shop. She looks fairly at ease, too."

"Baby steps," Beatrix reminded Hattie with a smile.

Nearly thirty minutes later, the three women, all hard at work, were interrupted by Det. Granger's large frame standing in the doorway of the shop. Harper looked up from her laptop as Hattie stopped what she was doing to see who came in the door. Hattie wasn't as surprised to see him as she was the constrained, worried look on his face.

"Det. Granger, can I get you some coffee?" Hattie offered.

He shook his head no. "Thanks, but I really came to talk. Do you have some private space?"

Hattie waved to Harper to follow, and the three of them went into Hattie's back reading room. She gave Det. Granger her chair and she and Harper took the couch. Hattie felt weird being on this side of the room, but Det. Granger's face was causing her even more distress.

"There's no easy way to say this, but Roxy Holland, Tucker's mistress, was found dead this morning in her apartment. She had been shot," Det. Granger informed them. Then he leveled a look at Hattie and asked, "Did you know her?"

"I didn't even know her last name," Hattie started to explain, "but she was here yesterday, Detective. We sat in this very room."

"What did she tell you?" It was clear from Granger's tone he wasn't pulling any punches.

Hattie shot straight. "Roxy informed me she thought that Tucker's murder was connected to a scandal or criminal activity at the parish. She wasn't sure of the details, but she said Tucker was looking into the priest, Fr. McNally, who Tucker had said was acting strangely. Roxy was filled with grief, and she was scared. She told me Tucker was sneaking around investigating. She didn't know any more though."

"Lizzie told me the same when I was over there yesterday," Harper added.

Hattie thought back to the day before. Filled with shock and guilt, she said quietly to herself, "The cards showed me Roxy was going to die. I just didn't realize it at the time."

Chapter Thirty-Three

"Excuse me? I didn't catch that," Det. Granger said, sitting back in his seat. He was watching them closely.

"Whether you believe in such things or not, Detective, I'm psychic. I can look at my cards and they can show me the past, present, and sometimes the future," Hattie explained.

She picked up the deck of Celtic Tarot cards that was sitting on the table between them. Gesturing with the deck in her hand, Hattie informed him, "I had looked for Roxy to see if there was any validity to Tucker's concerns about the parish. I got the cards for deceit, destruction and death. Then after that, I did a reading for Roxy about her life going forward without Tucker's financial support and got the same cards. I thought the energy was maybe off as Roxy had been very emotional. I assumed the reading was just a repeat of the one about the parish rather than seeing correctly that Roxy was in danger. I could have warned her." Hattie started to cry softly.

"You couldn't have known," Harper soothed as she wrapped her arms around her aunt.

Det. Granger sat forward with his hands on his knees. "I understand you're upset, Hattie, but Harper is right. You had no way of knowing that's what it meant. But this does explain a note tucked away in Roxy's bedroom. It simply read that she had talked to Hattie Beauregard, and you knew everything. Then there was a detailed note indicating what you just told me about the parish. But there's not enough to go on. It doesn't make any sense to us. Other investigators are interviewing Fr. McNally and staff right now. From what the investigators have updated me so far, no one at the parish seems to have any idea what Tucker may have been looking into."

"When was Roxy killed?" Harper asked.

"We believe sometime late last night. A friend of hers found her body early this morning. The medical examiner will do an autopsy later this afternoon. We should have a better time of death then."

Granger opened the folder on his lap, which contained a legal pad. He pulled out a pen and was poised to take some notes. "I need you to tell me everything Roxy said," Granger coaxed.

Hattie detailed everything Roxy had told her and included details that Tucker had added. Hattie hated lying, but she couldn't exactly say that a dead man came to her and told her about seeing the priest in Murray Park and about his undefined suspicions. None of it even made sense to Hattie, yet.

"You don't know who else Tucker told?" Granger pressed.

"As Harper told you, he had mentioned it to Lizzie. But no, I don't know of anyone else. I was surprised that Tucker had confided in Roxy that much."

Harper interjected, "I know someone told Dan Barnes. When I had dinner with him last night, he said he had an anonymous source. I wonder now if that was Roxy. Do you have any suspects?"

"We don't have much of anything right now," Granger admitted. "We are waiting for ballistics on the murder weapon. I can tell you someone surprised her. She was found in bed with a bullet hole in her head. Her place was ransacked like they were looking for something."

"Do you think they found the note she left?" Hattie asked concerned. If someone was killing off people who knew what Tucker might have been investigating, Hattie was worried she was next.

Granger shook his head no. "We only found it by accident. One of the crime scene techs knocked over a vase and it was inside."

Harper looked over at her aunt and detailed, "I was coming back from dinner last night, and I saw something strange behind Fr. McNally's residence. Hattie and Jackson didn't think much of it, but I'm just going to tell you and let you decide if it's important."

Det. Granger nodded so Harper continued. "I saw a car pull up. Fr. McNally handed the driver, a man, a large envelope full of something. I'm not sure what. Then he opened the back door to the car and a very pregnant girl stepped out. The three of them went behind the priest's residence. Hattie says it's a small brick building with stairs leading down to a large storm shelter. I don't know what it means, but I found it very strange."

Hattie added, "I didn't think much of it because there are beds down there, entire living spaces with bathrooms, showers, and kitchen. It's a living space. I thought maybe she just needed a place to stay. The Catholic church does that as many churches do."

Det. Granger seemed to take it and think about it. He commented, "They do that, but I find it strange if the girl needed shelter or a home, why not one of the many women's shelters in town. Holy Souls has an entire women's facility. Why put a pregnant girl in a storm shelter all alone?"

"Good point," Hattie agreed.

"I'll look into it," Granger assured. "That's all I have for now. I don't have anything more on your break-in, but as soon as I know more, you'll hear from me. Please, as I said before, let me know anything you find out immediately. Don't go looking for it, but things seem to fall into your laps. Call me anytime day or night."

Hattie saw Granger out. He grabbed a coffee to go. He thanked Hattie again for being so accommodating. She watched him leave, and then turned back and headed to Harper who was still sitting in her reading room.

"You okay?" Hattie asked as she sat down in her chair.

"I don't even know what to say about all of this. I feel like a murder magnet." Harper leaned back on the couch and closed her eyes. She sighed loudly.

"Are you regretting moving here?"

Harper sat forward and looked over at her aunt. "Not at all. This is just a lot and then with Nick calling."

"You want to look into what he wants? I can show you how these cards work, too?"

"Might as well." Harper sat on the edge of the couch, looking at the cards on the table.

Hattie picked them up, closed her eyes and shuffled them in her hands. Then she began to lay them out in a spread. Hattie explained each card's meaning in general and then their specific meaning in relation to where they fell in the tarot spread. To Hattie's delight, Harper really seemed to be listening and taking in what she explained.

"To summarize," Hattie said at the end, "Nick wants back in your life. He regrets his decision and the affair. He wants to repair things with you. I don't need to read the cards to know that won't happen, but he will be persistent. You'll need to be very firm with him. I don't see anything positive around him."

Hattie then smiled at Harper. "For you though, I see three suitors and eventually a marriage to one of them. Not just a marriage, but a soul connection. It's the man you're meant to be with."

Chapter Thirty-Four

Harper appreciated her aunt looking at her cards regarding Nick and was surprised to hear she'd marry again. She didn't always give Hattie much credit, but it was nice to hear regardless. Harper was tempted to figure out who her suitors were, but really, she just wanted to find out what was going on with Fr. McNally. She knew it was something. As Hattie told her to do time and again, she was trusting her instinct.

Harper said goodbye to Hattie at the shop and headed back to the house. Once there, Harper set up a workspace in her room and spent the next two hours going through more internet searches. She printed some photos from Fr. McNally's time in Brazil and studied them closely.

Harper was troubled by something. She studied the photos more closely. The way Fr. McNally looked in older photos was somewhat different when compared to now. She did an exhaustive search for a recent photo for comparison but oddly came up short. Harper tucked them in a file to explore more later.

Then Harper made a few phone calls attempting to dig more into Fr. McNally's life. She wasn't finding much since he arrived in Little Rock. It seemed for a priest who was overseeing such a large parish as St. Joseph's, Fr. McNally was really flying under the radar.

Harper looked out her bedroom window to see if Jackson was across the street. His truck wasn't there. She retreated to her bed to take a quick nap. Just as Harper was drifting off to sleep, she heard the floor outside her bedroom creak. Harper leaned forward and opened one eye to take a peek into the hall, expecting to see one of the dogs. There was no one there. She shrugged and laid back down, thinking she had imagined it.

Again though, Harper heard the creak. This time it was louder and almost like steps. Harper sighed loudly, got up and went to look in the hall. That's when she saw something move past the doorframe in Hattie's bedroom. It looked like the back of a person just passing by but not quite as solid. It was more like a shadow. Harper blinked once and then twice, questioning what she really saw. Then fear took hold. Harper raced down the hall, not sure what she would find.

Looking in Hattie's room, there no one there. Sparkle and Shine were sleeping peacefully on her aunt's bed. Harper stood there, surrounded by the silence of the room. The only thing she could hear was the soft snores of the dogs. Harper relaxed. She laughed to herself.

As Harper turned to leave, she caught sight of someone out her aunt's bedroom window. Fr. McNally was in the clearing, looking down at the grass and then in the wooded part where Tucker's body had fallen. Harper watched him for a few minutes. Fr. McNally was so lost in his mission, he never looked up. Eventually, he gave up and went back to the parish property.

Harper got an idea. She went back to her bedroom and dug through her closet for her comfortable cross-trainers. She hadn't been to the gym in months, but they were comfortable enough to hike through the woods. Harper laced up and went outside the back way. She retraced the steps she had taken the night before when she chased the prowler. Then Harper crossed the threshold into the woods and carefully watched the ground.

Harper took careful step after careful step. The ground wasn't flat. There was a bit of a hill to climb that then led to more flat ground. Hattie had told her that the woods eventually connected to other houses several blocks away. It was an undeveloped part of land that connected neighborhoods in the Heights. Standing at the top of one hill, Harper could make out much of the parish property through the trees. Not much was going on. Harper had no idea how many people worked in the buildings, but all seemed quiet.

Harper went farther. She had been walking for close to twenty minutes since she left the house and was just about to give up when she saw something flashy on the ground. It caught her eye. Harper picked it up, and then wished she hadn't when she saw what it was. It was a bright gold letter D key chain. The keys were missing and the latch was broken. It must have fallen off. Harper wished she hadn't gotten her fingerprints all over it. She slipped it carefully into her pocket.

Taking a few more steps around the area, she saw a screwdriver laying among the leaves and sticks. Harper contemplated going back to the house to get a bag to put it in, but she wasn't sure she'd ever find the spot again. Harper took a leaf and used that to pick up the end of the screwdriver, not touching the handle at all. Harper started a quick jog back towards her aunt's house.

As she was approaching the hill that would take her back down to the yard, Harper noticed a man moving suitcases into the small brick building Hattie said led to the storm shelter. At first, Harper could only see his back. He was average height and had short dark hair. When he came out of the building, Harper saw his face and thought at first it was Fr. McNally. But it wasn't. Their facial features looked incredibly similar. They had the same oval-shaped face, high forehead, straight pointed nose, and thin lips. They were both pale. Harper watched him bring suitcase after suitcase into the shelter and down the steps. Harper had no idea what she was witnessing.

Feeling brave, Harper continued her walk down the hill, keeping the screwdriver out of sight on her right side. She gave it a toss into her aunt's yard when she was close enough and then looped around to the parish property. Cutting through the woods, Harper came up to the door of the building just as the man was walking out.

"Hi," Harper said cheerily.

When the man didn't say anything she added, "I live next door. Just got a bit turned around exploring the woods."

"You're not supposed to be here." The man scowled.

"Right, I know," Harper conceded. "Just heading back next door. How's it going today?"

"Fine," he snapped.

Harper extended her hand, "I'm Harper."

He begrudgingly shook her hand. "Evan."

"Are you related to Fr. McNally? I thought it was him as I was walking down the hill," Harper said eagerly, pointing behind her to the way she just came.

"Brother," was all he said. Then he walked away from Harper, leaving her standing there.

Not wanting to come off too suspiciously, Harper headed back to Hattie's, watching Evan pull more suitcases out of the car. It was the same car she had seen the night before. Maybe Fr. McNally was letting family stay there. Harper thought that might make more sense, but it still was strange. Calling over her shoulder as she turned the corner into the clearing, Harper yelled, "Nice to meet you, Evan."

Chapter Thirty-Five

Harper quickly ducked back into Hattie's yard and ran into the kitchen to find a plastic bag big enough to put a screwdriver. As Harper came running out, she bumped right into Jackson who was poised on the steps about to knock on the door.

"What's the hurry, sunshine?" Jackson inquired, looking down at the bag and towel she had in her hands.

"I think I found the screwdriver you saw the guy carrying last night," Harper explained as she quickly moved around Jackson and scurried into the yard. Harper looked around until she found the screwdriver and used the towel to pick up the end, again not touching the handle. She carefully placed it in the bag.

Jackson was watching her. "Where did you find it?"

Harper pointed up into the woods. "I went for a walk. I wanted to follow the same path as the guy last night but in daylight. I found two things of interest right near each other. The screwdriver and a key chain with the letter D. I need to go put that in a bag next. It's in my pocket."

"Sounds like you had an interesting day," Jackson commented as he looked at her a bit funny.

"What?"

He didn't respond, but instead reached out and removed a twig from her hair and ran his thumb against her cheek. "You had dirt on your face," he said explaining his action.

"Thanks, I always seem to be a mess when I see you," Harper said a bit embarrassed. From the moment Harper met Jackson, she was not her usual poised self. First, Harper thought he was a handyman, then she showed up to dinner fresh from a shower with her hair all wet. Then Jackson saw her first thing in the morning and last night barely dressed at all.

"I don't mind," Jackson said, his voice deeper than normal.

Harper thought Jackson was acting a bit strange, but it had been such a strange day. She really didn't have time to get into it. She started walking towards the house. "We need to catch up. Did you find anyone that saw Inslee at the party all night?"

"No, I've pretty much talked to everyone that would talk to me. The consensus is the same. Inslee was definitely there early in the evening, and then he was gone. Last time I could get anyone to tell me they saw him was near eight, roughly two hours before you found Tucker's body."

"I wonder where he went. That's so strange to be there and then disappear, only to show up later like he'd never been there at all. Could Inslee have gotten called out to those burglaries?"

Jackson shrugged. "That's possible. That's been an ongoing case for a while. Maybe they found something, and they wanted him at the scene."

"You think Det. Granger would know if Inslee was there or not? I remember him saying something about the burglaries having been his cases before he got pulled off of them to handle Tucker's murder."

"You can always ask," Jackson said. Pointing to the screwdriver, he added, "You're going to have to call him to pick up that evidence anyway."

Harper walked back into the house with Jackson right behind her. She went to the tall cabinet near the stove and pulled out a smaller bag. Harper pulled the key chain from her pocket and dropped it in. She washed her hands and then pulled out the bread and meat and cheese from the fridge to make a sandwich. "Investigating makes me hungry," Harper joked and offered to make Jackson a late lunch.

Once they were sitting at the kitchen table, eating their turkey sandwiches and washing it down with Hattie's sweet tea, Harper said, "I'll call Granger when we're done. What were you doing today?"

Jackson took another bite and was quiet for a moment. Tentatively he said, "I had to go to a lawyer's office to sort some things out with my divorce."

Harper didn't press the issue. She gave him a sympathetic smile.

They ate in silence for a few more minutes, then Harper remembered Jackson didn't know about Roxy. Finishing the last of her sandwich, Harper told him, "I didn't tell you. I was in Hattie's shop today, and

Granger paid us a visit. Roxy was murdered last night."

Jackson looked at her with his eyes wide and his mouth slightly open. "Are you kidding me? Tucker and then his girlfriend? It's obviously connected, right?"

"I would think so." Harper then added quietly, "Hattie feels pretty bad about it. When she was in the shop yesterday, Roxy had gotten a personal reading and all Hattie saw was bad cards including death. She assumed the energy was off. Hattie feels like she could have protected Roxy."

"Well that's just silly," Jackson concluded. "I'm sure Hattie is gifted, but she couldn't have known." He stood and picked up his plate and Harper's. He took them to the sink, ran water over them and poured a little dish detergent. He stood there washing their dishes.

Harper watched him with amusement. Nick would never have done the dishes, even if she had begged for his help. "That's one of the reasons I don't want to tap into these gifts Hattie says I have. Who would want the responsibility of knowing something like that before it happens? Sounds like a curse to me."

"Depends on how you look at it. Cops have any leads?" Jackson queried as he finished the last of the dishes and started drying them.

Harper got up and put away the dishes as Jackson finished. "Det. Granger didn't say. They found a note Roxy hid indicating Hattie knew everything she did. I'm concerned for her safety even more. Mine too. Granger didn't think anyone else found the note, but who knows if Roxy told anyone she talked to Hattie."

"You want me to start spending the night here?" Jackson offered.

Harper laughed. "You just want to show off those sexy legs."

Jackson stood back appraising her. "You think my legs are sexy, huh?"

Harper blushed. She could start the flirting, she wasn't very good at seeing it through. She said demurely, "Not bad. But at least we're even now."

"What do you mean?"

"You saw me early in the morning, and I've seen you in your undies."

"You're not letting that go, are you?" Jackson laughed and shook his head.

"Nope." More serious, Harper added, "I think it would be great if you could crash in Hattie's spare room until this all is solved. I'd feel safer with you here. I'm sure Hattie would, too."

Then she remembered something else. Excitedly she tugged on Jackson's arm and said, "Come upstairs to my bedroom, there's something I want to show you."

The look on Jackson's face was priceless, a mix of uncertainty and amusement, but he followed Harper all the way up to her bedroom.

Chapter Thirty-Six

It was late in the afternoon, and Hattie was exhausted. After the excitement the night before, she never really got back to sleep. All Hattie had done was toss and turn. Then Det. Granger telling her about Roxy had set her on edge. Hattie had wanted to cancel her afternoon readings, but she knew clients were on edge too, hoping for answers so she prepared as best she could. Hattie smudged the reading room with sage. She had Beatrix smudge her, and then Hattie spent a good twenty minutes in meditation, just clearing her mind. The readings went well, but it wiped what was left of her energy.

Hattie was sipping some coffee at one of the tables, going over some accounting files on her laptop when Dan entered the shop. Hattie looked up, surprised to see him. She couldn't remember a time he'd been in there. She called over to him, "This is a pleasant surprise, Dan. What can I do for you?"

Dan came over to the table and pulled out the chair across from her. He sat down and folded his hands on the table. He looked stressed. Dan's brow was furrowed and the wrinkle between his eyes more apparent. Hattie looked at him for an explanation.

"I heard Roxy is dead."

Hattie nodded. She thought back to what Harper had said about his anonymous source. Hattie said, "She is. Did you know her?"

"Yeah, we had met several times," Dan said but didn't elaborate.

It was clear to Hattie that Dan was hesitant to speak about it, but he must want to otherwise he wouldn't be there. "Would you like to find a more private spot to talk?" Hattie offered.

"No, this is good. I'm not hiding anything anymore," Dan snapped. Then he apologized and said in a more normal tone, "Roxy was my source. She was giving me information about Tucker and what he was investigating with the parish. The police were at my office earlier today and are ransacking my house as we speak. They told me I couldn't be there."

"They searched my place, too, Dan. I think it's pretty routine. I'm not sure how I can help."

"There's more going on than you know," Dan said seriously.

She wondered why Dan came to her of all people. She also noted Dan never asked Hattie if she knew Roxy. Dan had either made an assumption or knew she had.

Dan hesitated. "I'm not sure how much I should tell you."

"Well," Hattie started, "you came here so you must need someone to confide in. We can just take our time."

Hattie clicked out of the accounting files, closed her laptop, and pushed it to the side. She got up and went to the counter. Hattie pulled out a mug and poured Dan a cup of coffee. She asked if he wanted cream and sugar. He shook his head no to both. Coming back over, Hattie sat the hot coffee in front of him. "Why don't you tell me your concerns, and I'll see what I can do."

"I've had a few threatening phone calls. At first, they were asking me what Roxy had told me. They said they'd spare me if I just told them," Dan explained. He took a long sip of hot coffee and sat with his hands around the mug. "First Tucker and now Roxy. Clearly he was on to something."

"Why did Roxy come to you?" Hattie inquired. She thought back to what Tucker said. If he was confiding in Roxy, he had a reason. Did he want the story to break?

"I've known Roxy from way back," Dan admitted. "She was a source on some stories back from when I ran the newspaper. Roxy had a knack for getting gossip. She had affairs with powerful men, and they let their secrets slip. I guess she thought she could trust me again."

"And could she?" Hattie asked directly.

"Of course," Dan said wearily. "What's with you and Harper suspecting me?"

"No one is suspecting you, but right now, given all that's happened, the questions have to be asked," Hattie explained matter of fact. "Go on. What did Roxy tell you?"

Dan dug through the messenger bag he had carried in with him, which was flung over the chair. He pulled out a small iPad. He touched the keypad and pulled up a note file. Dan read it over, and explained, "All Roxy told me was that Tucker was working on something big connected to the parish. At first, Roxy wasn't sure who it was connected to. Then a few weeks later Tucker had let slip that Fr. McNally wasn't really who he portrayed himself to be. I still don't know exactly what that means though. There was information about him being in Brazil, and something happening there, but no real solid details. But it was enough for me to press Tucker for more. It was something we had argued about."

"But you never found out specifically?"

"No, to this day I don't know more," Dan said defeated. "I didn't tell Harper this last night, but I have some leads to run down that I've dug up on my own, but now Tucker is dead. Roxy is dead. Am I next?"

"Let's hope not." Hattie breathed out an exasperated breath. "Do you think Tucker wanted you to break the story?"

"No, definitely not. We argued over that. So that was the weird thing. I assumed that's why he was telling Roxy at first, but after I talked to him, he definitely didn't want me to know. Tucker was frustrated and angry that I knew."

Hattie agreed, "Tucker was too smart to spill secrets like that casually. He had to have had a reason to tell her."

Dan looked to Hattie. He asked, "I heard Roxy came here to talk to you. What did she tell you?"

Hattie acted surprised. "How did you hear that?"

"Just around, but did she tell you what she told me?"

"I can't get into what a client told me, Dan, but I'll say I don't know any more than you just told me," Hattie explained cautiously. She wasn't in the habit of exposing her clients' secrets even if they were dead.

Dan looked frustrated. "Where does this leave us? There's not enough information to break the story, and we certainly can't find out why Tucker told Roxy. I don't even know if it's safe for me to keep digging."

"Who else was Roxy connected to?" Beatrix interjected, drawing both Hattie's and Dan's attention to where she was standing behind the counter.

Dan looked at Hattie and back at Beatrix. With confusion in his voice, he asked, "What do you mean?"

Beatrix came over to the table. She stood at the edge. "Let's assume that Tucker wouldn't just blab about a big case. Let's assume that if he was telling Roxy, it was for a reason. He had to have known she was a talker. Clearly, Tucker was letting enough slip that it would get out. If he really didn't want you to run the story, then he was hoping the information was making it to someone else."

"Who is the someone else?" Hattie asked mostly to herself. Turning to Beatrix, she commended the girl. "You are definitely smarter than your years."

"I read a lot of mysteries."

"Well then," Dan said, looking lost in thought. "Since we don't know who that might be, why do you think he'd share it?"

"Maybe to make someone nervous," Beatrix speculated. "If Tucker was really watching the parish, maybe he wanted to see how they'd react if they knew someone was digging around and getting close. People mess up when they feel cornered."

"Or they strike back," Dan said as realization struck him all at once.

As eye-opening as this conversation was, Hattie still didn't understand something. Looking at Dan she asked, "Why are the cops searching you?"

"I guess they suspect I'm involved somehow. They said something about Roxy having my contact info and my number being in her phone, which is all true. But I didn't kill her. In fact, depending on when she was killed, I was with Harper at dinner last night."

"Understood," Hattie said. "I'm still not sure how I can help you, but I know Harper has been looking into some things. Let me talk it over with her, and maybe we can all get together at some point."

Dan agreed. He pulled out a few dollars to pay for coffee but Hattie refused. Dan said he'd be in touch and got up and left.

Turning to Beatrix, Harper said, "I guess we are going to have to postpone that protection spell one more night."

Chapter Thirty-Seven

"I told you at some point you'd be begging to have me in your room. I just didn't think it would be this fast," Jackson teased as Harper pulled him by the arm up the stairs.

Harper rolled her eyes at him. "That is most definitely not why I dragged you up here. I was doing some research on Fr. McNally. I think I found something interesting. I want to show you."

"I see," Jackson said dryly, a hint of a smile tugging at the corners of his lips. "I was hoping for a little bit different show and tell."

"What has gotten into you?" Harper asked, crinkling up her nose at him. "You're all flirty all of a sudden, and we have work to do."

Harper went to her desk and started rifling through papers. Jackson sat down in the chair and gave Sparkle and Shine, who had tagged along, a good rub behind their ears. He said to the dogs loud enough for Harper to hear him, "We can't be flirting with the lady now. We have work to do. But what do you think, kids, once we solve the murder maybe I can take her to dinner and a movie?"

Harper barely registered what Jackson said. She was looking through the pages she had printed off to find the exact article that raised her suspicions. While Harper did that, the dogs wiggled around under Jackson's playful petting. He pulled dog bones from his pocket and gave one to each.

Harper found the pages and watched him. Nick always hated animals. Watching Jackson play with her aunt's dogs was sweet to watch. Walking over to him, Harper held out the pages and asked eagerly, "Look at that photo. Does that look like the Fr. McNally we know?"

Jackson stopped with the dogs who plopped down at his feet. He took the pages and studied them carefully. Harper watched to see if she could gauge his reaction. The photos were of Fr. McNally from just more than two years ago when he first started his work at a school in Rio de Janeiro.

Jackson looked up at Harper and back down at the page. He said with hesitation in his voice, "I'm not sure. It looks like it could be Fr. McNally, but he seems much heavier here so his face looks quite different and body frame doesn't appear to be the man next door. Maybe the difference is he's just lost weight?" Jackson suggested, and then looked to Harper for explanation.

"I thought about that," Harper admitted. Then pointing at the photo, she said, "Look at his eyes and nose though. His eyes here are wide-set and rounder. His nose is a bit full as well. The man next door, his eyes are more close-set and almond-shaped, and his nose is thinner. Weight gain or loss isn't going to change that."

"That's true." Jackson studied the photo again. "I wish we had a side by side comparison. Did you find any current photos of Fr. McNally?"

"No," Harper said with a satisfying grin. "That's the other weird thing. The parish doesn't have a photo of him on their website like other parishes do with their priests. Even in all the celebrations welcoming Fr. McNally, he's escaped getting his photo taken."

"That is weird. What do you think…?"

Before Jackson could finish his thought, Harper interrupted, "I called around and found an interesting nugget of information. The Catholic Diocese of Little Rock is without a bishop at the moment, which is usually the priest that would oversee the local parishes. The last bishop took ill suddenly and was close to retirement age so they relieved him of his responsibilities so he could get the care he needs. They didn't have an immediate replacement. That coupled with the shortage of priests and ongoing Catholic church scandals, the Little Rock diocese has been without local oversight for a few months. This could have easily left Fr. McNally unchecked."

"How did you find that out?" Jackson asked as his phone rang. He took his cellphone out of his pocket, looked quick, grimaced and sent the call to voicemail. Jackson looked back up at Harper, giving her his full attention.

Harper didn't ask who the call was from. For some reason, she assumed it was his ex. She sat down in the chair across from Jackson and explained,

"When I was searching for information today, I called the St. Joseph's parish pretending to be a donor. I wanted to see if I could get a little background on Fr. McNally. During the call I asked who the local bishop was overseeing the diocese. The woman that answered the phone explained the situation and that the diocese was without one right now. Then I found some older news on the parish website explaining the leave of absence."

"Did you find out more about Fr. McNally though?" Jackson asked.

"No, I was routed to a donor relations staff person and got voicemail. I didn't leave a message." Harper wished she could read Jackson's expression. He was sitting there with his legs crossed, ankle to knee and staring at her with a look of amazement.

Jackson picked up the papers again. He took a few more minutes to study them. "What are you saying though? That the guy next door isn't really this priest?"

"Maybe," she said and then more hesitantly, "I'm not sure. You would think the church would know who he is, right? Maybe before we make any wild claims, we need to really dig into the background of Fr. McNally and see what we get."

"How does this connect to Tucker's murder though?" Jackson asked.

"I don't know that it does, but Tucker was by all accounts digging into what was happening at the parish, and it's the best lead we have so far."

Chapter Thirty-Eight

A few hours later, Harper was standing in the kitchen making dinner. Jackson was sprawled out on the couch in the living room with the television on. Last Harper checked on him, Jackson was asleep. The scene was entirely too domestic for her, and Harper wasn't sure what she was feeling. But Hattie would be home from the shop soon, and Harper wanted to make sure she had a nice dinner given the events of the previous evening.

As she cooked dinner, Harper took quick glances at the day's newspaper. Local reports had an extensive report on the recent jewelry heists with photos of some of the missing jewels. Harper admired a gorgeous emerald ring that had diamonds around it. It was in a platinum setting. There were also ruby earrings and diamond bracelets and necklaces. *The thieves really targeted the right houses,* Harper thought. The newspaper said there were no suspects to date.

Harper was just putting the salad and chicken pesto pasta on the table when Hattie arrived. Harper called for Jackson. He padded into the kitchen, rubbing his eyes from sleep. Hattie gave him a once over and smiled, "I'm glad you're so comfortable here."

"I didn't mean to doze off. It's been a long day," Jackson said with a hint of embarrassment in his voice.

Hattie waved her hand at him, dismissing his concern. "I barely made it at the shop all day. I don't think any of us got much sleep last night. Harper said you're going to stay here, and I'm grateful for that."

Harper spooned out generous helpings of salad and pasta for each of them. She was just about to take a bite when the front doorbell rang. With the dogs at her feet, she got up to answer it.

Hattie raised her eyebrows in a question, and Harper explained, calling over her shoulder, "I didn't fill you in, but I found something today. I needed to call Det. Granger, but that was hours ago. He must have had a busy day. I assume that's him."

Harper went to the door and looked out. It was Granger. He apologized for showing up so late. Then he said inquisitively, "You said you found something of interest in the woods. Related to the break-in?"

Harper led Granger back into the kitchen. He said hello to Hattie and Jackson. Harper offered him some dinner, but he declined. She went to the side counter and pulled out both bags. Handing them over to the detective, Harper explained, "The first is what I believe is the screwdriver Jackson saw the guy last night carrying. Right near there, I found this key chain with the letter D. They were both found up in the woods, same path the guy took last night."

Det. Granger examined them through the bags. "Your fingerprints on these?"

Pointing to the key chain, Harper said, "I picked that up without realizing what it was, so yes. The screwdriver just the pointed end. I didn't touch the handle."

"You have no proof though the guy was carrying these. It could have been in the woods for a while," Det. Granger countered, turning over the bags looking at the evidence.

"True," Harper conceded. "But I thought it better to grab them and bring them to you than not. Did you ever get a chance to check on the pregnant girl over in the parish building?"

"No, not yet. We had people here early this morning, questioning their staff about Roxy, but I never made it over. I was going to do that while I was here now." Setting the bags down on the counter, Granger added, "Mind keeping this until I go check next door? I'll grab them when I come back through."

Det. Granger went out the porch door. Harper sat back down to eat. Jackson nodded his head towards Hattie. "You should tell Hattie what you found?"

Hattie put down her fork and her eyes opened wide in interest.

Harper chewed a bite of salad. "I don't want to say anything to Granger because I'm not sure what I'm looking at, but I found some photos of Fr. McNally from years ago when he was working in Brazil. It doesn't look like the same man as next door."

"What does that mean?" Hattie asked with interest.

"I don't know," Harper said honestly. "It could mean nothing. He lost weight. He looks different or maybe it's not really Fr. McNally. I want to dig into his background more to see what I can come up with."

The three ate in silence. Harper was lost in thought speculating what it could mean and just how strange the whole thing was. Nearly thirty minutes later, as they were finishing the last of their dinner, Det. Granger was back. He looked to Harper and asked with confusion in his voice, "Are you sure about what you saw?"

"I'm one hundred percent sure. I'd stake my life on it," Harper insisted. "Why?"

Det. Granger leaned back against the counter. "There's no pregnant girl down there. There's not much of anything down there."

"No suitcases and boxes?" Harper asked, thoroughly perplexed. She saw it with her own eyes.

"No, nothing," Granger insisted. "I didn't search the entire area, but it's pretty wide open. Fr. McNally brought me down there without hesitation. I gave it a quick look. He said he doesn't know anything about a pregnant girl, and there was no one meeting that description at his residence or anywhere at the parish."

Frustrated, Harper said angrily, "I don't know what is going on over there, but I saw a pregnant girl go down there last night with her suitcase like she was staying. Today, I saw a man who said he was Fr. McNally's brother bring down several suitcases and boxes."

"His brother?" Granger asked with interest.

"After I came back from my walk in the woods, I saw a man bringing suitcases down there so I walked over, pretending I took a wrong turn. He said his name was Evan and Fr. McNally's brother. He wasn't very talkative, but looked like Fr. McNally so I didn't question it."

"Well there's no brother, no pregnant girl and no suitcases now," Granger said. He breathed out. "Listen, I'll come back. I'm spread thin right now. I'll send a car by occasionally to keep an eye on things. With Roxy's and Tucker's murders and this jewelry theft case, we are working around the clock. I can tell you my investigators found nothing suspicious this morning."

He looked to Jackson and Hattie and then back at Harper. "Between us, I'm not making any headway on any of the cases."

"I heard y'all searched Dan Barnes office and home today. Find anything?" Hattie asked, taking a sip of her drink.

"You know I can't tell you that," Granger said with a faint smile. "But no, we didn't find a darn thing. He's not telling us something, that's for sure. I don't know what it is though."

Jackson perked up at that. "You think he's dangerous?"

Granger crossed his arms. "I can't say. He knew both Roxy and Tucker. Dan had several public fights with Tucker, but he insists it was over a story. It seems unlikely he'd kill someone over a story, but stranger things have happened. We didn't find anything suspicious in Dan's house or office to tie him to the murders. We don't even have a good suspect yet."

Harper walked back over and picked up the smaller of the two bags. "The D key chain," she said, turning directly to look at Hattie. "You don't think this is Dan's, do you?"

"No," Hattie insisted. "I can't imagine why Dan would have any need to break into this house. He was just at my shop today, telling me about Roxy and that the police were searching his place. Why come and tell me if he's the culprit?"

"Maybe he's trying to gain your trust to see how much you already know," Det. Granger offered. "Criminals will do that. Did Dan ask you any strange questions?"

"No, nothing strange. I think he and I are both confused though as to why Tucker would disclose anything about his investigation to Roxy."

"That seems to be the question of the hour," Det. Granger confided absently. Then clearly frustrated, he added, "Everyone keeps talking about this investigation, but we have no information about it at all. No one can even confirm Tucker was looking into anything. We went through his files at home and at his office including all his computers. There's nothing. Unless we get a confirmation from someone with something credible, I think we have to conclude that it's another dead end, so to speak."

Chapter Thirty-Nine

The next morning Hattie was sitting in the kitchen sipping coffee and feeling a bit nervous and jittery. The caffeine probably wasn't helping, but she had another night of fitful sleep and needed the boost.

The previous night as Hattie was getting ready for bed, she thought back to her conversation with Dan. He had pressed Hattie for what she knew. Dan also knew Roxy had talked to her, but wouldn't disclose how he knew that. Hattie hadn't wanted to make Det. Granger more suspicious about Dan, but the exchange had been strange. Dan had shared information with Hattie so she chalked it up to him digging on a case. Hattie hoped it wasn't more than that.

"Hattie, my dear, you look completely lost in thought," Beau said as he suddenly appeared in the kitchen. He looked the way he did in his last year of life. He was gray like Hattie and wrinkles blanketed his face. Beau had on the comfortable green cardigan sweater he always wore.

Hattie smiled at him and said wryly, "I'm sure if you've been watching you know we are in over our heads."

Beau sat his ghostly presence across the table from her. "I do. I shooed the dogs into action last night to scare off the intruder and then I spooked the guy in the woods. The screwdriver and key chain are his. I saw Harper find them."

"Thank you for keeping watch. Did you see who he was?" Hattie asked as she got up and poured herself some more coffee. She added extra milk and grabbed a blueberry muffin from a tin on the counter.

"I saw him, but I don't know who he is. If I saw him in a picture, I could identify him. It wasn't the priest next door if that's what you're curious about," Beau explained.

"I'll have to get some photos and show you," Hattie offered. "Not that I'll know how to explain if you identify him. I can't really say my dead husband made the identification."

Beau stood and went to look out the back window. He added, "That priest is strange. There was a pregnant girl. Harper really did see that. I was out there when Harper was. And I was standing in the living room last night and overheard that detective explain that there was no girl. But she was there. I saw her, too. I don't know where she is now."

"Oh Beau," Hattie sighed. "I was so exhausted last night, I didn't even sense you were here. I'm sorry."

Beau waved her off. "You were busy and tired, my love. But I have to tell you something…" He hesitated, almost as if he wasn't sure he should. Hattie looked at him waiting.

"Out with it," she demanded.

"Harper nearly caught sight of me yesterday," Beau admitted. "She was working in her room, and I was worried about her being here alone. She heard me moving around, and she looked down the hall just as I was passing by the door in our bedroom. Harper rushed down the hall, but I made myself disappear before she saw me."

Hattie laughed to herself. "I assumed Harper would start to get some of her gifts at some point. At least maybe now Harper will be understanding if I ever tell her I can talk to dead people."

Just then Hattie heard movement in the hallway. She got quiet, and Beau made himself scarce. Jackson appeared in the kitchen. With raised eyebrows, he said, "You can talk to the dead?"

Hattie just stared at him unsure of what to say. Finally, she nodded a simple yes.

Jackson didn't respond. Instead, he poured himself a cup of coffee and warmed hers. He sat right next to her. He took a deep breath. "Have you ever wondered why I never question your gift?"

"Sometimes, but I can tell you're an old soul. I asked you once when we first met, and you laughed and told me I had good snacks. I let it go at that."

Jackson laughed. "You do have good snacks, and you immediately became my friend when I needed one."

Jackson took a sip of his coffee. Then he explained, "My sister, Sarah, is a medium. It plagued her all of her years growing up. Our parents didn't know what was wrong with her. They were scared for her. They thought she was having a mental breakdown. My brother and other sister thought Sarah was faking for attention. I knew though. Our great-grandmother had the same gift. She never told anyone but me that I'm aware of. I told Sarah and together we navigated it. She embraces her gift today as much as she can while raising a family. If you want me to keep your secret, I understand and will. But you don't have to hide it from me."

Hattie had tears in her eyes. Brushing the tears from her cheeks, Hattie breathed out a sigh of relief. "You have no idea how relieved I am to hear that. I've been hiding it for so long. Harper doesn't even know, and I'm not ready to tell her. I don't think she'd be ready to hear it."

"I don't either," Jackson agreed, taking another sip of coffee. "You mind if I ask who you were just talking to?"

"My husband. Beau pops in and out from time to time. I've seen Tucker though, twice," Hattie explained.

"I wondered when I heard you talking." Jackson asked curiously, "Was Tucker here at dinner when you were acting strangely?"

"Yes, he was very distracting," Hattie admitted, a faint smile on her lips. "I've never had to do that before. Usually Beau is only here when no one else is. I didn't even know until the other day that I could see anyone besides family."

Hattie added thoughtfully, "This isn't a gift I've worked to develop or even wanted to."

"I can understand that. It was really hard for my sister. It started happening to her much younger and she never seemed to be able to control it," Jackson detailed. He got up and poured himself more coffee. He held the pot up to Hattie offering more. She declined. Sitting back down, he asked, "Has Tucker told you anything of value?"

"Not really," Hattie lamented. "So far talking to him hasn't really proven useful at all. Not that it's his fault. With my husband, it took a few months before he even showed himself to me and even longer for him to have full memories back. With Tucker, it was sudden and trauma so who knows." Hattie got up and got herself together. She dropped her cup in the sink and started going through her bag, making sure everything she needed was there.

Turning to Jackson, Hattie said, "I need to leave for the shop. Harper went for a run, but she should be back soon. I'm a little worried about her. She is going full-on with this case. I'm concerned about her getting in over her head."

"You're asking me to keep an eye on her," Jackson stated. It wasn't a question. "You have nothing to worry about. I'm not letting her get too far ahead of herself, but she's strong-willed."

Hattie smiled at him. "She's always been. Harper just lost her way for a while in Manhattan. Her father has a way of bullying people into submission." Hattie headed towards the door.

Calling out to Hattie's back, Jackson, who was looking down at the floor absently petting the dogs, mumbled awkwardly, "I feel weird even asking you about this," he paused and took a breath, "but I'm having some serious issues with my ex-wife. I'm wondering if I stop by the shop if you could give me some insight and maybe some ideas of what to do?"

"I thought you'd never ask," Hattie assured him. "Stop in midmorning. I'll be free then."

Chapter Forty

Harper was a sweaty mess by the time she got back to her Land Rover from her run. She had gone down to Murray Park and ran the trail that crossed over the Big Dam Bridge. Harper had heard that the bridge was the longest pedestrian and bicycle bridge in North America. She thought it would be a good spot to start back into an exercise routine. Harper had run in Manhattan in Central Park during the nicer weather and then in the gym in her office building during the winter. It had been a few months though, and Harper felt it. Her pace was off. Harper felt like she was running through quicksand, but she got four miles in.

Harper sat in her vehicle, wiping her face with a towel. When she was done, she noticed Drew off in the distance, sitting at a picnic table. He was alone at first, but then a man who looked like Fr. McNally's brother, Evan, met up with him. It was hard for Harper to see from her vantage point, but it looked like a heated exchange. Harper couldn't hear them at all, but as the minutes passed by, they seemed to get angrier and angrier with each other. Drew was clearly yelling, waving his hands around, and the man she suspected to be Evan was doing the same. Finally, they stopped and looked around, probably wondering who had just witnessed their outburst. Harper was so far off in the distance and ducking low in her Land Rover, she figured they probably couldn't see her. To be sure, Harper waited until Evan walked off and Drew sat back down at the table before she left.

Once home, Harper unlocked and opened the back door and was greeted with Sparkle and Shine who were happy and eager to see her. She filled their water bowls and dropped off treats. Harper headed for the stairs, ripping off her sweaty shirt as she bounded up the steps. She went into her room, pulled off her sports bra and dropped her shorts. Naked except for a pair of panties, she padded towards the bathroom. Harper made it about three feet when she saw the shadow again in her aunt's room. She froze in place. Quietly this time, Harper crept toward the room. Popping her head in, again no one was there. Harper shook her head and went into the bathroom to shower. She was getting more annoyed than spooked.

A few minutes into the hot water beating down on her head and back, just as Harper was starting to relax, she heard the hallway floor creak again. Running her fingers through her sudsy hair, Harper demanded aloud, "I don't know who you are, but you have to leave me alone. I don't know what is happening, but I'm not dealing with this!"

Then Harper went back to finishing what she was doing, ignoring the noise. As Harper was finishing up and rinsing the conditioner from her hair, she laughed to herself for saying something so ridiculous. Her aunt and this house were definitely getting to her.

After her shower, Harper gave her hair a quick fix, applied some minimal makeup, threw on jeans and her favorite emerald green lightweight shirt, and padded barefoot back down the steps. She found Jackson sitting on the couch watching television. Harper teased, "Don't you have something to do besides sit around and stalk me?"

"I'm headed to Hattie's shop in a few minutes, but I saw you come home. You looked like hell so I thought I'd pop over and say hello," Jackson teased right back.

"You're right, I looked dreadful." Harper laughed and plopped down in the chair across from him. "I saw something shady on my run."

Jackson shut off the TV and turned toward Harper, giving her his full attention.

Harper detailed seeing Drew and who she thought was Evan at the park and what she saw. When she was done explaining, Harper asked, "What do you think about doing some surveillance on Drew? I wasn't able to find much about him in my search besides his insurance fraud convictions."

Jackson seemed to consider. Harper thought for sure he was going to say no, but he surprised her. "Why don't we head out tonight after dark? Let's take your Land Rover though. It blends in better than my truck. I'll drive."

"Still don't trust my driving?" Harper said with a wide grin.

"Not at all. What do you think that meeting was about?"

"No idea, but don't you think it's strange that Fr. McNally's brother would know Drew? I didn't think Fr. McNally or his family was from around here. I wonder if it was someone he met in prison."

"That's a distinct possibility," Jackson agreed and got up from the couch. As he was heading out, Jackson asked, "Will you be here when I get back?"

"I have a meeting with Dan," Harper explained. She knew Jackson wasn't going to be happy about it, but she had signed a contract to do work, and she wanted to see what else Dan would say about Roxy.

"I don't like that one bit," Jackson said from the doorway. He was clearly frustrated. "I assume arguing with you won't work. Call me when you're back and if you need anything while you're there. In fact, just check in with me every thirty minutes."

Harper shook her head at him. "Not happening, Dad. I'll see you later though."

After Jackson left, Harper got the last of her things together, found her favorite pair of boots and headed out. She was getting more comfortable behind the wheel. She navigated through the city streets and back down to Dan's office.

After finding a place to park on the street, Harper climbed the steps to the second floor and entered into the workspace. While she knew the magazine didn't have many staff, just two writers and a graphic designer, Harper was surprised to find the large open workroom empty.

Taking a couple of tentative steps towards his office, Harper called out, "Dan, it's Harper, are you here?"

Dan's door was closed, but she heard muffled voices coming from the other side. Harper had already called out and no one responded. She wondered if they knew she was there. Her first thought was that Dan was in trouble, but it was his voice she heard raised.

"I told you, I don't know anything," Dan said, his voice full of frustration.

"What do you know about Tucker's murder?" Matthew Inslee barked.

Dan responded adamantly, "I don't know a thing about Tucker's murder or Roxy's. I've told you that. I've told the cops that. Leave me alone."

"You know more than you're letting on. I know you do. Who are you protecting?"

"I'm not protecting anyone!" Dan yelled.

"It's that witch, isn't it?" Inslee spat.

"You leave Hattie out of this. She has nothing to do with this."

"You can't stop me from doing anything," Inslee mocked. "I'll run her out of town as soon as I'm elected. It's a shame though, that niece of hers looks like a good time, if you know what I mean."

"You're a pig," Dan said, his voice full of disgust.

"What does Harper know about the murder, Dan? I know she's talked to you."

"She's doing some work for me on the magazine. That's it," Dan countered.

"She knows more than she's letting on, and you are going to find out for me," Inslee insisted.

Harper heard some things being moved around. It sounded like a struggle. Something was knocked over, and she heard them grunting. Dan yelled, "Get out of my office!"

"Find out what Harper knows if you don't both want to end up dead. You're in over your heads with Tucker's murder."

Chapter Forty-One

Harper couldn't believe what she just heard. She was panicked and didn't want to be seen. She looked around the office for a spot to hide. Harper wouldn't have time to make it back to the main door, but to the far right of Dan's office was a dark hall. She could see light, probably coming in from a window. An office maybe. It seemed to be the only option.

Harper made a mad dash and slipped into the darkened hall and into the room as she heard their voices grow louder. She assumed they were in the large open workspace now. Harper looked around the room she was in, and it seemed to be a library of sorts. There were shelves of books on metal shelving units that went from the floor nearly to the ceiling. There was also another shelf that held antique-looking vases, nicely framed black and white photos, and small abstract sculptures. Harper moved farther into the room away from the door.

Standing near the shelf, she looked over the items. Harper picked up a small sculpture, turning it around in her hands to get a better look. It looked like an abstract giraffe. It was an intriguing piece. Harper admired it and set it back down. As she steadied it back in place, Harper bumped a vase next to the sculpture with her arm. Horrified, Harper watched the vase begin to sway and tumble forward. She caught it midair. As Harper did, she heard a distinct clinking sound at her feet. With the vase still in hand, Harper looked down and was left speechless by what she saw.

Right next to Harper's booted foot was a very expensive-looking diamond necklace, suspiciously like the one she had just seen in the newspaper. Mixed up in the chain and jewels of the necklace was also the emerald ring she had admired. Harper froze not sure what to do, even more confused about what it meant.

Harper put the vase down and pulled her cellphone from her pocket. She called Det. Granger, who answered on the second ring. Harper explained where she was and what she had found. She also told him what she had overheard between Dan and Inslee. He said he was sending a squad car right away, and he'd be soon to follow. Just as he was asking if Harper would be able to sneak out, she heard someone approaching.

Dan walked in the room and absently flipped on the overhead light. He froze when he saw Harper on the phone and the startled expression on her face. Harper was sure she looked like she had just been caught red-handed for something, when really it was the other way around.

Harper pretended to hang up, but really kept the call engaged. She held the phone in her hand, screen down. She didn't budge from the spot. The key chain with the letter D flashed in her mind. Harper wondered if Dan could really be the one that tried to break in.

"What are you doing in here?" Dan asked, confusion evident in his voice. He stepped towards Harper. As he did, she looked down at the ground, which caused him to look down. Dan noticed the jewelry at her feet and popped his head up sharply, looking at Harper with his mouth open and eyes wide. But Dan's voice was calm and level. "What's going on, Harper? What is that?"

"That's what I was going to ask you, Dan. I found the stolen jewelry in your vase. Can you explain that?" Harper asked accusingly. She stayed firmly planted and did not move.

"I've never seen them before in my life," Dan said, looking back down at the jewelry and then back up at Harper.

"Well then how did it get here?" she demanded.

"It looks like you're planting evidence on me," Dan accused.

"Hardly," Harper snipped. "I nearly knocked over the vase, and this fell out. I just saw these pieces in the newspaper. What are you doing with stolen jewelry, Dan?"

For the first time, Dan looked scared. He held up his hands in surrender. "Harper, I swear to you I've never seen that before. I don't even understand what you're doing back here."

Harper explained, "I got here early for our meeting, but you were in your office with the door shut. I heard you with Inslee. When he instructed you to find out what I knew before we both ended up dead, I didn't stick around to come face to face with him. I ducked in here. Is that why you tried to break into our house the other night? To find out what we know or to scare us?"

Dan backed up slowly. Harper thought he was leaving the room, but instead, he sat down at the only table in the room. It was a small round four-seater taking up most of the middle of the room.

Dan looked at her and said sincerely, "Harper, I'm not going to hurt you. I didn't try to break into your house. I didn't steal that. The cops already searched here. I can't account for it, but I think someone is trying to frame me."

"I don't believe you," Harper scoffed. "You know far more than you're letting on. Jackson was right not to trust you. The cops are on their way."

"You called the cops?" Dan groaned, putting his head in his hands. "Why would you do that?"

"Dan, you have stolen property. What was I supposed to do?" Harper asked incredulously.

"Trust me, know that I'm not a thief. You could have started there," Dan mumbled. He looked at his watch. "How long until they get here?"

"Any minute," Harper replied. "Dan, if you did nothing wrong then you have nothing to worry about. But I can't trust you, I barely even know you. And what I do know is that you've been holding back on me and with Hattie regarding Tucker's murder."

"I was trying to keep both of you safe," Dan grumbled.

"It doesn't seem like that to me," Harper said. She walked over to the table and set the phone down. She ended the call, not having any idea if Granger had still been on the other end listening.

Harper looked Dan in the eyes. "If you really didn't do anything wrong, you should tell me what you know before the cops get here. It's the only way we are going to be able to help you. Do you know who killed Tucker?"

Dan looked across the table at her. "Harper, I was with you when Roxy was killed. I was standing in the tent when Tucker was murdered. I was there the whole night, everyone saw me. I have no idea who killed them. And I certainly wasn't burglarizing houses. I don't know how or if these burglaries are connected to Tucker's murder, but I do know there are things you don't understand. Dangerous things that could get you hurt if you knew."

Harper heard the sirens off in the distance. She leveled a look at Dan and got straight to the heart of it, what had been bothering her all this time. Her gut told her Dan already knew. "The priest is an imposter, right? He's not really Fr. McNally."

Chapter Forty-Two

Dan's jaw practically hit the table when he heard what Harper said. His eyes darted around the room before finally settling back on her. Dan started to try to convince Harper that she was wrong, but Harper stood firm. Dan wiped beads of sweat that were forming on his brow and relented, "How long have you known?"

"Yesterday. I saw photos of Fr. McNally that don't really match up to the priest. I've been suspicious since the night of Tucker's murder. I don't know with absolute certainty."

Dan explained, "I've been suspicious for months, but it was Tucker's murder that got me really digging around. I probably saw the same photos that you did. It's not him, but like you, I haven't had a chance to fully confirm it. I haven't told a soul though, Harper, and you shouldn't either. This is bigger than I think we know. Two people are already dead. I'm being framed. You need to walk away from this."

"She needs to walk away from what?" Det. Granger said from the doorway. He had his gun drawn and had several uniformed cops behind him. Harper waved him off, letting Granger know that she was okay. Granger hesitated but Harper nodded her head. Finally, he turned to the other cops and sent them back.

With his gun still at his side, Granger motioned for Dan to stand. He frisked him and asked if he had any weapons.

Dan sighed. "Just my pen, Detective. As I've been telling anyone who will listen, I'm just trying to break the story, not be the story. I have no idea how the jewelry got here. You searched this office already."

Dan sat back down. Granger went to look at the jewelry on the floor. He turned to Harper. "Did you touch this?" Harper shook her head. He radioed down to a crime scene tech to come up and bag the evidence.

Turning to Dan, Granger said, "I don't know what to believe so we are going to the station and talk about this while my guys go through this office again. I know you have an alibi for the night of the Saints & Sinners Ball when all those houses were robbed, but I need to know your alibi on the other nights, and who might have access to this room."

Dan got up but hesitated. "I need someone to lock up the office. My staff is all out on assignments. I can't just leave it open."

"I can do it," Harper offered quickly.

Dan didn't hesitate. He leveled a subtle but knowing look that Harper caught. He explained, "The keys and that contract you were here to sign are in the left bottom drawer in the far back. Sometimes the key slips down so you'll have to dig around, but it's in there."

Before they left the room, Det. Granger turned to Harper and sternly advised, "You need to stop being in the middle of my investigations. This is two cases now. You need to let me do my job. You are to go get the key, touch nothing else and wait downstairs at the deli. When the crime scene techs are done, they will come get you. Understood?"

Harper said she understood, but she knew she couldn't hold to the promise. She was itching to get out of the room and into Dan's office. She had already signed the contract. Harper wasn't sure what Dan was indicating she'd find, but she was getting to it before the cops searched.

Det. Granger and Dan walked out of the office as crime scene techs walked in. Granger gave them the same instructions he had just given Harper. She practically ran to Dan's office. Once there, she pulled out the drawer and fished around inside. There were old magazine issues on top, which she pulled out and set on the desk. She didn't see a file or a key. The desk appeared empty.

Harper slapped her hand around inside, growing frustrated. A crime scene tech was walking towards the door, but she wasn't leaving without what was inside the desk.

Dan's words, *far back, slips down,* rang in her mind. She traced her fingers to the back of the drawer and her fingertip hit a tiny nearly unnoticeable lip. Harper dug her fingernail underneath it and lifted the false bottom of the drawer. Inside was a thick file holder but no key. She grabbed the folder and slid the false bottom back in place. A crime scene tech walked into the office as she stacked the magazines back in place.

"Ready?" the tech asked.

Taking a quick glance at the top of Dan's messy desk, Harper lamented, "He's a bit messy. I found the contract he said to take, but I'm still looking for the key."

The crime scene tech walked farther into the office and glanced down at the desk. He shook his head in disgust. "How does he find anything? I'll give you a few more minutes."

Harper moved things around on the top of the desk. It was then she noticed a note. It simply read: *Meet tonight Drew eight o'clock Murray Park*. Harper grabbed the note and slid it in her pocket. As Harper moved another stack of papers, she found the key.

Harper watched the door to make sure no one was watching her. She grabbed the thick file folder, slipped the key in her pocket and took quick steps toward the door. Harper nodded to the tech as she passed and reminded him that she'd be downstairs at the deli when he was done.

Chapter Forty-Three

Jackson opened the door to Hattie's shop and stopped. He breathed in the air and smiled. He called to Hattie and Beatrix who were standing behind the counter, "I love the smell of whatever you are baking. It's warm and sweet. It's a little like walking into my grandmother's house. What are you making?"

"It's always about your stomach," Hattie teased. She looked back towards the kitchen. "I think my baker is trying something new. He mentioned something about chocolate butterscotch muffins. They should be ready soon if you want to try one."

"Always," Jackson said. He came around the counter and poured himself a cup of coffee. He'd been coming to the shop so regularly that Hattie had instructed him to help himself. After grabbing coffee, Jackson took a seat at the table he liked. He flipped through the day's newspaper until Hattie said she was ready for him.

Together they went into her back room. Hattie sat down and let Jackson get comfortable. Concerned, Hattie asked him, "What's going on? I've noticed that you've seemed not quite yourself, but I didn't want to pry. I was glad you asked for my help."

"I feel a bit silly doing this. I've never had a need for psychic insight. I'm just a bit stumped and not sure what to do," Jackson admitted. He sat back, took a deep breath and volunteered, "My ex-wife has been calling more than usual. She's making hints about getting back together, which she knows I have no interest in doing. She's been calling my parents and my sisters. Basically, she's just causing all kinds of stress for me. I'm just not sure what to do."

"What's her name?"

"Cora," Jackson told her.

"Are you okay with whatever I pick up? It might be personal. I don't want to embarrass you or make you angry."

Jackson agreed he was fine. Hattie asked if he had a photo. He pulled out his phone and scrolled through for a moment. Handing Hattie the phone, Jackson said, "I don't keep photos of her. I pulled that from her social media. Will that work?"

"It will," Hattie began. She took the phone and stared down at the photo. Then Hattie closed her eyes for several moments. Finally, Hattie opened them and detailed, "Money. That's her motive. It's all financial. I see you've helped her more than you probably should have. When you first got together, you paid her debts. She ran up your credit, you paid it off. She ran it up again, and you paid it off again. She's never been responsible. She's going to your family to try to gain sympathy."

Jackson confirmed Hattie was accurate in what she was seeing.

Hattie continued, "Forgive me for saying, but I think your sister, not the one you told me about but the other, is playing both sides of the fence. She placates Cora while she's on the phone but when she hangs up, she wishes Cora would just leave you alone. She doesn't really want to get back together. Cora is very afraid you are going to move on, and her financial support will go away. She's holding on to keep you focused on her. She thinks if she can stress you out, you won't have another relationship. I know you can't cut her off completely, but you shouldn't give in and give her anything else."

"Is there another man?" Jackson asked. He ran a hand down his face, seemingly a bit lost in thought. He added, "I want her to move on, but I don't want to fund their relationship."

Hattie closed her eyes again. She hated readings like this. She didn't ever want to hurt anyone, but Jackson deserved the truth.

"I see you are still paying for the house she lives in. He's living there with her," Hattie said matter of fact. Hattie scooted to the edge of her chair. She set Jackson's phone down and reached across the coffee table for Jackson's hands. He sat forward in the chair and put his hands in hers.

"I see you having to go back to court and renegotiate, but you'll need evidence he is living there. You'll get it by an unexpected means. You'll win, and eventually free yourself from her. The more you stand up to her, the more Cora will start to move on and find someone else she can use."

Jackson looked at her thoughtfully and squeezed Hattie's hands. "Thank you. I suspected it all, but the confirmation is nice. I feel guilty for being firm, but I just want to move on with my life."

Still holding his hands, Hattie asked, "Do you want to know what else I see? It's good."

"Good news would be terrific. It's been a rough few days."

"You're falling for Harper," Hattie picked up. Jackson didn't confirm or deny. "You're worried she doesn't feel the same for you. Harper does. It will just take a little time. You need to open up to her and she will do the same. Did you ask her on a date?"

"I did," Jackson admitted. "Harper never really answered. I don't think she took me seriously."

"Ask her again. She will say yes this time," Hattie assured him. She let go of Jackson's hands and handed his phone back to him. She felt the energy of his heavy heart. Hattie got up, told Jackson to wait where he was. She went to the front of the shop, waved hello to Lottie who was sitting at a table reading the newspaper. Hattie went to the stones she had lined against the back wall. She pulled a black tourmaline stone and a rose quartz.

Walking back into her reading room, Hattie opened the palm of her hand so Jackson could see the stones. Pointing to the tourmaline, Hattie informed him, "I don't know if you meditate but you need to start. Keep this stone with you all the time, especially when dealing with Cora. It will protect you from her negative energy. It will send it back to her."

Jackson took the stone and looked at it in his hands. "I don't meditate much, but I can start if it will help."

Next, Hattie placed a tiny pink stone in the center of his outstretched hand. It looked small and too feminine for Jackson's big, masculine hand. Hattie indicated, "Use that one to bring love into your life. It will revive self-love. Improve your self-esteem. Even those of us who feel good about ourselves can use a boost after dealing with tough situations and negative people."

"How do you know all this?" Jackson asked, tucking the stones in his pocket.

"Years of learning from my grandmother and aunts. This is what I'm hoping to teach Harper as soon as she's ready," Hattie explained. "Do you need to know anything else?"

"I'm good, how much do I owe you?" Jackson asked, standing and pulling out his wallet.

Hattie waved him off. "Nothing at all. I'm happy to help you. Look at how much you are helping us."

She reached out to Jackson and wrapped her arms around him. "You've become family to me."

"Thank you," Jackson said sincerely. "I don't know what I'd do without you. Harper, too, she's a handful but she keeps me on my toes."

"Come on," Hattie said releasing him from the embrace. "Let's go try out those muffins. We deserve a treat."

"You don't have to ask me twice," Jackson laughed, following Hattie out of the room.

Chapter Forty-Four

Once at the deli, Harper ordered a sweet tea, a turkey wrap and found a table in a back corner, far removed from all the other patrons. As soon as she sat, Harper moved her food to the other side of the table and started digging through the file. It was all about Fr. McNally. There were photos of him in Brazil, the same ones Harper had found. There were others though, that looked like they were from years ago, tracing some of his previous assignments at different parishes around the country.

There were other notes too, indicating some of his early schooling in Concord, a town northwest of Boston, Massachusetts. It struck Harper that the few times she heard the man speak there wasn't even the slightest hint of the Boston accent that was so common for people who grew up in the region. Not that over years and moving around the country it couldn't have been lost, but there was no trace of it.

The file also contained phone numbers and people's names. Harper had no idea how they connected, but the more she flipped through the file, the more she became convinced that the Fr. McNally she met was an imposter.

Harper was flipping through page after page and didn't notice the person standing next to her until she heard him speak. "Interesting meeting you here," Matthew Inslee commented.

Harper looked up sharply and closed the file. Without being asked, Inslee slid into the seat across from her. He peered at her across the table, his arms folded across his chest. "What are you doing here, Harper?"

"Not that it's any of your business, but eating lunch," Harper snipped. "Last time I checked I was free to do that."

Inslee hitched his jaw at her and asked, "What's in the file?"

"Nothing that concerns you," Harper responded. "If you'll excuse me, I didn't invite you to sit, and I'm not open to company right now."

Inslee tisked at her. "Harper, if you're going to make it in the south, you're going to have to lose those harsh Yankee ways. We are friendly down here. I'm just being neighborly."

Harper slid the folder off the table, resting it on her lap. She pulled the turkey wrap that was sitting squarely in front of Inslee to her side of the table. Harper unwrapped it and took a bite. Then she took a sip of her tea. Harper looked at him and said coolly, "I didn't realize it was a southern custom to force your presence on a lady. That must be new."

"We don't get along much do we?" Inslee asked. He leaned forward on the table, resting his arms. "I like you. I had hoped we could have become friends, but I'm off-putting for you, aren't I?"

"I don't like you, but more importantly, I don't trust you," Harper said matter of fact. "You've insulted my aunt, you're arrogant and you're up to something. I just don't know what yet."

Inslee gave her a slick, conniving grin. "See that's why I'd never live up north. You're too direct, all sharp points. I like my women a little smoother around the edges."

"You mean quiet and compliant," Harper interrupted.

Inslee scoffed. "Those are your words not mine. I might as well tell you, Harper, I'm running for Prosecuting Attorney for the Sixth Judicial District in the special election that they will hold to fill Tucker's job. Bill Myers is running, too." Inslee leaned in and looked Harper in the eyes and threatened, "And when I win, I'm going to make sure you and your aunt go back to where you belong."

"I guess we will just need to make sure you don't win," Harper retorted. "Now, leave me alone. I have things to do."

Inslee didn't budge, just stared defiantly across the table at her.

Harper threatened, "Do I need to call Det. Granger and let him know you are harassing me? I can certainly do that. Starting a campaign with a harassment charge won't do much for you though."

Inslee held Harper's gaze for a moment and then got up, pushed in his chair and walked away. Harper just stared after him, unmoving. She knew Inslee was trouble, and giving him power over the entire prosecutor's office would be even worse. They'd have to make sure that didn't happen.

A few moments later, the crime scene tech walked in the deli door and gave a wave to let Harper know they were done. She grabbed the file and headed up to lock the office. Harper stood at the threshold for a moment and wondered if she should search the place herself, but she assumed the cops would have found anything incriminating.

Harper tried to call Jackson on her walk back to her Land Rover, but he wasn't answering. She remembered Jackson said he was going to Hattie's so she decided to head there. Before starting the engine, Harper pulled out the note she had found on Dan's desk and reread it. She wondered if it was Dan meeting Drew or Drew meeting someone else. She also wondered if the meeting had already taken place or if it was that night. Clearly, Drew liked Murray Park, she had seen him there that morning. That's where they'd start their surveillance Harper decided.

Harper went to put the SUV in drive when she remembered she still hadn't asked Det. Granger if Inslee was investigating the break-ins the night of the Saints & Sinners Ball. She wanted to know definitively if that's where Inslee went. Harper placed a quick call to him letting him know she had locked up Dan's place, but that she also had a question and to please call her. Granger was already angry with her, Harper had no idea if he'd even answer her question.

The sun was shining, and it was a beautiful day. Harper clicked the button to put the window down and turned the radio up. She sang as she drove. She was pulling up in front of Hattie's shop before she knew it. Humming to herself as she opened the door, she stopped cold when she saw Lizzie sitting at a table with Jackson, the two lost in conversation.

Harper waved to both of them and made a beeline to Hattie behind the counter. "What's going on there?"

Hattie was putting away coffee and tea cups. They clanked as she added another in the row. "Jackson and I were talking in back and when we came out, Lizzie said she wanted to talk to Jackson. They have been sitting there for the last hour."

Harper kept one eye on Jackson while she filled Hattie in on what happened with Dan. She told Hattie Dan's suspicions about Fr. McNally, some of the notes in the file and the jewelry she found. Harper admitted, "I feel bad for calling the police, but I'm not sure who to trust. And Dan did have stolen jewelry hidden in his office."

Hattie frowned, clearly dismayed by the information. She countered, "Couldn't someone have hidden the jewelry there? Do you really think Dan would hide it out in the open like that?"

Harper worried, "I really don't know. I just hope I didn't cause trouble for an innocent man. He seemed readily willing to share the information about Fr. McNally with me. But that was only after Granger was taking him to the station."

"Dan's always been such a nice guy," Hattie fretted, moving the cups on the shelf around to add more. "Maybe Det. Granger will just talk to him and release him quickly. That still leaves the question of how the jewelry got in this office if he didn't put it there."

"We seem to have far more questions than answers," Harper muttered to herself while still watching Jackson's animated conversation with Lizzie.

Chapter Forty-Five

Nearly thirty minutes later when Harper was so antsy she could barely stand still, Lizzie finally got up from the table, shook Jackson's hand and left. She gave a quick wave to Harper and Hattie as she opened the door and stepped out into the sunshine.

"New girlfriend," Harper said with a smirk as Jackson approached the counter. Her tone came off more annoyed than teasing, which wasn't how she intended.

Jackson looked at her, a curious expression on his face, and set his cup down on the counter. "Jealous?"

Harper laughed at herself. "No I just really wanted to catch you up and you were taking forever. What did Lizzie want?"

Jackson looked around the shop. It was empty at this point so he explained, "She said she felt bad after we had spoken the other day because she knew she threw her brother under the bus. Lizzie said that she didn't really believe that her brother could kill Tucker, but that Drew had become a financial drain, and she was frustrated. She said that frustration spilled over into our conversation when she accused him. She asked me what I thought."

"That's odd. Lizzie didn't really accuse Drew, just said he wasn't home and that he was up to no good," Harper said, walking out from behind the counter and taking a seat at a nearby table. "Why come tell us now that she changed her mind? We aren't the police. It's not like we can arrest him."

"Maybe she wonders who we might have told."

Harper shrugged. "Still seems strange."

Taking a pause, Jackson added thoughtfully, "I think Lizzie feels conflicted. I think she wanted to make it clear that she didn't think Drew could have murdered her husband, but she's clearly tired of dealing with him."

"I can understand that," Harper mumbled.

"But that's not the weirdest part," Jackson stated. "While Lizzie wanted to make sure we didn't think he was a suspect in the murder, she did hint around that Drew might not be so innocent when it came to the jewelry heists."

Surprised, Harper questioned, "What do you mean? Lizzie thinks her brother robbed those houses?"

"I think she might," Jackson began. "Lizzie reiterated that Drew didn't have an alibi that she knew of for the night of the Saints & Sinners Ball. That Drew was out for most of the evening, and when he got back to the house, he seemed flustered. Lizzie said his pant leg was torn, and he would barely make eye contact with her. When Lizzie read about the crimes in the newspaper, she started thinking back to the dates of the other burglaries. She told me she's concerned that Drew was out those nights, too."

"Does Lizzie have any proof of anything?" Harper asked skeptically.

"No, she didn't offer anything like that. Lizzie just said it and left it at that."

"So, Lizzie comes here to tell you that her brother probably didn't kill her husband, but that he might be a jewelry thief, robbing their rich friends?" Harper clarified.

"You just hit the nail on the head," Jackson affirmed. "Lizzie said she knew several of the couples whose houses had been burglarized. She told me that Drew had been at a few of the houses prior."

"That's completely bizarre that Lizzie would come here to tell you that, but she may not be that far off the mark. I have my own information about the jewelry case." Harper pulled out the note that she had taken from Dan's desk and handed it to Jackson. "What do you make of that?"

Jackson studied the note. "I think it means we are starting our surveillance at Murray Park tonight. Where did you get this?"

Harper went over in detail everything that had happened with Dan that morning. Jackson sat there watching her carefully, his eyes growing wide when she told him about finding some of the stolen jewelry and calling the police.

Jackson was even more shocked when Harper got up and walked back behind Hattie's counter and brought back the thick file folder. Harper plopped it down on the table in front of him. "Dan told me where to find it. He pretended that's where the key to his office was not to alert Det. Granger. Dan had a false bottom in the drawer, and it was tucked in there. Dan's been investigating the priest longer than we were even suspicious."

Jackson flipped through the file. When he got to the section that held the photos, he lifted up several to get a closer look. Then Jackson grabbed two and slapped them down on the table facing Harper. Jackson tapped his index finger on the more recent photo of Fr. McNally, one that had obviously been taken by surveillance. The priest had not posed for the photo. "Dan's got it right here. I don't know how he got these, but looking at this side by side with older photos of Fr. McNally, there is no way they are the same man."

Harper agreed. "That doesn't tell us who the guy is though masquerading as Fr. McNally. And more importantly, it doesn't tell us where the real Fr. McNally is."

Jackson thumbed through some more of Dan's notes. "Let's start with the placement before Brazil, when he was here in the states. Last place says Dallas. Let's make some calls there and find out what we can. It's close enough we can always drive down if we need to. We can find out family and friends, too. We can go back even farther if needed. Then we can check out Brazil. Clearly, the man who came back from Brazil is not the same man that went. But I want to be armed with more information first."

"I think that's a good plan." Harper thought about Det. Granger's warning. Then she thought about the people working at the parish not knowing who they were really working with. Harper asked, "Do you think we should tell anyone yet? Granger gave me another lecture about staying away from his investigation."

Jackson sat the file down. He said thoughtfully, "Normally, I'd say go to the police with your concerns and let them handle it, but you've expressed your concerns a few times and no one is taking you seriously. I say we run with this on our own and when we have definitive proof, we hand it over."

Harper agreed, but she knew she still looked worried, which she was. Inslee's words about being in over their heads rang in her ears.

Jackson got quiet. He leaned into Harper and said quietly, "Besides, no one knows about this. Granger isn't looking into this. Dan clearly had a reason to keep this hidden and wanted us to have it. He's gained some of my trust with that. We tip off the police, everyone will know. I have a feeling whoever that guy is, pretending to be Fr. McNally, will just slip away."

Jackson and Harper spent the next hour going through Dan's file. They pulled out important pages and took some notes. Jackson grabbed Hattie's laptop and started a search for some phone numbers of potential witnesses listed in the file.

Harper found both a name and a phone number for a teacher. Dan's note indicated she had once worked with Fr. McNally when he was in charge of a small Catholic school in Vermont. It had been early in his career. It was one of the only phone numbers Dan had listed in the file so she tried it first. She reached the woman on the first try. The woman, who said she had retired from teaching more than ten years ago, was willing to talk. Harper gathered all the information she could.

After the lengthy conversation, Harper ended the call and turned to Jackson. Punching him in the arm in excitement, Harper exclaimed, "You are not going to believe this!"

Chapter Forty-Six

Jackson rubbed his arm, feigning pain. He looked to Harper eagerly. She detailed, "According to the teacher I spoke to, Fr. McNally had been placed in an orphanage as a young boy. His mother had died when he was small, and there was no father that had claimed him. This teacher told me Fr. McNally spoke about it often because some of the students in the school were in foster care or didn't have families. The teacher said he used to tell stories about his own childhood to connect with the kids."

"Well that certainly makes him an easier target for identity theft than most. My mother would know it wasn't me showing up for Sunday dinner. If you have no dinner to show up to and no real family that's keeping an eye on you, you've got a bit of a bigger target on your back," Jackson detailed.

Harper read through some of the notes she had taken. "There's something else," Harper added, getting Jackson's attention. "Granted this was more than twenty years ago, early in his career, but the kind, gregarious man the teacher described does not in any way seem like the grumpy, secretive man living at the parish."

"When was the last time she had contact with him?"

"She said it's been years. But that's still a big detail into the priest's life for a first call."

They both went back to their searches. An hour later, Hattie was just bringing them each coffee and a pastry when Det. Granger walked into the shop. Harper looked up to Hattie and then closed the file in front of her. Jackson, who was sitting right next to Harper, clicked out his internet search.

With a worried expression on her face, Hattie greeted him, "Detective, I hope nothing is wrong this time. Each time I see you, there's been another incident."

"No, nothing like that," Det, Granger assured. "Just wanted to talk to Harper about this morning." Det. Granger went to the table where Harper and Jackson were sitting. Jackson moved his things to make room.

"Can I get you some coffee or something to eat?" Hattie offered.

"Sure," Granger said. "I haven't had much of a break today. Well really in the last few days as you can imagine. Coffee would be nice."

"Anything in particular you want to eat?" Hattie asked from behind the counter.

"Everything looks and smells great so whatever you decide is fine." Turning to Harper, he asked seriously, "Do you think Dan knew that jewelry was there? How did he react when you found it?"

"I don't even think Dan noticed at first," Harper said, reflecting back to that morning. "Dan was more surprised to see me in the room. He didn't really give any bad reaction to me being there. He just seemed startled to see me at all."

"And when he saw the jewelry?" Granger pressed.

Harper thought for a few moments. She emphasized, "Same. Now that I really think about it, Dan really gave no acknowledgment at all until I asked him why he had jewelry from the burglaries."

Hattie dropped off Det. Granger's coffee and a blueberry muffin. He thanked her and then rephrased his question to Harper. "If I'm hearing you correctly, Dan didn't give any hint that he cared you were near the vase or that he was hiding something?"

"Not at all," Harper confirmed. "Actually, Dan's first reaction after I told him that it was some of the stolen jewelry was to accuse me of planting evidence."

"How did you know it was the stolen jewelry?" Granger asked, curiosity apparent in his voice.

Harper got up and went behind Hattie's counter. She dug through the bin of newspapers she knew Hattie kept there. Harper found the article she was searching for. Bringing the paper over, Harper put the paper in front of Det. Granger. Pointing to the emerald ring, she explained, "I had just read this article. It has several photos of the missing jewelry. I thought this ring was pretty so it stood out to me. When I found the jewelry, it was obvious it was the stolen pieces."

Jackson interjected, "Do you not think Dan is involved?"

Finishing a sip of coffee, Det. Granger said, "No. There's nothing to tie him to the case. Dan has been an upstanding member of our news community for years. No prior arrests, not even so much as a traffic ticket. We had just completed a thorough search of his house and office the day before, and nothing. Dan has an alibi for all but one of the burglaries. That night Dan said he was home alone. I tend to believe him. But I still think he's hiding something. I just don't know what."

"I don't believe he stole any jewelry," Harper offered. "I probably shouldn't have made such a quick assumption, but I had just heard him arguing with Matthew Inslee. I was being cautious."

Det. Granger looked at her sharply. "Why was Inslee there?"

"I'm not really sure," Harper said, knowing she wasn't giving him the full story. "They were arguing when I came in, which is why I was in that back room. As you know, I don't like Inslee so I ducked in that room to avoid him. I saw the sculptures and the vase. It really was just dumb luck I found the jewelry at all."

Det. Granger seemed to consider this. Before he could say anything else, Jackson asked, "I'm curious, Detective, many people saw Inslee at the Saints & Sinners Ball early in the evening, and then he showed up after the murder like he'd never been there. Did he get called out to the burglaries?"

"Not that I'm aware of," Granger said, finishing the last of his muffin. He seemed a bit thrown off by what Jackson said. He asked, "What do you mean Inslee was there and then no one saw him?"

"That's exactly it," Jackson reiterated. "Inslee was at the event for maybe the first hour. Then he showed up to Hattie's house after the murder in completely different clothing and acted like he hadn't been at the party at all."

"Why wouldn't Inslee have made mention that he was there?" Granger asked. "He never once told me he had been at the event. I would think he'd know that people could confirm he was there."

"That's what I was thinking," Jackson said. "Unless Inslee didn't think we'd have reason to be asking. He does act like he's beyond reproach so maybe Inslee believes nobody would ever look into it or question his actions."

Det. Granger seemed really thrown off by the whole conversation. He wondered, "Was Inslee there during the murder?"

From behind the counter, Hattie offered, "Don't you think if he was there and heard his boss was killed, Inslee would have run right over? He didn't come to the house until nearly forty minutes later."

Harper interrupted, "And in different clothing than he had been wearing earlier."

"I have no idea what to make of that," Granger said perplexed. "This case gets weirder and weirder by the second." He finished his coffee. After forcing Hattie to take his money, Granger got up to leave.

Before heading out the door, Granger turned back to Harper and said, "I nearly forgot. Dan wanted me to tell you to keep the file he gave you. He said to work on the project yourself right now. That after what happened he wants to lay low for a while. Hopefully, you know what that means. If not, you can probably call him."

Chapter Forty-Seven

Hattie spent close to twenty minutes shoving Harper and Jackson out the door, assuring them she was fine being alone in the house. They were concerned now that they strongly suspected Fr. McNally was not who he said he was. Hattie finally convinced them she was fine. After all, she had been living next to the man for several months.

Hattie thought back over that time to see if anything had sparked her intuition about him. There was nothing, but really, she hadn't paid much attention to the priest at all.

After Jackson and Harper left, Hattie went around the house and triple checked the doors and windows to make sure all were locked. Then she made herself a simple dinner and relaxed until Beatrix came over to perform the protection spell on the house. Neither felt like their energy was very strong, but Hattie thought that it would have to do for now.

Once they were done, Hattie and Beatrix ate some apple pie Hattie had made earlier that day, and talked about spells and Voodoo and the inner workings of trying to balance a normal life with their gifts.

Beatrix admitted she didn't date much and felt out of place among her peers. Hattie assured the girl she had the same experience in her youth, but eventually found her husband and her community. Hattie was sure that Beatrix would, too. But it was a good reminder for Hattie to reach out to her more and include her. Hattie was hoping that Harper and Beatrix would take some time to get to know each other as well.

After Beatrix left, Hattie was resting comfortably in the living room when her cellphone rang. She looked at the screen and debated whether to answer. It was her brother, Harper's father. She took a deep breath. "Hello, Maxwell."

"Hattie, I hope all is well with you. I'm calling to check on Harper. I want to make sure she's behaving herself accordingly."

Hattie rolled her eyes. "Harper's fine, Maxie. She's not a child. Why don't you call her yourself?"

Hattie heard her brother cluck his tongue at the name she had called him all through childhood to annoy him. Max brought out the worst in her. Frankly, he could bring out the worst in anyone. Hattie thought he was insufferable.

"I've tried calling Harper several times, she doesn't return the call," he barked.

"Well then, Harper's not ready to talk to you. And after how you treated her, I can't say I blame her."

Max sighed. "I was only doing what I thought was best for her. Her birthday is coming up. Tell Harper to call me."

"I will, but I make no promises. She's a grown woman," Hattie said flatly. "Don't you even ask how I'm doing? I'm your only sibling, Max. We are the only family we have."

"I assume you're fine. You've got your shop and your lifestyle. You know I don't agree with how you live," Max groused at her.

Hattie laughed. "You know I don't agree with how you live so I guess we're even." She softened her tone. "Actually, I'm glad you called. I need some information. Do you happen to know where Greg Borger is these days?"

"Fr. Borger," Max corrected, "is at a parish in Austin, Texas. He is semi-retired but is helping the parish there. What do you need with our old school friend?"

"Nothing, really," Hattie skirted the truth. "I haven't caught up with him in years. It would be nice to talk to him. Do you have his number by chance?"

Hattie waited while Max went through his phone and provided her Fr. Borger's phone number. She thanked him, promised again to remind Harper to call, and they said their goodbyes. Hattie checked the time. It was nine-thirty and far too late to try Fr. Borger tonight. It was lucky he was in Austin. Hattie hoped he'd be a good resource for Harper and Jackson.

Hattie turned the television back on and pulled the throw blanket around her. There was a chill in the air tonight. She had just started to doze off when she heard movement behind her chair. Calling over her shoulder, Hattie squawked, "Tucker, don't you dare sneak up on me."

Tucker poked his head around her chair. "How'd you know it was me?"

"How many other ghosts do you think I have bothering me?"

"Well," Tucker started, "I've seen at least five around here, but I don't know who they are. They don't seem to want to talk to me. I'm not a part of the ghost clique."

"My husband and his family," Hattie explained. She sat up farther in the chair. "What can I do for you?"

"Did you solve my murder yet?" Tucker asked eagerly. But before Hattie could answer, he complained, "They still have my body lying on a cold slab at the city morgue. I'd like a proper service where I can watch everyone mourn for me, and say nice things. Isn't anyone getting close to solving who killed me?" Tucker planted his spiritual body on the couch, across from Hattie. Her dogs sniffed at him, but then went and laid down on the rug near Hattie's chair.

"No, the police don't seem close. I have no idea, but Harper and Jackson are hard at work," Hattie assured him. "You don't remember any more from the night it happened?"

"I've been trying to think. Bits and pieces come to me, but it's just flashes I can't make any sense of. I did remember standing there arguing with a man in a devil mask. That was clear as day, but I don't know who he is or what we were arguing about. That felt like progress though. That mask also looked familiar, but I couldn't place it."

"You have to remember him," Hattie said a bit excited. That was more than progress for him. "That's who shot you. Keep focusing on that memory and maybe more will come."

Tucker sighed loudly. "I saw Roxy. She was confused. Didn't even know she was dead. I tried telling her, but she just stared at me. She's not any smarter here on the other side."

"That's not very nice."

"But it's true," Tucker lamented. "I haven't seen her since. I don't know where she went. I can't find her. Do you know where she could be?"

"No, I don't know how any of that works on that side." Hattie yawned absently. "Just focus on the memory of the man in the devil mask. If you can remember, we can solve your murder."

"Lizzie can't see me. I've been hanging around the house, but she can't see me. She doesn't seem too upset I'm dead though," Tucker complained.

Hattie was growing tired. Talking to spirits zapped her energy. Beau never stayed for long for that very reason, but he usually brought positivity. Tucker was just weighing her down, and Hattie was starting to fall asleep.

"You weren't the best husband. Maybe you can find a way to make amends."

"If I could do anything, I'd drag her brother to this side. Drew is nothing but trouble," Tucker said sternly, and he then disappeared.

That worried Hattie since Harper and Jackson were watching Drew tonight. She sent Harper a quick text and confirmed they were okay, and then she went to bed.

Chapter Forty-Eight

Harper was sitting on the passenger side of her own Land Rover, and she was bored. She had no idea that going out on surveillance would be quite as boring as it was proving to be so far. After leaving Hattie's earlier that day, she and Jackson had gone home, eaten dinner and headed out for the evening. Harper let Jackson drive although she had given him a hard time in the driveway. Jackson won. He seemed to always win and that vexed her.

Jackson drove them straight to Lizzie's house and found that Drew's car was gone. They hightailed it down to Murray Park. No one was technically supposed to be in the park after dark, but it was rarely enforced. Jackson and Harper were sitting in her parked Land Rover in the parking lot near the boat ramp. There were a few other cars scattered in the lot, which was good so they didn't stand out.

Then the waiting game began. Sitting in such quiet, dark confines, the conversation had turned personal quickly. They talked about their childhoods growing up. Jackson's youth seemed much more normal than her own. He had siblings and parents that were together. Jackson explained he grew up in Richmond, Virginia. His father had been in the Navy and then ran his own woodworking business. His mother was a schoolteacher. Jackson played football in high school and studied criminal justice in college. He joined the Army instead of becoming a cop and the rest is history. Harper looked at him across the console knowing there was far more to the story than that, but she let it go.

"What about you?" Jackson asked, shifting the focus back to Harper. He tapped the steering wheel with his finger, staring straight ahead, only occasionally stealing a glance at her across the SUV.

"Nothing about my childhood seems normal to anyone outside of Manhattan, but it's all I knew at the time," Harper explained. "My mother passed away when I was very young so I was raised by my father. He was strict but consistent. Not very loving or fun but present. I had the best education money could buy and a life that was plotted out for me. I met all the right people, took all the steps in life he wanted me to take. I made all the decisions he wanted me to make and went to work for our family's magazine."

"That doesn't sound very fun," Jackson suggested.

"It wasn't at times. I visited Hattie here during the summers and on school breaks. She was my fun. Her and my Uncle Beau, they were my outlet. I could run and play and be messy."

"You could be a kid."

"That's right," Harper said. Then she added wistfully, "I loved it here, even though as I got older, Hattie's witchy ways seemed odd to me, but still, it was the best part of growing up."

Harper grew quiet. After a few moments, she said, "When my life fell apart, my father blamed me and banished me from the city. He's been calling since I arrived here. I haven't called back."

"Are you going to?" Jackson asked, looking directly at her. His eyes were soft and full of concern. Jackson shifted his body so he was facing her.

Harper smiled at him. "Eventually. I'll call. I'm not really sure what I'd say to him right now. Plus, I'm still angry with him."

"Understood."

Harper started to speak, but then noticed off in the distance by the picnic tables, there was a man with his back turned to them. Harper turned to Jackson and whispered, "I think we may have something."

Jackson was looking at Harper intently, his eyes searching her face. "I think we do, too," he said, his voice catching.

Harper nudged Jackson in the stomach. "Not us," she groaned, "over there!" Harper took hold of Jackson's chin and directed his face towards the picnic tables.

"Oh." Jackson laughed, embarrassment in his voice. "I think you're right. Who is that?"

"I don't know." Harper pulled out the binoculars she had borrowed from Hattie. Jackson had his own, and they were significantly more official and high-end than hers.

"Steal those from the Army?" she teased, breaking the tension that hung in the air.

"No," Jackson replied. "He's clearly waiting for someone."

Out of the passenger side window, Harper saw the headlights from a car entering the park. They wound their way through the curved road of the entrance and came to a stop near the man. The man walked to the back of the car, which looked to be a four-door sedan of some generic brand. Harper couldn't be sure. The driver got out and they both went to the trunk. Because they were standing side by side, Harper couldn't get a good view of what was happening.

"Can you see anything?" she whispered.

"Not much. It's too dark and the angle is bad. But that's definitely Drew."

"Where did Drew park? He just kind of showed up out of nowhere."

"I don't know. I think they are exchanging something. It looks like the guy has some sort of case he's opened," Jackson explained.

"You think it's jewelry?"

"Maybe," Jackson said. "Did you see that?" He nudged Harper with his elbow. "Drew handed the other guy something that looks like it's wrapped in cloth, and the guy handed Drew what looks like a thick envelope."

"That looks exactly like what I saw Fr. McNally hand the guy who said he was his brother. Cash, maybe?"

"I think so," Jackson confirmed.

Harper watched for a few minutes longer. Then she started to panic. Drew was walking off in one direction and the other guy in the car was looking directly over at them. He quickly got in his car and was headed right for them. Harper dropped her binoculars at the same time as Jackson. Harper turned to him, "What do we do?"

Jackson hesitated for a second. Then in a flash, Jackson leaned into Harper and wrapped his arms around her. He slipped his fingers into her hair and pulled her face closer to his. "Kiss me," he breathed.

Her eyes flew open. "What?"

Jackson's only answer was to close the distance between them himself. He kissed her, softly at first and then more passionately. Jackson's tongue teasing hers. Jackson cupped Harper's face, traced his thumb down her jawline.

Harper lost herself. It was one of the best kisses she'd had in her life.

After a few moments, Harper regained her senses. She pulled back slightly and whispered, "I think he's gone."

Jackson looked at her, his eyes full of passion. He seemed to hesitate not sure what to do. Then Jackson sat back, but his hand remained on her, his fingertip tracing over her bare arm. He cleared his throat. "Good, good," was all he said.

Chapter Forty-Nine

Harper swallowed hard, not sure what to say to Jackson. Her lips felt swollen and well-kissed. She stared ahead, hoping he'd say something, but he didn't. He just sat there. Finally, Harper said, "We should go. See if we can find Drew someplace. He clearly didn't park here, but maybe he walked from the Riverdale area."

Jackson started the Land Rover. He looked over at Harper and started to speak, but stopped. He put the SUV in drive and took off. They drove out of Murray Park and took a left on Rebsamen Park Road. They got five minutes down the road and saw Drew walking. Jackson pulled over into an apartment complex and watched him. Drew walked to a parking lot that housed commercial buildings and office space. Jackson edged the SUV closer to the road so they could keep an eye on him. When Drew pulled out, so did Jackson.

"I'm surprised we found him," Harper remarked, hoping to break the ice.

"Hopefully, we can keep up with him, and see where he's going," Jackson responded. He looked over at Harper as he drove. "Should we talk about that kiss?"

"I don't know," Harper said honestly. But she didn't stay quiet for long. "I thought at first you were kissing me so we could pretend that we were just a couple making out in the park…"

"I was," Jackson interrupted. He kept one hand on the wheel and reached for her hand with the other. "That's why I kissed you because that was the only thing that came to mind to get us out of the situation. I couldn't just take off because then that guy would have known we were watching them. I wasn't sure what else to do so I kissed you. Then…" Jackson didn't finish his thought.

"I know," Harper offered, letting him off the hook. "We got carried away. I haven't kissed anyone in a long time."

"Me either," Jackson admitted quickly. "You just felt so good in my arms. Your lips were so soft…" he trailed off again.

Harper let out a nervous laugh. "I think we're being silly. We are in our forties, well I'm nearly forty. This isn't a big deal. We said we were going to be friends, and we kissed. People do this all the time."

"What? Make out on surveillance?" Jackson teased. He looked over at Harper and smiled genuinely at her for the first time.

"Right." Harper laughed, too. "Let's just keep the kissing to a minimum right now, and focus on finding out where Drew is going with whatever is in that envelope."

Jackson cleared his throat and looked at her with eyebrows raised. "A minimum right now? So, there will be more kissing?"

Harper smacked him on the arm and then put her face in her hands, embarrassed. She felt like she just gave herself away. "I just meant…"

"I knew what you meant," Jackson said. "We're good, cookie."

Pointing at Drew turning right on Kavanaugh from Cantrell, Harper said, "Look Drew's nearly back into the Heights. Where do you think he's going?"

"We can find out. I don't think he has any idea we're right behind him."

They continued to follow Drew through the Heights, past Hattie's shop, all the way to the light at University. They took a right and turned into the Heights neighborhood. At Z Street, Drew took another right and then abruptly pulled over. Jackson drove up University, passed Z street and then took a right and doubled-back coming down Pierce Street. Jackson pulled over and waited. The tree-lined streets were narrow with large homes on either side. Within minutes, they saw Drew crossing Pierce right in front of them.

"What do we do?" Harper asked. "We can't follow him in the car."

Jackson debated for a second. Then said, "Let's take a walk in this wonderful evening air."

The two got out and started walking. They turned down Pierce in the same direction as Drew. They had no idea where he was at the moment, but they kept walking. Harper was all ready to pretend they were out for an evening stroll if they happened upon him.

"We actually aren't that far from home, right?" Jackson asked. "I don't think I've driven this way too much, but I think we're close."

"We are, just a couple blocks down is Hawthorne and then a few blocks down on Hawthorne is your house."

They kept walking, keeping an eye out for Drew. Most of the houses had lights on. It was only ten o'clock. One house at the corner of Pierce and W Street caught Harper's attention. It was a large home on the corner lot. It was completely dark, but there was a light shining from the inside. The beam bounced from spot to spot, not staying still. Harper grabbed Jackson's arm and pointed.

Jackson looked in the direction of the home. He whispered, "I think he broke in. Looks like he's using a flashlight. Do you have your cell? We need to call Det. Granger. If we can't reach him, then 911."

Harper pulled out her phone and immediately called Det. Granger. He picked up on the third ring. He sounded like Harper had woken him from sleep. She didn't waste any time. "Jackson and I are walking in our neighborhood. We think Drew, Lizzie Reese's brother, is breaking into a house at the corner of Pierce and W."

Granger seemed to go from nearly asleep to awake in seconds flat. His voice clear and strong, he commanded, "Stay out of sight. I'm sending a unit right now. I'll be there, too."

Harper and Jackson walked back up Pierce and ducked out of sight in the trees between two houses. If the owners had seen them, they probably would have called the police, thinking Jackson and Harper were up to no good. She hoped no one saw them.

"You think the cops will get here in time?" Harper whispered.

"I don't know, but Drew has to walk back this way so if it's him, we will definitely see him. How do these houses not have alarms? You've got million-dollar homes back here, and the burglaries have been all over the news."

"I don't know," Harper said, moving closer to Jackson. The normally safe neighborhood felt ominous tonight. She shivered. Jackson put an arm around her and pulled her close. Harper looked to him and said, "I guess Lizzie was right about her brother. She must really be tired of him to rat him out like that."

"You never know with some people. Maybe Lizzie just wanted to do the right thing. Drew's obviously been in trouble with the law many times before. Lizzie said he'd been a drain on her and Tucker, maybe she was just tired of it. She's grieving too, which people can do funny things when they are faced with death."

Harper had a split second of wondering just how close Jackson came to death when he was deployed. The thought was quickly replaced by the distraction of the flashing lights of the police cars coming towards them. They had their sirens off, but they were rapidly approaching.

Jackson and Harper watched and the cops came to a screeching halt and jumped out of their vehicles. Harper counted at least eight officers on the scene. Det. Granger arrived a few seconds later. Harper and Jackson stepped out from the trees into the road.

Granger waved to them and they started to approach. At that point, many of the neighbors were also coming out of their homes, probably wondering what was disturbing their normally quiet neighborhood this late at night.

As they got to where Det. Granger was standing, two uniformed cops had Drew in handcuffs and were walking him to the car. He looked over at Harper and spat, "I warned you. Should have killed you when I had the chance, but those damn barking dogs."

Granger looked at Harper. "Well that answers who was trying to break in the other night." He walked off and said something to the officers and then came back to Harper and Jackson. "You'll need to follow me to the station. We will need your statements."

Granger started walking back towards his car as Jackson and Harper turned to walk back to her Land Rover. Det. Granger called to them over his shoulder, "I don't know how you caught him, and I almost don't want to know, but thanks."

Chapter Fifty

Harper blinked herself awake. The sun was shining through the closed blinds and the air was warm. She and Jackson had been at the police station until close to two in the morning. They came back to Hattie's and went right to sleep, separately. Harper had left a note in the kitchen for Hattie that there had been a break in the jewelry case, but that she'd have to wait for an update. Harper had been exhausted. Never one to sleep late, Harper knew her body needed rest.

Once fully awake, Harper reached over to the nightstand and picked up her cellphone. It was nearly eleven in the morning. Harper had already missed two calls from her father and one from the prison where Nick was. She wasn't calling anyone back. Harper scrolled through the news, catching a brief story about the missing jewelry case and Drew's arrest.

Then she noticed a text from Jackson. It read: *Went for a run, then back to my place. I want to talk about last night.*

Harper didn't want to talk about last night. She knew if she had to talk about it, she'd end up admitting how much she liked kissing Jackson. He was so different from Nick, everything about him. He felt solid, warm, and comfortable. Actually, it was way too comfortable with Jackson, and instead of feeling good, it was unnerving. Harper ignored the text for now and headed for a shower. As she stepped into the hallway, Sparkle and Shine were sitting at attention at the end of the hall, looking like they were listening intently to the air.

Harper muttered, "Crazy dogs." She walked into the bathroom, dropped her clothes, and stepped into the shower. She let the hot water run over her, washing away the stress of the night before. Thoughts of Jackson kept invading. She pushed them aside, scolding herself. Harper couldn't get involved with him. They just met. She was going over the list of reasons why it was all a bad idea when she heard her phone ring again. She let it go to voicemail.

Harper wrapped herself in a towel and went to check her phone. It was Matthew Inslee. He left a quick message that he needed to speak to her immediately and to call him. She would not be calling him back.

After getting ready and blowing out her hair into soft waves, Harper went to the kitchen. She fished around in the cabinet for a bowl and poured herself some cereal. Sitting down at the table, it was then Harper noticed a note from Hattie. The note reminded her to please call her father and provided a phone number to a Fr. Borger in Austin. Hattie indicated that he was an old school friend of hers, and he might be able to give some direction into how best to look into Fr. McNally's past. The note also asked Harper to come to the shop when she finally got up and around.

Harper took another hour to savor her alone time and then headed to Hattie's. Like Hattie, Harper enjoyed the walk. But as she approached the four-way stop at Country Club Boulevard, an SUV came screeching to a stop in front of her. Harper jumped back out of its way. Her startled heart was racing. Matthew Inslee got out of the SUV and was in Harper's face in seconds.

He stood toe to toe with her, pointing in her face and screaming, "How dare you tell Detective Granger that I was missing from that party! It's none of your business when I was there or where I went! You are nothing but a no-good trouble maker, and I'm going to see you are run out of this city if it's the last thing I do."

Inslee's finger was so close to Harper's face that it made her step back. She bumped into the curb and nearly fell on her behind. Inslee's face was red, his eyes like saucers, and he was practically foaming at the mouth. Harper was trying to regain her composure to respond, but Inslee kept yelling the same thing over and over again.

From her right, Harper noticed a shadow cross her vision. Before she could even register what was happening, Jackson had grabbed Inslee by the shirt and twisted his arm in an unnatural position around his back. Jackson slammed Inslee face down on the hood of his car. Jackson growled low and deep, "If you ever, and I mean ever, lay a hand on Harper again, I will ensure it will be the last thing you ever do."

The way that Jackson was holding him, there was no way for Inslee to move or fight back. He struggled against Jackson's hold, but Inslee was no match for him. "Get off me," Inslee squeaked.

"Not yet. Apologize to Harper for your ignorant behavior."

"Screw that," Inslee spat. "I'm not apologizing."

Jackson twisted the man's arm again. Inslee winced in pain. He grumbled, "I'm sorry."

Jackson let him go and stood back. Inslee got up, spun around and had his fist raised like he was going to hit Jackson, who was squared off waiting for the punch. Jackson laughed. "Thirty years in the Army, four tours in the Middle East, I'm the last person you want to go hand to hand with. But please, try me. Nothing would give me more satisfaction."

The two men stood ready for a fight. Finally, Inslee dropped his fist, adjusted his clothes. He looked over at Harper. He bellowed, "This is the last time I'm telling you. Stay out of my way." With that, he turned and got back into his SUV and sped away.

Harper reached for Jackson, and he jumped when her hand touched his shoulder. Then he softened his posture. "Thank you," Harper said sheepishly. "You okay?"

Jackson searched her face. He calmed down. "Yeah, I'm fine. It's you I'm worried about. I was just getting back from my run and saw you. I figured you were walking to Hattie's, but then I saw Inslee roll up on you like that."

"He called me this morning, but I was in the shower. He left me an angry message and told me to call him, which I hadn't planned on doing. I was on my way to Hattie's. She left me a note that she wanted to talk to me." Harper reached for Jackson and put her arms around him. She hugged him tightly.

He wrapped his arms around her but said, "I'm all sweaty. I'm going to make you a mess."

"It's okay," Harper whispered into his neck. "Thank you for rescuing me. I really don't know what I'd do without you here."

They parted and locked eyes. Jackson smiled and brushed a strand of hair from Harper's face. "Why don't you head on to Hattie's, and I'll be there after I shower and change."

Harper agreed. She continued on with her walk, but turned back to watch Jackson as he jogged back to his house.

Chapter Fifty-One

By noon, Hattie had already run through eight pots of coffee, been completely cleaned out of Danish and muffins, and had sold more cups of tea than she had sold the previous three days total. The store was filled with people. She had Harper and Jackson to thank.

Apparently, Det. Granger had let it slip that it was thanks to a tip from them that the police were able to arrest Drew for jewelry burglaries. The people in the community were so relieved and happy that they were coming in to thank Hattie.

Many of them asked Hattie if it was her psychic gifts that enabled Harper and Jackson to figure out it was Drew. Hattie laughed and explained that it was just good old-fashioned investigative work, but that she didn't even really know the whole story because Harper had come in so late.

Several of the women who had never been in the shop before were impressed with how cozy it was.

They told Hattie over and over again how much they loved it, and that they'd definitely be back. Two of the women had pulled Hattie aside and asked what she recommended to put a little spice back in their marriage. Hattie put together some simple lust spells with rosewater, pink tapered candles and honey. She explained how to write the name of their husband on the candle with a pin, rub the candle with rosewater and a little honey and burn the candle late in the evening for nine nights while envisioning passion in their marriages.

After giving the very grateful women the spells, Hattie also added, "Never discount how good you'll feel after pampering yourselves, too. Go get a massage, get your hair done, spoil yourselves." Then Hattie added with a laugh, "It's easier to seduce when you're feeling like a seductress."

"You're terrible," Lottie laughed, calling over to her from one of the tables. "You give great advice but when was the last time you felt like a seductress?"

Hattie threw her hands up. "Who am I seducing? Better question, who'd want an old gal like me?" She gave a little twirl in the middle of the room.

"I know the feeling," Lottie said. "My husband is asleep on the couch at four-thirty."

"It happens," Hattie sympathized. "Where's Judy?"

"She was meeting with her friends that had been robbed. They had to go down to the police station. Do you really think it's Drew? I had been sort of kidding the day I said maybe he had killed Tucker. I never thought he'd be robbing houses."

"Speak of the devil," Hattie said, hitching her jaw in the direction of the front door. "Harper's here. She can fill us in." Turning to her niece, she yelled over the crowd of people, "Grab a seat here with Lottie, and I'll get you some coffee."

Harper came over and joined Lottie. She was barely in her seat when Lottie pounced. "Well, tell us what happened. How did you catch Drew?"

Harper looked at the older woman surprised. "How did you hear already?" Looking around the crowded shop, Harper asked, "Why is it so crowded in here?"

"Det. Granger told some people that you and Jackson helped catch Drew, and it spread around the neighborhood the way all gossip does here," Hattie told her. She set the coffee down in front of Harper and kissed her on the head. "People are proud of you as am I. Now what the heck happened last night?"

Harper went through the whole story about what they saw in Murray Park. She explained they had parked in the neighborhood and followed Drew to a house. "There are still so many questions I have though. Drew clearly met someone in the park last night, but we couldn't see who it was. And really, why was Drew stealing jewelry when the Reeses are so rich?"

"I know that one," Lottie interjected proudly. "Judy had lunch with Lizzie yesterday. She cut him off and was going to kick him out of the house. It had been a long time coming. Apparently, Tucker had been threatening it for years. Drew had no job. He was probably doing it as a way to earn money."

"You can't just sell jewelry like that easily though," Harper commented, taking a sip of her coffee.

"What do you mean?" Hattie asked. She looked up the counter to make sure Beatrix was not too overwhelmed with customers. The shop finally seemed to be clearing out some. The din of noise that had permeated the place was finally dulling and you could hear yourself think again, which was good because Hattie had been waiting for hours to hear the story from Harper.

"Well," Harper started. "That kind of high-end jewelry can't just be sold at a pawn shop. Some of those pieces were worth millions of dollars. Drew would need to connect to a fence to sell it. Then the fence would move it out of the state probably, maybe even out of the country. Sometimes they even cut it up, take the stones and put it in other settings or sell the stones separately."

Hattie looked at her quizzically. "How do you know all this?"

"We covered a story on jewelry heists for an edition of *Charlotte* a few years back. You'd be amazed at the complex network."

"Do you think this means he killed Tucker?" Lottie asked. She was picking apart a cheese Danish in front of her and taking sips of tea.

"I have no idea," Harper admitted. "I was hoping that Det. Granger would have given me a call. He said he'd let me know when he knew more. Maybe he doesn't know anything else yet."

Harper excused herself to go to the bathroom. When she did Lottie said, "The poor dear looks exhausted."

Hattie agreed. She'd never seen Harper so tired. This was definitely not the life Hattie had envisioned for her when she suggested Harper move to Little

Rock. She was picturing that Harper would have found some friends her own age. She'd take long lunches, maybe pick up some freelance work, be lazy around the house, and learn the magic she needed to learn before the entire Ryan family legacy went down the drain. Crime fighting wasn't high on the list.

Chapter Fifty-Two

Hattie followed Harper to the bathroom. She waited outside and then asked her niece to join her in the back room. Harper yawned and sat down in Hattie's chair. She snuggled into it and rested a pillow on her lap. "What's up?"

"You look exhausted," Hattie started. "I'm so sorry you got so involved in all this."

"You don't know the half of it. Matthew Inslee screamed at me in the street on my walk over."

"He did what?" Hattie barked. Hattie did not do dark magic, but she was coming close to pulling out the family grimoire and finding the nastiest spell imaginable she could perform on him.

"It's fine," Harper assured her, snuggling farther into the chair. "Jackson took care of it. He's really strong. It's funny. I know he's a retired Army Colonel, and I know he's been to war, but he's so mild-mannered and unassuming. You kind of forget he's probably got some ninja skills."

"Ninja skills?" Hattie asked, her face breaking into a wide grin.

"He threw Inslee on his car face down and did this twisty thing with his arm so he couldn't move. I think we have our own personal superhero."

"You've got a little crush, don't you?" Hattie asked.

Harper just stared back at her aunt but didn't actually answer her.

Hattie waved it off. "Never mind. I won't give you a hard time today. I really called you back here because I have a present for you."

"You do?"

"It's not a big deal, just a little something that I think you are ready for," Hattie said and handed Harper a tiny, clear pouch.

"What's this?" Harper asked, as she unsealed the opening and pulled out a pointed amethyst stone attached to a chain.

"It's a pendulum. I know you aren't into this whole psychic witch thing, but it is our family legacy. Whether you want to practice or not, it would at least make me feel better if I could start teaching you so it's not all lost when I'm gone."

Harper was looking at the pendulum with a mix of curiosity and fear. "What do I do with it?"

"It's not going to bite you," Hattie teased. She pulled out her own pendulum. Hattie's was made of calligraphy stone. She held the top of the chain with one hand and placed her other under the stone.

Hattie explained, "You can use it to tap into your intuition. You can ask it yes or no questions, and it will swing on its own, giving you an answer. You have to take some time to get to know your stone though and learn which way means yes and which way means no."

Harper looked at Hattie with a puzzled expression on her face. "Show me what you mean."

Hattie explained that with her pendulum side to side meant no and front to back meant yes. When it spun in a circle, it meant maybe or something needed more clarity before a real answer was given. Hattie asked if her niece's name was Harper, and the pendulum swung yes. Hattie then asked if her own eyes were brown. It said no, which was true, they were green.

"It takes time," Hattie assured her. "Just something for you to practice with. It may not answer questions accurately if you have an emotional investment in the answer. For instance, I've not been able to ask who murdered Tucker because I'm so close to the situation. I care about the outcome. Plus, spirit doesn't always answer us when we want. It's not one hundred percent, but it's a good tool to start tapping into your intuition. Clean the stone with water, put it on your windowsill to charge it under the moon, and keep it with you to absorb your energy. Just practice. That's all I ask."

Harper got up and hugged her aunt. She promised, "I will and thank you. Thank you for being patient with me, too. I know I'm not so quick to believe."

Hattie smiled. At least Harper didn't outwardly fight her on it, which was what Hattie had been expecting. Excited, Hattie said, "I nearly forgot to tell you, I put a call into Fr. Greg Borger. I'm just waiting for him to call back. I think he can probably help you with Fr. McNally if you want to continue. If you want to stop, I understand."

"We aren't stopping," Harper said determinedly. "There's no way I'm giving up on this now."

Hattie nodded towards the door. "I'm going back out there. Beatrix probably needs help."

"I'm going to sit here and rest. Let me know when Jackson gets here." Harper held up the pendulum. "I might even practice this for a bit. Maybe it can tell me if Jackson likes me."

"I don't think you need the pendulum to tell you that. I don't even need to be psychic to see that he does." With that, Hattie slipped out of the room and headed down the hall back out into the main area of her shop. She was happy to see that Jackson was already there and chatting with Lottie. She sent Beatrix over with some coffee.

"I heard you were a hero today," Hattie called.

"Something like that," Jackson said modestly. "Is Harper here?"

"She's resting in the back," Hattie said, busying herself behind the counter.

Hattie spent the next several minutes cleaning up the morning rush. Hattie was just putting on yet another fresh pot of coffee when her cellphone rang. It was Fr. Borger finally returning her call. She answered quickly and waved to Jackson to join her and Harper in the back room.

Hattie found Harper asleep in her chair. She nudged Harper's shoulder and pointed to the cellphone. She mouthed that it was Fr. Borger. Sitting on the couch, and holding the cellphone in her lap, Hattie turned on the speakerphone. She made a quick introduction all around and then explained what had been happening with Fr. McNally and what they all suspected.

When Hattie was finished, Fr. Borger said, "I think the best bet is for you to come to Dallas, and I can meet you there tomorrow morning if that works. Together we can go to the parish where Fr. McNally worked previously and ask some questions."

Harper turned to Jackson and said, "I guess we are headed to Dallas."

"I guess so," was all he said.

Hattie noticed the brief smile on both their faces. She wasn't sure if it was because they were getting another lead or they'd have a few days away together.

Chapter Fifty-Three

Harper and Jackson had been on the road for over an hour. After they made the decision to go to Dallas, they both went home to pack. It was three in the afternoon when they left. They had a four hour drive ahead of them left. Jackson insisted on taking his truck so he was happily and comfortably behind the wheel. Harper was staring out the window, seeing parts of Arkansas she had never seen before. It was really just lots of trees and open land. She had attempted to change the radio station at one point, but Jackson smacked her hand away.

Jackson liked modern country music, which Harper knew nothing about nor did she really care to. If it had been Harper's choice, they would have been listening to some seventies classic rock or even the grunge and angry women rockers of the nineties she loved so much. But Harper was stuck listening to songs about beer, trucks and women. To be completely fair, the more Harper listened, the more she softened to it. But there was no way after the stink she put up that Harper would admit that to Jackson, who was singing right along with the song currently coming out of the speakers.

Thankfully, Jackson had a great voice so Harper was more than happy to listen to him sing, even if she thought some of the lyrics were unrelatable and silly.

Almost as if reading her thoughts, Jackson pipped over the music, "It's because you're still a Yankee. Once you get accustomed, you'll love it. We just need to get some of that stuffy city girl out of you." And then he went right back to watching the road and singing.

Harper rolled her eyes but smiled as she looked out the side window. They bumped along nicely for another hour. Harper pulled out the file that Dan had given her and was going through it again. She turned to Jackson and asked, "If this isn't the real Fr. McNally what do you think happened to him?"

"I don't know, but if I had to guess, he isn't alive."

Harper winced. "Do you think someone killed him?"

"That or he died and this guy just assumed his identity. It happens," Jackson explained, matter-of-factly.

"Wouldn't the church know that? Where do you think the switch happened?"

"If I had to guess, I'd say sometime after leaving Brazil and coming here," Jackson speculated. "The early photos of Fr. McNally in Brazil looked the same as his older photos in Dallas. But the man who arrived in Little Rock does not appear to be the same man. What gets me though is the resemblance. Too many coincidences to just bump into someone whose life you want to steal and you just happen to look like him."

"Right," Harper agreed. "I wondered the same thing. But the woman I spoke to said Fr. McNally was an orphan with no family that she knew of so it's strange to say the least."

"How did Hattie say she knew Fr. Borger?" Jackson asked, switching lanes to go around some slow-moving trucks.

"She and my father went to school with him. He's from Manhattan. Hattie let it slip he was her prom date their senior year."

"The witch and the priest," Jackson laughed.

The conversation was interrupted by Harper's ringing cellphone. She pulled it out of her purse and looked to see who was calling. It was Det. Granger.

Jackson lowered the music, and Harper answered. Harper barely got out a hello and Granger said, "I stopped by Hattie's shop to talk to you, but she said you were headed out of town for a couple of days. I want to let you know Drew confessed to breaking into those houses. Most of the victims were Lizzie's friends or at least people in her social circle. He'd know when the big events in town were happening and find out who was attending. When you're running in the same circles, it's not hard to find out. Then Drew would target those houses on those nights."

Harper interrupted, "Was he working with anyone?"

"No, he says he was working alone," Det. Granger indicated. Then he added, "We have a lot to still sort out, but he's definitely our guy."

"I'm glad he's caught, but really it was Lizzie and Dan who tipped us off. You should thank them. Call it a gut feeling, but I don't think he was working alone. Twice we saw him meet with other people."

"Maybe he was trying to sell some of the pieces. The only pieces recovered so far are what you found. Drew claims he sold the rest to online buyers and at some pawnshops."

"He isn't selling that jewelry online or at pawn shops, I guarantee you that," Harper said tersely, growing frustrated. "I'm not questioning how you do your job, but have you ever had a case with this much million-dollar jewelry?"

"I can't say I have. As you know these kinds of cases don't happen every day around here. We mostly handle smaller burglaries, electronics, money and such," Granger admitted.

"I've written about them," Harper explained. "Drew is not working alone. He can't move that kind of jewelry alone. He's working for someone or with someone or has a connection he's selling it to that will move the jewelry out of here. Unless you found jewelry he hasn't sold yet, you're not going to find the rest."

"He's still talking. Thanks for the info. I'll see what more we can get."

"You hear anything about who killed Roxy or Tucker?"

"Not yet, but Drew is still talking so we might get something," Granger explained. Then he added more seriously, "I spoke to Inslee about being at the Saints & Sinners Ball. He was more than a little insulted I was asking. Inslee said he went to the event early in the evening and met up with a woman he's been seeing. They left early. Inslee said he was called away from her bed when he was notified about Tucker."

"That's his story," Harper groaned.

"Harper, I asked for the woman's name, and I spoke to her. Inslee was with her. The whole conversation embarrassed her and Inslee. He wasn't happy. You…"

"I know he wasn't happy," Harper snapped. "Inslee practically assaulted me on a city street. He screamed at me, got in my face. I don't care what he says, I don't believe him."

"This isn't a fight you're going to win," Granger argued. Then more softly he said, "I don't trust him at all. But unless there is some solid, irrefutable evidence, Inslee is too powerful in this city. No one is going to believe you. You get something you can prove beyond any shadow of a doubt, bring it to me. Until then, let it go."

Harper breathed heavy. She wanted to argue her point. She knew in her gut there was something more with Inslee. Although Harper hated to admit it, Granger was right. She needed proof.

Granger asked, "Where are you headed?"

"Dallas," Harper said without offering more of an explanation.

"I find it a little strange you were so gung-ho and stepping all over my toes, and now you're just up and skipping town," Granger said skeptically. "Anything you want to tell me?"

"Nope, just going to visit a friend. We will be back in a day or so. You asked me to back off, so this is me backing off."

"I find that hard to believe," Granger said, his voice low.

"Well, you don't have to worry. Down in Dallas, I won't be in your jurisdiction. I can make some other cops angry for a change." Harper heard Granger sigh loudly and the call ended.

Chapter Fifty-Four

After ending the call with Granger, Harper turned to Jackson and said with frustration in her voice, "He's really not getting it. They are treating this like it's the run-of-the-mill burglary. Granger said Drew told him he sold the jewels to pawn shops and online. What person that can afford millions in jewelry is shopping at a pawn shop?"

"You told him. Det. Granger is smart," Jackson reassured. "When I met with him to go over my statement after Tucker's murder, Granger was telling me about some of the cases he worked before coming to Little Rock. He's not from here either. He's been a detective for years. Granger's good, trust him."

"I guess." Harper filled Jackson in on what Inslee had told Granger. Then she added, "It seems like a pretty tight alibi, but Inslee's so slick and slimy, I just don't trust him."

"Granger's right though. I hate to admit it, but we probably need to back off of Inslee until we have real proof."

Harper nodded in agreement, but she wasn't happy about it. She thought back to her conversation with Hattie yesterday and the pendulum. Harper wondered if she could ask it if Inslee was lying. She'd have to try it later when she could concentrate better.

After several more minutes of silence, Jackson asked, a bit of tension in his voice, "Where are we staying tonight? I need the address."

Harper pulled out her phone and gave Jackson an address, which he programmed into his GPS. Then she detailed, "It's a Hampton Inn. There were several conferences in Dallas this week so it was hard to find a place. We are sharing a room."

Jackson's eyes opened wide as he looked at her.

"Eyes back on the road, Romeo. We are sharing a room, not a bed."

Jackson grinned like a cat. "You're away from Little Rock for the first time. Who knows what you had planned?"

"Not that," Harper deadpanned. She insisted, "I'm not a convenience store cookie. You're going to have to bake."

Jackson cracked up laughing until he had tears rolling down his cheeks. He turned to her, still laughing. "Where do you come up with this stuff? No one said you were a convenience store cookie."

"Who knows with you? You think you can just grab a girl and kiss her while you're supposed to be watching the suspect. We don't know who the other guy is because you were so focused on getting hot and bothered," Harper said with a straight face.

Jackson argued, "I was trying to make sure we weren't caught. Do you really think…"

Jackson didn't get to finish his thought because Harper started to laugh. She reached over and rubbed his arm. "What was it you told me when we first met? That I was too uptight, that I needed to get used to your teasing. What's good for the goose."

Jackson shot her a look then put his eyes back on the road. "You're exasperating," he muttered under this breath.

"Well, that makes two of us."

The pair drove in silence for nearly the rest of the trip. Harper napped. Jackson sang. She opened her eyes a few times and caught him staring at her. Harper just grinned and went back to napping.

A few hours later, they were checked into their hotel room and had grabbed a late dinner at the diner next to the hotel. Back in their room, Jackson took a shower while Harper changed into pajamas. She made a quick call to check in on Hattie. After Hattie convinced her all was fine, Harper settled into her bed. She pulled out the pendulum Hattie had given her and stared at it, unsure of how to start.

Harper positioned her hand underneath the way Hattie had shown her. She asked the pendulum to show her the answer yes, and to Harper's surprise, it moved front to back. She asked for the answer no, and it swung side to side. Harper steadied her hand and tried a few more yes or no questions she already knew the answer to. Harper was sure that she was not moving the chain and stone. Harper sat amazed she was getting responses.

She got a little bolder and asked if Jackson thought she was pretty. It swung front to back quickly, strongly indicating that yes, he did. Harper immediately felt silly, like she was back in school at sleepovers she used to have with her friends. Harper concentrated and asked if Inslee was with a woman the night of the ball. To her dismay, it said yes, he was. She tried again and got the same answer. Maybe she needed to ask a different way. Harper was trying to come up with a different way to ask when she heard Jackson clear his throat.

"What are you doing?" he asked curiously, from across the room. Jackson's bald head was still damp and he was wearing a gray Army tee-shirt and shorts.

"Hattie gave me this," Harper explained, holding up the pendulum so Jackson could see it. "She said it's a pendulum that will help me tap into my intuition. Hattie said I can ask it yes or no questions and my energy will guide me to the right answer."

"Interesting," Jackson commented. He pulled back the covers to his bed and threw some pillows up against the headboard. He climbed in, pulling the covers up to his lap. Turning to Harper, Jackson asked, "Is it working?"

"That's the thing, it's just my intuition so who knows if it's really right. I asked some questions I already know the answer to and it gave me the correct answer, but when I asked if Inslee was with a woman that night it says he's telling the truth."

"Maybe he wasn't there the whole time," Jackson offered. He clicked on the television and started flipping channels.

"That's what I was thinking, but I'm tired now so I'll ask again tomorrow."

Harper got up and went into the bathroom. When she came out, Jackson had shut off his light and was snuggled more into his bed watching television. Harper climbed into her bed and shut off the nightstand light. She wasn't sure what she was feeling. Harper had thought sharing a room with Jackson might be awkward, but it wasn't. She felt safe with him. Harper fixed her pillow and was getting comfortable when she felt eyes on her.

Jackson was watching her intently. He smiled. "You want some company over there?"

She groaned and grabbed the pillow next to her head and flung it back at him, hitting him squarely in the head. Harper playfully barked, "You stay over there. Go to sleep, we have an early morning."

"Your loss." He yawned.

Chapter Fifty-Five

Hattie had thought that maybe the rush in the shop yesterday was an anomaly and all would go back to normal today, but it had been a mad rush all morning again. Hattie had navigated through it without any help because Beatrix was in class. Hattie would have to hire more staff if things continued like this. She was brewing another pot of coffee when Judy and Lottie walked in.

"Hi, ladies, pull up a chair where you can, and I'll have your usual right over," Hattie called from behind the counter.

Instead of sitting, Judy and Lottie grabbed dirty plates and cups that were left on tables and brought them to the back of the store to be run through the dishwasher. Lottie wet a rag behind Hattie's counter and cleaned off tables while Judy picked up scraps of paper, refolded newspapers, and put the shop back in order.

Hattie fussed and told them to sit, but they weren't hearing it. They ignored Hattie's pleas and went right on cleaning.

"We can't relax in this mess," Lottie said, washing the last of the tables. "You need help, Hattie. You are too old to be doing this on your own so we can pitch in."

"Well then you aren't paying for anything," Hattie chirped. She stacked their goodies on a tray and brought them over to the table. Finally, the ladies came over and plopped down in their seats.

"We are excited that business is picking up, but you really need some help. You can't carry on like this," Judy said, taking a bite of her raspberry cheese Danish.

"I will," Hattie said, sitting down next to them. She had grabbed a chocolate chip muffin and cup of coffee for herself when she was preparing Lottie's and Judy's. She took a sip of coffee. "Tell me, what's the gossip for today."

"Lizzie is like a new woman," Judy chirped. "I saw her this morning, and you'd think the woman would be upset her brother was arrested, but no. She was practically gushing about having her freedom now."

"Does she feel any embarrassment that her brother robbed her friends?" Lottie asked what Hattie was thinking.

"If she does, Lizzie's certainly not acting like it. She told me that Drew is finally getting what he deserved. The only thing Lizzie expressed regret over was that she wasn't going to have the satisfaction of dragging Tucker through court."

"Did Lizzie say anything about holding any memorial service for Tucker when the coroner releases his body?" Hattie asked.

"I asked that," Judy said, "and Lizzie didn't seem concerned about it in the least. She's already started going through his closet and pulling out clothes to donate. She's called the car dealership about turning in his Mercedes. She's liquidated some of their assets. I heard from a friend that Lizzie even talked about selling the house and traveling. She's definitely not missing a beat having those two gone from her life."

Taking a sip of her coffee, Lottie leaned into the table. "That's terrible. I understand he was not the best husband, but he kept her financially comfortable. If Lizzie didn't want to be married, don't be married, but don't deny the man a memorial service. Don't act like you never cared at all. The least Lizzie could do is fake it until it all blows over. This community deserves to say goodbye properly to one of our own."

"I agree. He needs the rite of Christian burial," said a deep voice from behind the woman.

Hattie turned and was surprised to see Fr. McNally standing there. She was so tired and lost in thought, she hadn't heard him come in.

Knowing what Harper suspected about the man, Hattie was a bit startled. He was the last person she'd ever expect to come into her shop. Fr. McNally was dressed in black pants and a shirt with his white collar. Hattie stood. "Hello, Father, can I help you?"

He walked towards her and shook her hand and that of Lottie and Judy. "I was just walking through the neighborhood after hearing confessions at the church and thought I'd stop in. I've never been inside, but I've heard so much about it."

"Would you like some coffee or something to eat?" Hattie offered.

"No, thank you." Fr. McNally looked at Hattie and said sincerely, "I know we haven't gotten off to the best start as neighbors, but I hope you believe now that I had nothing to do with Tucker's death. It was all just a misunderstanding that evening. Matthew Inslee assured me he's cleared it up with you."

Hattie didn't believe a word he was saying, but she wasn't brave enough to say that. "I think it was an overwhelming situation as you can imagine," Hattie said finally.

"Have the police made any progress in finding out who killed him? I've gone to the spot several times to pray that they would."

"Not that I'm aware of, but of course the police aren't updating me," Hattie explained nervously. "I've seen you at the spot a few times. I wondered what you were doing."

"Praying," Fr. McNally reiterated. "Is your niece here? I wondered if I could ask her a question."

"No, Harper's out for the day, but I can send her over to you when she's back."

"That won't be necessary. I can catch up with her here another time. I thought she might be back already. I saw her leave yesterday with that other neighbor of yours. Are they on a trip? They had luggage with them."

Hattie was starting to get more suspicious about the reason for the man's visit. She didn't like that he knew that Harper and Jackson were away. "Jackson had to take care of something and Harper tagged along. They should be back later today," Hattie lied.

"Oh good, good," Fr. McNally said. "Well I'll just take a little look around your shop if you don't mind, and then I'll be on my way."

Hattie sat back down with Lottie and Judy. Hitching her jaw in Fr. McNally's direction, Lottie whispered, "That's a bit odd, don't you think?"

"Very," Hattie agreed. Then she said loudly, "Well you ladies enjoy the rest of your coffee. I have to get back behind the counter." With that, Hattie got up, went behind the counter and got out her laptop. She pretended to do some work while she watched the priest over the rim of the screen. Fr. McNally was taking in the stones Hattie had, reading descriptions on each one. He walked over to the candles and picked up a couple, reading the labels on those as well.

Fr. McNally stopped browsing the store. He stood in the middle of the room seemingly hesitating, then he approached Hattie at the counter. "I wanted to ask, do you speak to the deceased?"

"I wouldn't think as a Catholic priest you'd believe in such a thing," Hattie said a bit surprised.

"I believe all things are possible, now whether I believe it's a gift from God or a source of Satan, that's another story. As you know all forms of divination and clairvoyance are more than frowned upon. They are sin."

"Well, Father," Hattie said angrily, "while I don't really care about your opinion of my gifts, I can assure you there is nothing negative or demonic here. As for your question, speaking to the deceased is not something I do."

Fr. McNally and Hattie stood eyes locked for several seconds. Hattie was not backing down. Finally, the priest nodded his head and left the shop.

Chapter Fifty-Six

After a hearty breakfast at the diner next to the hotel, Harper and Jackson drove to the St. Jude's Parish in Park Hollow, a wealthy neighborhood in northern Dallas. They met with Fr. Borger, who was a tall man with a handsome face, striking blue eyes and an affable demeanor. Harper liked him instantly and quickly saw what Hattie might have liked about him when they were young.

They met in the parking lot of the parish office and then were escorted in. The three had been waiting in a conference room for nearly an hour. Sipping coffee that had been provided to them, Fr. Borger was regaling Harper and Jackson with stories from Hattie's youth. Hattie and Fr. Borger, who just went by Greg then, had been quite a duo in their upper eastside elementary and high school.

According to Fr. Borger, they remained great friends through college and well into their forties.

Hattie had even written him letters while he was serving in Vietnam before coming back and entering the seminary. Fr. Borger admitted time and distance separated the friendship, but he was happy to hear from her.

Jackson and Fr. Borger shared some war stories and the differences during each of their time in the Army. Fr. Borger then turned his attention back to Harper. He noted he had also been friends with Harper's father Maxwell, who as they aged, he saw more frequently.

"Your father was never one for trouble. Hattie and I would skip school and just cause lighthearted mischief, but Max wanted no part of that. I think he felt a sense of responsibility to one day take over the family magazine and prove himself as a capable young man in spite of coming from a well-known and wealthy family. He always wanted to ensure people knew he earned it rather than it was handed to him. That was important to Max."

"My father was never one for having fun or letting loose. It's pretty much how he raised me," Harper lamented. Harper frowned thinking back to her sterile childhood. She was grateful for all she was given and the opportunities she had, but she never really felt like she had a father. He was more like a warden whose rules she had to follow and never step out of line or disobey.

"I know that must have been hard, Harper," Fr. Borger commiserated. "I've spoken to your father a number of times over the years. He had more grief than you know after you both lost your mother. In a lot of ways, Max felt extra pressure to make sure you grew up to be successful because it was a direct reflection on him. Right or wrong, he wanted you to succeed. Max is very proud of you."

"Really?" Harper asked in amazement. She'd never heard her father say he was proud of her. The fact that he told other people was shocking.

"Really," Fr. Borger reiterated. "All through school and even with how well you did at the magazine, Max has been so proud of you." Fr. Borger must have taken note of the shocked expression on Harper's face. He laughed and added, "I'm a priest. I can't lie."

Harper explained, "When everything happened with my husband, he practically threw me out of Manhattan. That's why I'm here. My own father fired me."

Fr. Borger leaned across the table and locked eyes with Harper. "Did he fire you or unlock your cage?" He let the question hang in the air. Then he said, "I spoke to your father while it was all going on. Harper, Max knew how unhappy you were at the magazine and your entire lifestyle in New York. Max said it was like constantly watching someone going through the motions. He saw an opportunity, and he took it. His delivery was terrible, but his heart was in the right place."

Harper was floored. She hadn't thought about it that way. If her father hadn't fired her, she would have stayed on out of family obligation and to make him happy. He forced her to make the decision she had wanted to make anyway.

A knock on the door interrupted the conversation and Harper's thought. An older woman, probably closer to Fr. Borger's age than Harper's came in. She had a blue skirt and patterned yellow and blue blouse. She held out her small hand to Harper, and said to the three of them, "I'm Edna Parker, the administrator here at St. Jude's. I was here while Fr. McNally was our parish priest. While I'm very glad you're here, I can't help but wonder what took you all so long to follow up on our report."

"I don't think I understand," Jackson said perplexed. "What report?"

"We called the police when we heard Fr. McNally was missing. You aren't from the Dallas Police Department?" she asked hopefully.

Both Jackson and Harper shook their heads.

"Then who are you?" Edna asked concerned.

"They're from Little Rock, which is where Fr. McNally is right now," Fr. Borger began to explain.

Edna cut him off, "I don't understand. Fr. McNally has been missing since last June. When did he get to Little Rock?"

Fr. Borger looked at Harper. She explained, "From what I understand, someone indicating he was Fr. McNally showed up at the St. Joseph parish in Little Rock last July. I don't know the specific date."

"What do you mean someone claiming to be him? I don't understand that," Edna pressed.

Jackson politely waved his hand to cut them all off. "Mrs. Parker, why don't you sit with us and explain what you know and then we can explain what we know. The bottom line is we have concerns that the man saying he is Fr. McNally is not in fact him. Hearing you say you filed a missing person's report is concerning. Maybe we can just start at the beginning and tie all the pieces together."

Harper laid a hand on Jackson's arm. She appreciated his reason and logic. Her brain was starting to spin. "I think what Jackson said is a good idea. We need a frame of reference."

Fr. Borger agreed. Edna shut the door to the room and sat down at the table with them. She folded her hands in front of her on the table and began, "Fr. Patrick McNally started here at our parish nearly ten years ago. He quickly became a staple of our community. The children at our school adored him. The parishioners loved him and he seemed to absolutely love being here. He connected very well with the youth in our programs. On Saturdays, you could find him shooting baskets on the basketball court. And he played on our parish softball team."

Harper looked at Jackson and said softly, "He sounds nothing like the man who lives next door."

Edna continued, "We have a very wealthy parish here. Our families are very comfortable, but Fr. McNally made sure families were giving back not to the church but to the community. He hosted food drives and events to bring in people from all over Dallas. He worked with other churches, from all denominations across Dallas to coordinate efforts to help those less fortunate."

She pulled a tissue from her pocket and wiped away the tears that were starting to form. "You have to understand, we absolutely loved Fr. McNally. The entire community was heartbroken when the Catholic Diocese here asked him to help with a sister church at the Catholic mission in Rio de Janeiro. But Fr. McNally felt it was his calling so he went, and that's when the trouble seemed to start. We had heard…"

Edna did not get out her last sentence. A woman a few years older than Harper pushed open the conference room door. She had been crying. Her face was red and her dark hair was in messy curls around her face. She looked frantic. "Did you find Patrick?"

Chapter Fifty-Seven

"Patrick?" Harper asked, looking at the crying woman. Clearly, this woman was familiar enough with Fr. McNally to call the man by his first name. Harper was a good distance away from her Catholic roots so she wasn't sure how common that was.

Edna looked embarrassed. She got up, embraced the woman by the arm and lead her to the table. Edna handed her another tissue and explained, "This is Camille. She's a fourth-grade teacher here at the school. She and Fr. McNally were quite good friends. They spent a lot of time together."

With her eyes cast down at the table, tears still running down her cheeks, Camille quietly explained, "Patrick, I mean Fr. McNally, and I became great friends. We are close to the same age and both grew up in the northeast. What we really had in common was neither one of us grew up with our birth families. Neither of us were ever adopted, and we aged out of the system. We had a lot in common. I took the teaching job here without knowing anyone in the city, and Fr. McNally made me feel welcomed and like I had a family for the first time."

Camille turned, looking at Edna. "I knew Fr. McNally as the wonderful priest who ran this parish and school, but I also knew the man who was my friend."

Turning to look across the table, Camille locked eyes with Harper. "Please tell me you found him."

Harper took a deep breath and let it out slowly. With sympathy in her voice, she said, "I'm so sorry, we had no idea Fr. McNally was missing. There is a man that lives at the parish behind my aunt's house who claims he is Fr. McNally, but we have our doubts."

"No, that can't be him," Camille sobbed in disbelief. "If it was Patrick, I would have heard from him. I've been emailing him for months and nothing. He wouldn't ignore me. We were too close of friends."

"When was the last time you heard from him?" Jackson asked. He had pulled out a pad of paper from Harper's messenger bag and started to take some notes.

"I know the exact date. It was June 17. I had emailed him about one of the students here who had received a college scholarship, and he emailed right back," Camille informed them. "I emailed him on June 22 and that was met with no reply. I've emailed several more times since then and nothing. Even messages begging for a response were met with silence."

Fr. Borger shifted in his seat. Turning to Edna, he said, "You had started this conversation telling us you had made a police report, can you tell us more about that? What made you call them?"

"It was a number of things." Edna got up and poured herself a glass of water from a pitcher that was sitting on the counter on the side of the room. Water and coffee had been left for Harper, Jackson and Fr. Borger when they first arrived.

Sitting back down, Edna continued, "Fr. McNally was going to be placed there for two years. He left here in July 2016. He came back to visit a number of times during his first year. It was a rough area in Rio, but Fr. McNally thought he was making a difference."

"He really did," Camille said interrupting. "At first Fr. McNally really didn't like Brazil at all. Then he got to know some of the people and felt more settled. He expressed to me that people told him they were very grateful for the church and the work he was doing."

"His first year and a half had seemed to be okay. Then there was a turn in January 2018," Edna added. "In a letter he had sent back here, Fr. McNally expressed concern for his safety. He was working in a very rough neighborhood and in a parish filled with youth who had been in trouble with the law. The church rectory where he was living had been burglarized. It was youth who had been caught, but then let go by the police. The gang activity was increasing and even the police seemed stymied to stop it. In February 2018, Fr. McNally got word from the diocese that he would be coming back to the states in July of that year. He had asked to come back to this parish, but from what we knew that hadn't been approved yet. Fr. McNally had expressed relief that he'd soon be back in the United States."

"What was the point though that you called the police?" Fr. Borger asked. He got up and walked around the room, stretching his legs. Harper felt like doing the same. They had been sitting there for a couple of hours.

"We knew Fr. McNally was supposed to receive his orders from the diocese in mid-June. With the shortage of priests, there were a number of places he could have been sent to, but then we just never heard. He never came back here. There was no word from Fr. McNally and all communication ceased."

"Why not just ask the Dallas diocese where they placed him?" Harper asked, wondering what she was missing.

The question seemed to spark a memory for Fr. Borger. He looked to Harper, worried he said, "I have a feeling Fr. McNally got lost in the shuffle. We had a major merger of dioceses here last year. With so many Catholic churches and schools closing, we no longer had a need for so many dioceses, so smaller ones were absorbed by some of the larger. Each diocese had their own record keeping, some were more tech-savvy while others were still using paper files."

"That's exactly right," Edna agreed. "When we stopped hearing from Fr. McNally, we called the parish in Rio. Fr. McNally didn't have much staff the way he had here, but we spoke to his housekeeper. We also spoke to the principal of the school. We heard the same story. Fr. McNally had packed up and left."

"Could he have taken some vacation time?" Jackson offered.

"Possibly but we could never get a straight answer as to where he went. Actually, we never got any answer," Edna remarked. "We waited a few weeks and then called the Dallas diocese."

Edna turned to Fr. Borger. Frustrated, she detailed, "The merger caused more than just a record keeping issue. We had significant staffing changes including a new bishop. We called the diocese several times, and each time we were promised someone would get back to us. They never did. Finally, we called the police there in Rio and here. No one would take a report. Both said it wasn't their jurisdiction. Rio indicated that according to passport records, he left the country. Dallas police department said because he didn't go missing here, it wasn't their problem. We have been in the middle of this jurisdictional red tape while a man is clearly missing."

Camille was softly crying again. She wiped her eyes and blew her nose, "It's such a shame, too. Patrick had just found some of his birth family."

Chapter Fifty-Eight

Harper, Jackson and Fr. Borger were at an Irish pub down the road from the parish. After Camille had said what she did about Fr. McNally finding his birth family, she had been called back to her class at the adjacent parish elementary school. Edna had to leave to attend a meeting that had been on her schedule. Before she left, Edna provided Fr. Borger some contact information for the Catholic mission in Brazil.

Camille had promised she'd call Harper as soon as school let out for the day so they could continue the conversation. She had pulled herself back together to go attend to her students, but it was clear below the surface, Camille was still distraught. Harper had no doubt they'd hear from Camille as soon as the last child was on a bus headed for home. Until then, they could do nothing but wait.

Once in the parking lot outside the parish, Fr. Borger had placed a call to the mission in Brazil, but no one answered. He left an urgent message, but again all they could do was wait. The three were stymied at the moment so they found the pub and ordered lunch. They sat discussing what they knew to date when Harper got a call on her cell. It was Det. Granger so she stepped away to take it. Harper had planned to call him as soon as they had more information, something concrete at least, but Granger had other news.

Granger sounded elated. "We found the gun used to kill Roxy and Tucker in Drew's storage locker," he effused. "While Drew didn't confess outright, he said enough that we believe he killed Roxy and Tucker."

"Did Drew give any reason why?" Harper asked. She was skeptical for some reason. Harper had no reason not to believe that Drew had killed them, just something felt wrong to her. She couldn't place it though.

"Drew was very concerned that Tucker would find out about his burglaries, and he said he assumed that Tucker had also told Roxy," Det. Granger reported, a bit out of breath. "The bottom line is Drew had means, motive and opportunity."

"But did he really?" Harper asked, a bit frustrated. "According to Drew and the reports called in, he robbed five houses that night. How did he pull that off and come over to Hattie's and kill Tucker all in the same night?"

The question was met with silence. She heard Det. Granger's breath return to normal. He countered, "We will sketch out the timeline, but Drew had plenty of time. Most guests arrived at the Saints & Sinners Ball by seven that evening. Tucker's murder wasn't until ten. Even by his own account, Drew had been in most of the homes before with Lizzie so he knew the layout. Drew admitted he was in and out in under fifteen minutes."

Harper was doing the math in her head. Most of the homes were in close proximity to each other, some as close as a few houses apart on the same street so Harper begrudgingly admitted that while it was technically possible, it still didn't seem probable. She asked, "Did you find anything else at his storage unit?"

"If you're asking if there was any other jewelry, no, there's wasn't. Drew said he sold nearly all of it," Det. Granger detailed.

"In a few days, he sold it all?" Harper knew that unless there was a fence involved, that was nearly impossible.

"Harper," Det. Granger said, clearly annoyed and frustrated with her, "there are no perfect cases. Sometimes we don't get all the answers. We may never recover all the jewelry for those families, but this is a win. We got the bad guy. I thought you'd be happy to know."

"Congrats, Detective," Harper said tersely.

"No, Harper, thank you. Without your annoying persistence and help, we might not have wrapped this up so quickly," Granger congratulated.

Harper had no idea what to say because she didn't think he had it wrapped up at all. Det. Granger started to speak again, but he stumbled over his words. Harper couldn't quite make out what he was saying.

Finally, Granger cleared his throat and said more clearly, "I really appreciate your help. Maybe once I get things squared away here, I can take you to dinner and thank you properly."

Harper was taken aback. Was it a date or a professional courtesy? Maybe he just wanted to be friends. Harper remembered Jackson had said Granger wasn't from Little Rock. Harper said what she felt was politest, "That would be nice, thank you."

Hanging up, she rejoined Jackson and Fr. Borger at the table.

"You look stressed out. You okay?" Jackson asked as she sat down. He reached over and put his hand on top of hers.

Harper gave him a weak smile. Then she related everything Det. Granger had shared. She also went over all of her concerns. When Harper was done, Fr. Borger asked, "Do you doubt this Drew fellow killed them? Sounds like he had ample motive."

"I don't really know," Harper admitted. "It seems like Drew would be the strongest suspect. He definitely had motive. Plus, he's burglarizing people's homes. He's been to prison before. It's not like Drew's a stand-up guy. Something just feels off. I can't really explain it better than that."

Fr. Borger laughed. "I used to have conversations with Hattie like this. She'd always have these gut feelings, little pings of intuition."

Jackson squeezed Harper's shoulder. "Harper's more like Hattie than she knows or cares to admit."

Turning to Fr. Borger, Jackson asked, "I'm sure you know what Hattie does. How do you feel about that with your Catholic teachings? I know Hattie's gifts are considered against most Christian values."

"It is," Fr. Borger said solemnly. "Hattie has been a friend for years though. I've seen her gifts first hand. It's a bit of a challenge for me. I know church teachings, but I also know Hattie is one of the kindest, nicest people I've ever met. Sometimes you just have to accept people for who they are and try not to question it too much. Many people do not believe what I believe, but I don't think they are bad or that there is something wrong with them for it. We all have a different path."

"That's an interesting and good perspective to have," Jackson commented.

Fr. Borger looked at Harper. "So, if you don't believe Drew is the one, what are you going to do about it?"

"Well," Harper started, taking a drink and washing down the last of her sandwich. "I think that's why we are here. We've been suspicious of the man saying he's Fr. McNally. If Drew didn't kill them, then certainly this guy is a good second suspect. He came running out that night towards where the body was found. He was muddy, and Hattie was instantly suspicious of him. She doesn't do that lightly. If anything, I've seen her give people far too many chances."

"Do you know why this imposter might have killed the prosecutor?"

"We know Tucker, the victim, was investigating something at the parish. Maybe Tucker wasn't investigating at all, but rather had found out what we are finding now, simply that the priest wasn't who he said he was. Is that enough of a reason to kill?"

"Could be," Fr. Borger stated. "Maybe it's not so much hiding who he is now, but whatever crimes he committed to get there."

Harper shot a worried look to Jackson who returned it.

Chapter Fifty-Nine

After Fr. McNally's visit, Hattie wasn't feeling the best. She was concerned about her interaction with him and worried about Harper and Jackson. More than anything, given how busy the shop had been, Hattie hated to admit it, but she was feeling her age. She found it curious that given the protection spell she and Beatrix had done, that Fr. McNally even entered the shop. Maybe they had been too focused on Matthew Inslee when they performed it.

Around two o'clock, after the shop had cleared out, Hattie's cellphone buzzed with a storm warning. There was a line of strong storms headed for Little Rock later that afternoon into the evening. It wasn't quite peak tornado season, which ran April through June, but storms could be notoriously bad any time of year. Hattie was used to it, but decided to close up the shop early and head home. The dogs would be going crazy with the thunder and lightning, and Hattie wanted to make the walk home before she needed an ark.

The sky was gray and the wind was picking up. Hattie stepped through the door and into her back porch when the sky opened up and a torrent of rain fell. Sparkle and Shine rushed to her, wiggling and brushing up against her legs. Thinking they might need to go, she opened the door and held it open. The dogs looked at the rain and back at her. They turned and went into the kitchen. "Well I didn't think you'd want to go, but I gave you the option," Hattie called after them.

Putting her things down on the kitchen counter, Hattie stood still for a moment, just breathing in the quiet. Actually, if Hattie was going to be honest with herself, it was too quiet. She had become accustomed to Jackson being around over the last few months, and then with the addition of Harper, Hattie felt like she did back when Beau was alive.

She opened the fridge and pulled out a can of ginger ale in the hopes it would settle her stomach. Hattie let it sit while she climbed the stairs to her bedroom in search of some medicine for her headache and aching joints. Hattie entered her bedroom and pulled up short, startled by the sight of her husband Beau, who was standing at the window in the farthest part of the room. "Oh, you're here," Hattie blurted.

Beau turned to her. "Sorry, my dear, didn't mean to scare you. I was going to meet you downstairs, but I noticed the flurry of activity across the way."

"There's a storm coming," Hattie explained, walking over to him. "Maybe they are just rushing around to prepare."

"It doesn't look that way," Beau said. Pointing at the scene below, he indicated, "They are bringing things into that building back there. I think I'm seeing what Harper saw a few days ago. It's happening again."

Hattie looked at where Beau was pointing and sure enough, there was Fr. McNally, another man and the pregnant woman. Hattie wondered if it was the same person that Harper had seen. If it was, in the light of day, she did not look like a girl but a grown woman. They were bringing suitcases down into the storm shelter.

Hattie rubbed her temples, her headache pounding. "I'll be right back," she told Beau. Hattie went into the bathroom, pulled out some pills and swallowed them with a glass of water from the bathroom faucet.

"Not feeling well," Beau observed, still watching the neighbors.

"Not really, I'm just very tired." Hattie kicked off her shoes, took off her skirt and blouse and grabbed a pair of cotton pajamas that were tossed on the chair. She put them on and then pulled the covers back to climb into bed. Turning to Beau, she whispered, "I wish you could still hold me."

Beau came over and brushed his hand over her face and hair. Hattie couldn't feel him, but she could feel his energy. Slowly she drifted off to sleep.

A few hours later, Hattie heard the thunder boom and saw lightning illuminate the darkened room. She opened her eyes and closed them again. She took a big breath in and let it out slowly, reorienting herself awake. She sensed that she was not alone. Hattie assumed Beau was still there. "What time is it? How long have I been asleep?" she croaked, her voice still gravelly from sleep.

"I don't know, I've only been here for about ten minutes," a man said from her doorway, but it wasn't Beau.

Alarmed, Hattie sat upright and blinked rapidly, trying to see clearly in the dark. When her eyes were finally focused, fear set in. "What are you doing in here?"

Hattie quickly got out of bed and planted her feet on the floor, but she wasn't sure where she could go.

The man who claimed to be Fr. McNally was blocking her exit.

"You and me are going for a little walk. We have some things to discuss," he said sternly.

"I'm not going anywhere with you, get out of my house," Hattie demanded and moved to walk past him.

He blocked her way and pulled up his shirt to reveal a gun in his waistband. Hattie looked at it and back to his eyes. She had no doubt that he might shoot her. Grabbing her by the arm, he shoved her into the hallway and down the steps.

He mocked, "You can stop with the charade. You know I'm not the priest."

Hattie's eyes darted back and forth. Her mouth was dry, and she had trouble swallowing. "What should I call you then?"

"Paul will do just fine," he grunted at her with a shove down the steps.

Once they reached the landing, Hattie turned the corner into her kitchen and stopped cold. Her hand flew to her mouth, and she let out a shriek. Her beloved Golden Retrievers were lying unmoving on the kitchen floor.

Paul jerked her arm hard. "They're fine. I drugged them. They will wake up, but after we are gone so they don't give me reason to shoot them."

Hattie looked down at them as she passed. "Where are you taking me?"

"Just put your shoes on," he snapped.

Hattie got to her back porch and grabbed a pair of old sneakers she had next to the door. There were socks stuffed in them, too. She had planned to go for a walk a day earlier and had pulled out the socks and sneakers, but had never had the chance to wear them. Hattie leaned over and pulled them on.

The rain was coming down hard. The thunder was roaring and the lightning fierce.

Hattie contemplated escape, but she didn't see a feasible means. She stated, "You can't be serious that we are going out in this. We can talk right here."

"Move," Paul demanded.

Hattie turned the door handle and stepped outside. The wind whipped against her. The pajamas were thin and immediately soaked. She shivered against the cold. Paul pulled her along, practically dragged her through her own backyard. She'd yell but there wasn't anyone around. With the whipping rain and thunder who would hear her anyway. As they got to the top of the clearing, she saw Tucker. He was standing in the middle near where his body had been found, watching them.

He shouted, "Hattie, watch out!" And that was the last thing Hattie heard before blinding pain ripped through her skull and the ground came charging towards her face.

Chapter Sixty

It was close to six-thirty by the time Harper, Jackson and Fr. Borger were able to meet up with Camille and Edna. The five of them were presently seated around the same conference table in the parish as earlier in the day.

"I apologize we had to stop earlier, we had meetings and students to attend to," Edna said.

"We understand. After all, we barged into your office unannounced," Fr. Borger acknowledged.

Turning to Camille, Harper proposed, "You had started to say earlier that you were especially upset because Fr. McNally had just found his birth family. Let's start back there if we can."

"As I mentioned before, Fr. McNally and I were both placed in orphanages as infants," Camille began, more composed than she'd been earlier in the day. "He had always wanted to find his birth family, but it's never easy especially when children are placed for adoption or in an orphanage so early in life, especially back then. Many times, the records are sealed."

Camille flipped through some pages that were in front of her. She held them up. "These are some of the email exchanges I had with Fr. McNally. He had uncovered some information that gave him access to his original birth certificate. He didn't detail how he came to find it."

Harper held out her hand, and Camille handed the pages over.

"What happened next?" Jackson asked.

"At the time, we both had been searching for our birth families. I found my mother last year, but Patrick, after he gained access to his birth certificate, learned his parents were deceased. He found a half-brother through some of the records he had uncovered."

"How did he feel about that?" Harper asked. She was fighting the desire to start reading through the pages in front of her, but she thought it best to listen first and then read.

Camille continued, "We talked in March last year. Fr. McNally was going to wait until he got back to the states to make contact. The brother was in Chicago, I believe. He just thought it best to be back in the states where he had normal phone service and could fly to meet him should a meeting be desired. He wanted to be as accessible as he could be."

"Did he stick to that plan?" Jackson asked.

"I don't know, but I have a feeling he didn't," Camille speculated.

"Why is that?"

"Because Fr. McNally was so excited about the opportunity to have family. He wanted to know where he came from, who his people were, and even his ancestry. For people who don't know their birth families, there are a lot of missing pieces," Camille explained. "Given Fr. McNally's excitement, as you can read, he asked me several times what I thought was the best way to make contact. He finally decided on an initial introductory letter. He thought that was probably least intrusive just in case his father had never told his new family that he had a child earlier in life. Fr. McNally also wondered if the father had even known about him. He decided a call or showing up was too much."

Harper handed Jackson one of the email pages. Jackson read it. "He was already writing the letter so it seems you may be correct that Fr. McNally didn't wait to send it."

"Right," Camille agreed. "That email is from late April. I don't think he would have waited to come back here to the U.S. before sending it. He sounded ready to go."

"Do you know anything at all about this half-brother?" Jackson asked, jotting down some notes.

Camille closed her eyes. She seemed to think back. Finally, she opened her eyes and looked across the table to Jackson and detailed, "Not all of our communication was email. Sometimes we would Skype. I remember him mentioning that the brother was from Chicago. He also said his name was Paul. Fr. McNally had wondered if the P name was a family thing."

"You have a last name?" Jackson asked, sounding hopeful. "Was it McNally as well?"

"No, McNally was a name given to him in the orphanage. I know that much. I think Fr. McNally said the family name was something like Daniels or Davidson, something like that."

Camille leaned her arms on the table. Her eyes were filled with worry. "I wish I had paid better attention, but you have to remember at the time, I wasn't paying so much attention to detail. I was focused more on how he was feeling about it all."

"How was he feeling?" Harper asked. She couldn't imagine what that must feel like, not to know your birth family. For as hard as it was with her father sometimes, at least she had a home, knew her roots and had the connection. She couldn't imagine as an adult meeting family for the first time like that.

Camille shrugged. "It was hard to tell. One minute, Fr. McNally seemed really happy and excited, then another he was full of fear about making contact. I think he was more concerned about rejection. There was also a part of him that wondered why, if his father could have been a good father to other children, why not him."

"But Fr. McNally didn't really know his father was a good man, correct?" Fr. Borger interjected.

"No, that's true," Camille conceded. "He just knew there was a half-brother so maybe Fr. McNally had worked it up in his head that his father was this great man supporting another family but not his own."

Playing on a hunch, Harper pulled the file Dan had given her from her bag. As she flipped through it, she hoped, "Did Fr. McNally have a photo of the brother or show you one?"

"No. I don't know that he had one. I don't know what if any research or information he had on his brother other than a name and a city."

"But you knew Fr. McNally really well, correct?" Harper pressed.

"Yes, I saw him nearly every day for years, and then we were in constant communication while he was in Brazil until he disappeared."

"What are you getting at?" Jackson asked Harper.

In response, Harper laid a photo on the table in front of Camille and asked, "Who is this?"

Camille picked up the photo and studied it. She looked back to Harper and said, "I don't know. I've never seen him before." Turning to Edna and Fr. Borger, she asked, "He's a priest, do either of you know him?"

Edna took the photo from Camille and studied it. With confusion in her voice, she said, "I don't know him either. He does look a little like Fr. McNally. There is a resemblance."

Harper took the photo back and laid it on the table. She laid other photos of Fr. McNally next to them. Pointing with her finger, she indicated, "This one is Fr. McNally." Pointing to the more recent photo the two women were just looking at, "This is the man claiming he's Fr. McNally."

Camille sucked in a sharp breath and started to cry. Edna turned to Fr. Borger. "We need to get ahold of someone in that mission in Brazil now."

Chapter Sixty-One

Fr. Borger spent the next hour tracking down his contacts both locally at the diocese and over in Brazil. One person reached out to another and then to another. Finally, they got someone on the phone connected to the local mission where Fr. McNally had lived. The story Edna initially received that Fr. McNally had packed up and left was not the full story. The story they now heard caused them all to sit back in shock.

Fr. Borger detailed, "Two weeks before Fr. McNally was supposed to return to the states, he had a visitor. He told people it was his half-brother Paul. The man didn't seem too friendly or nice, according to others at the church. In fact, Fr. McNally expressed to them some reservation about the man's visit. Apparently, it had been unplanned. Paul just showed up. But Fr. McNally said that he wanted to take the time to get to know his brother so they were going to stay at a place Paul had rented in Cabo Frio on the beach."

As Fr. Borger was speaking, Harper was struck by blinding violent images. She wasn't sure where they were coming from, but they were vivid. A pain shot to the front of her forehead and she reached to rub the spot. Jackson looked at her with eyebrows raised. Harper nodded that she was okay, rubbing the spot gently with her fingers.

Turning his attention back to the group, Jackson asked, "Did Fr. McNally go on the trip then?"

"He did," Fr. Borger responded. He looked down at his notes from the call. "The man I spoke to, who was a caretaker at the church, said that Fr. McNally packed up all his belongings and left them in his room. Fr. McNally said that as soon as he was back from his trip that he'd be headed back to the U.S. But, according to the man, Fr. McNally never returned. When the new priest started, and they hadn't heard anything, they assumed Fr. McNally went back to the U.S. without his things. They are currently in storage in the church basement."

Camille started to cry again, and Edna reached over to comfort her. She asked, "What does this mean? Where is he?"

Harper, Jackson and Fr. Borger shared a look. Jackson, his voice quiet and kind, speculated, "We can't know for sure. This is pure speculation on my part, but Paul could have killed Fr. McNally on that trip and returned to the U.S. as him."

Camille looked at him through red, swollen eyes. "You really think Fr. McNally is dead?"

"I do," Jackson said solemnly. "If he's not, where is he?"

"I think that's the question whether he's deceased or not," Harper said. Looking to Fr. Borger, she asked, "Is there anyone who can go through his things looking for information? Clearly the police aren't going to do anything so someone should check his belongings."

"Let me make some calls," Fr. Borger said. He stepped out of the room.

"Edna, do you have a laptop or tablet connected to the internet we can use? I'd do this on my phone, but it's too small," Jackson explained.

"We do," she said. Edna got up and walked out of the room.

Turning to Harper, Jackson explained, "I want to see if we can find anything on Paul. We can search under the two last names Camille provided." Handing the file of emails to Harper, Jackson added, "Why don't you skim through there, maybe there are more clues you can find. If we can find a photo of him, I think we'd have some more answers."

Harper started with last year, right around the time Fr. McNally and Camille started talking about finding their birth families. Harper read each of the priest's emails very carefully. It was clear he was at first excited to find his birth family. After gaining access to his original birth certificate and finding that his parents were deceased, his tone became more apprehensive. He had even cautioned Camille that sometimes it was almost better not knowing because the picture wasn't always what's imagined, but Fr. McNally didn't provide any specifics on what he meant.

The door to the room opened and Edna handed a laptop to Jackson. "How can we help?"

"Is there any way you can track down someone at the Dallas Diocese? We are going to need them on this as soon as possible," Harper indicated. "I'm going to call the detective we know in Little Rock as soon as Jackson does his search. The more information we have the better because otherwise the cops there will continue to dismiss our concerns."

Edna and Camille left the conference room explaining they would go to Edna's office where she kept the contact information for the diocese. She said she'd bring Fr. Borger with her if he was done with his call. That left Harper and Jackson working alone in the conference room.

As soon as the two women left, Jackson turned to Harper. He asked suspiciously, "What was with your head a little while ago?"

Harper swallowed. "When Fr. Borger was explaining the trip Fr. McNally took with his brother, I had a sharp pain that ran from the back of my head to the front, and then I had vivid images of Fr. McNally being struck in the head. Something like that has never happened to me before. Do you think it means anything?"

"I don't know, but if you were anyone else, I'd probably say no. Given Hattie's gifts, don't discount it," Jackson said seriously. He reached out and rubbed the top of Harper's head affectionately. "Does it still hurt?"

"It's okay, throbs a little," Harper said honestly. She got back to searching the files. On the second to last page, she got a name. She tapped Jackson on the shoulder frantically. "It's here," she said, shaking the page at him. "His name is Paul Davidson. He's two years younger than Fr. McNally so that would put him right at fifty-one. Fr. McNally found a birthdate, city of Chicago address, and full name."

Jackson typed the information into the search engine, and within seconds he pulled up a few articles. He read each one as Harper watched in anticipation. Then Jackson turned to her with a mix of fear and understanding. "This is all starting to make sense."

Jackson turned the laptop to Harper. She was looking at a photo of Paul Davidson in a federal court in Chicago. He was being arraigned for a slew of charges related to fencing millions of dollars in precious gemstones and high-end jewelry. Subsequent articles showed that Paul had fled the country before trial. One of the articles indicated that although they had taken the man's passport, they believed he had used a forgery and had left for an unknown location in South America. The articles were dated nearly a year before Fr. McNally started his search for his family.

In another article, they indicated that Paul's brother Evan was getting out of federal prison in Arkansas for his part in some money laundering scheme. Harper looked at Jackson. "You think that's where Evan and Drew met?"

"I think you were right about Drew needing a fence for that jewelry and who better than someone who already has a network. What do you want to bet that Evan and Drew cooked up this burglary scheme using Lizzie's connections and then Paul fenced the jewelry?"

Harper let out a long, slow breath. "I'd say you're about right. It was the perfect storm. We need to call Det. Granger."

Chapter Sixty-Two

Hattie woke in a darkened room. She sat up slowly, but her head was throbbing. Her vision was blurry. As Hattie looked around the room, she slowly took in her surroundings. She was in a small square room made of gray cinderblock. The room was sparse. It had a simple cot with a blanket and a thin pillow, and that was it. There were no windows, and the door was closed.

Hattie stood up, felt dizzy and immediately sat back down. She rubbed a bump on the back of her head, which felt wet. Hattie brought her hand around to her face and was alarmed to see blood on her fingers. She looked down at the bed and there was a small circle of blood on the pillow. She tried to recall the last memory she had before waking in the room. Hattie remembered seeing Tucker. He was yelling, but she couldn't remember what he had said.

Fr. McNally, or at least the man who had pretended to be him, had been behind her. What did he say to call him? She couldn't remember. She tried to focus. The memory of waking up from sleep with him in her home struck her. He must have taken her. Hattie's breathing quickened and her pulse raced. She had to get out of there. But no one even knew she was gone. She had no idea what time it was or how long she'd been missing.

Hattie tried standing again. She inched herself off the cot slowly and steadied herself as she stood, taking a slow deep breath to fight off the nauseated feeling that overcame her. She walked to the door and pounded her fist against it. "Hello, anyone out there? Let me out of here!" Hattie yelled once, twice, then three times, her voice growing stronger with each. Nothing in response.

Hattie shivered against the cold. Looking down, she was reminded she only had on her cotton pajamas. Pressing her ear up to the door, Hattie heard voices. There were three distinct – two men and a woman – coming closer. Hattie stepped back into the room as someone approached the door.

The door opened and there was a woman standing there. She was very pregnant. She barked, "He wants to talk to you. Let's go."

"Who wants to talk to me? Who are you? Where are we?" Hattie demanded to no avail. The woman didn't say another word. She led Hattie down dark corridors, one leading to another. Hattie was lost already. It was like a maze. Dark hall after another finally opened to a large room. Hattie recognized it as the storm shelter below the St. Joseph's school and church grounds. This was the only room Hattie had ever been in. During a storm a few years ago, she had taken shelter in this room with people in her neighborhood. Hattie had no idea until now what the rest looked like.

Waiting for her in the open room was Paul. Hattie remembered his name as soon as she saw his face. As Hattie came into the open space, he pointed to a chair in the middle of the room. "Sit there." Talking to the woman, Paul ordered, "Go get her that blanket. I need her comfortable."

"You care about my comfort?" Hattie mocked. "If you really did, you wouldn't have hit me in the head or dragged me down here."

"You wouldn't have come willingly," Paul countered. "And yes, for what I need, you should be comfortable."

"And what is it you need?" Hattie asked cautiously.

"I need you to do that thing you do. The magic. Talk to the dead," Paul demanded, pacing around the room. He kept rubbing and scratching at his head. Hattie assumed it was a nervous tic she had only now just noticed about him.

Hattie shook her head. "I don't talk to the dead. I told you that."

Paul stopped and pulled the gun from his waistband. He pointed it at her. "I've seen you in your window talking to no one. I've seen you in the yard. I know you can. Now do it for me."

Hattie swallowed. "I'm an old woman. I talk to myself a lot."

"You're lying," Paul said, gun aimed at her.

Hattie took a big deep breath. "I don't have control over it," she said honestly. "I'll see what I can do. Who do you want to connect with?"

"The dead guy."

"Tucker Reese, the man who was murdered in my yard? Why?"

"Yeah him," Paul said nervously. "I need to know what he knows about me."

The pregnant woman whose name Hattie still didn't know came back into the room with the blanket. She dumped it on Hattie's lap and left. Hattie pulled it around her shoulders for warmth.

Hattie looked at Paul and conceded the truth. "I've spoken to him. He doesn't remember anything about that night or the events leading up to it. He just shows up. I don't know how to make him appear."

Paul started pacing again. He muttered to himself, "I have to know what they know. I have to know how close they are."

"How close who is?" Hattie asked. "Listen, I don't know what you've done, and I don't care…"

Hattie was interrupted. The metal door at the top of the stairs that led to the small interior of the building that accessed the storm sheltered opened. She saw the man who Harper had called Fr. McNally's brother come down the steps. Hattie recalled his name was Evan.

He yelled to Paul, "They got Drew for the murder of that attorney. You think he's going to give us up?"

Hattie looked between the both of them. She daringly asked, "Are you saying it wasn't you who killed Tucker Reese?"

Paul looked to her. She saw fear in his eyes for the first time. "No, that's what I've been trying to say. We didn't kill him, and I don't know who did. But Drew knows things."

Turning to Evan, "Can you get to him? Shut him up?"

"No, no," Evan repeated. "They have him in the cell. Can't see him or get a message to him."

Paul cursed loud enough for Hattie to hear it. Turning back to her, Paul pointed the gun. "Get Tucker here now. I need to know."

"I told you it doesn't work like that," Hattie started to say, but then she was distracted. Suddenly standing right behind Paul was a man that Hattie assumed only she could see. She looked carefully at his face and suspected it was the real Fr. McNally.

The man looked to Hattie. He said with fear in his voice, "You're not safe with him. He killed me."

Chapter Sixty-Three

Harper and Jackson waited for Edna, Camille and Fr. Borger to come back to the conference room before they called Det. Granger. Edna confirmed she reached someone at the Catholic Diocese of Dallas who took the report and was going to act immediately. She said they may follow up for more information as needed. Fr. Borger also confirmed he at least got a detective on the phone in Rio de Janeiro, now whether they did anything about it was another story.

"Let's call Det. Granger in Little Rock," Harper encouraged. "He's at least in close distance to Paul to bring him in for questioning. We just need him to take us seriously."

It was later in the evening, nearing eight o'clock at night. Harper wondered if Det. Granger would still be at the office. She tried his office phone to no avail and then tried his cellphone. He picked up. Harper said hello and explained where she and Jackson were.

Then Harper told Det. Granger she was putting him on speakerphone.

Placing her cellphone in the middle of the table, she hit speakerphone and turned up the volume. She made quick introductions of everyone around the table. Harper said, "You told me not to come back to you until I had proof, and I do. That man is not Fr. McNally."

"I'm listening," Det. Granger said with skepticism in his voice.

Harper detailed, "His real name is Paul Davidson. He's from Chicago and has a number of pending federal charges related to fencing millions of dollars in gemstones and jewelry."

Harper then spent the next twenty minutes going over in detail how they came to learn his real identity, what they know of the real Fr. McNally and what they suspect happened to him. She gave Edna and Fr. Borger a chance to speak. Then Harper turned it over to Camille who made a passionate plea for justice for Fr. McNally. Harper raised her eyebrows in a question to Jackson and he shook his head. He had nothing to add.

When the group finished, Harper took a deep breath and asked, "Is that enough now for you to look into this? At the very least call Chicago and talk to the prosecutor handling the case. They will tell you all about him."

"You've made your case, Harper," Det. Granger conceded. "This is going to be messy and complicated, but I'm on it. I want to call Chicago and do a little research and see what they need before I bring him in. What's the contact in Brazil and at the Dallas Catholic Diocese?"

Edna and Fr. Borger detailed that information. Granger added, "Bring home copies of those emails and anything else you think is relevant. When will you be back?"

Harper turned to Jackson and he whispered to her that tomorrow would be best. She told Granger, "Given the storms and the hour, we will head back in the morning."

"Come on in as soon as you get back. We can get your formal statements."

Harper and Jackson agreed. The group picked up their things in the conference room. As they were leaving, Harper leaned in and hugged Camille. She said sweetly, "I'm sure Fr. McNally cherished your friendship. I know all of this is probably unbearable right now, but you were very brave to help us."

Camille gave a weak smile. She gave Harper a big hug and thanked her. Then she walked off with Edna while Harper, Jackson and Fr. Borger stepped out into the night air.

"You did good," Fr. Borger said. He shook Harper's hand and then Jackson's. "It was a good idea for Hattie to have called me. I'm glad I was there for you. I'll keep following up with the diocese here to make sure they take care of what they need to. I'm available if anyone needs anything else."

"Thank you for all of your help," Harper said. She reached out and gave him a hug. "If you're ever in Little Rock please let us know."

"I will. I definitely want to catch up with Hattie." Fr. Borger turned to leave. He made it a few feet, then stopped and called over his shoulder, "Harper, don't forget to cut your father some slack now and then. He means well. He just always seems to make the wrong decision."

Harper and Jackson walked to his truck. Once inside, Harper rubbed a spot on the back of her head. It still hurt, and she wasn't sure why. Maybe the weather was giving her a headache. She tried to call Hattie, but there was no answer.

"You okay?" Jackson asked, as he started the truck and pulled out of the parking spot.

"I don't know," Harper said unsure. "I feel weird. My head still hurts. I can't reach Hattie either. You think we can just drive back tonight?"

"Sure, honestly I thought tomorrow would be better, but I'd like to get back, too. It feels like we've been down here for days. At least we accomplished what we set out to do."

They sat in silence for a few more minutes. "Hey, Harper," Jackson started. She turned and looked at him. "You did a really good job with this. No one believed you at the start but you kept following your instinct and you figured it out. Hattie would be proud of you."

They rode back to the hotel in silence. Once there, Harper tried Hattie again and got voicemail. They gathered up their belongings, checked out of the hotel, and started their trip back. It was uneventful until they were about fifty miles from Little Rock. It was close to two in the morning, but Harper's ringing cellphone broke the silence in the truck.

It was Det. Granger. Harper answered and listened. She grew frantic with each word he said. Harper asked all the questions she could, but Granger didn't have many answers.

"What happened?" Jackson asked concerned as Harper ended the call.

"Hattie is missing," Harper said, her voice sounded hollow even to herself. "Det. Granger said that one of the neighbors called the police. The house is dark, but the back porch door was swinging wide open and the dogs were in the yard barking like crazy. They went out, but didn't see Hattie so they called the police. She's not in the house, but her car is there. They've started a search."

Jackson hit the gas and they sped towards home. The streets were eerily quiet at that time of night so they had a clear path. Although they were going at least twenty over the speed limit and miles were flying by, Harper counted nearly every second. She felt completely paralyzed to help. She turned over in her mind every place Hattie could be. Then it hit Harper like a flash.

She picked up her phone and called Det. Granger. She shouted, "Hattie's in the storm shelter with Paul! I know it. Go there now. We will be home in less than thirty minutes."

Granger didn't even argue with her. He assured Harper they were on their way.

Chapter Sixty-Four

Hattie flinched at the dead man's words. That was all it took for Paul to come over to her. He demanded, "What are you seeing?" Hattie looked beyond him, and he spun around the room. "Is he here now? What's he saying?"

"No, Tucker isn't here," Hattie said honestly. Hattie didn't want to give away what she was seeing. She assumed it would only enrage Paul. She needed to stall him. Frustrated and tired, Hattie added, "I'm cold. It's uncomfortable down here."

Paul ran a hand through his dark hair. "I don't care about that. You have to connect with that lawyer now."

Hattie sighed. "I told you, that's not how it works. I don't have control over it. Let's go back to my house or even the yard. That's where I've seen him before. I don't know that he'll know where to find me."

"No, call him. Get him here now!" Paul shouted.

"Tucker, Tucker," Hattie called, her voice flat. "I need to talk to you."

Hattie had to figure a way out. There were three of them though, and Paul had a gun. She wondered who the pregnant woman was so she asked, "Who was that woman? She looks too pregnant to be hanging out down here."

"My wife, and she's fine. That's none of your concern. You just need to get that lawyer here now," Paul said clearly frustrated with her.

"All we can do is wait to see if he shows up. I called him. I told you I can't just summon him."

The dead man, who was dressed casually in shorts and a polo shirt, started to tell his tale. He came over to Hattie and stood by her side. His voice was quiet, pleasant and solemn. "I'm the real Fr. Patrick McNally. This guy is my half-brother. I was searching for my birth family and found him. I sent him a letter to introduce myself. It was after that I found out he was a criminal in the middle of a trial. He must have noticed how similar we looked and hatched a plan."

Hattie tried to stare straight ahead as the priest told his story. She was watching Paul who was frantically pacing around the room. His wife was still nowhere to be seen. The other man, Evan, sat across the room watching the scene play out.

"Call him again. Now!" Paul shouted at her.

Hattie closed her eyes. She willed with all the energy she had left in her body for Tucker to show himself. Then she yelled his name loudly one more time and then again. When she opened her eyes, she was relieved to see Tucker standing across the room.

He had a confused expression on his face as he looked from Paul to her and then he noticed the other spirit.

Tucker looked at him carefully, and as if finally connecting the dots, Tucker said to Hattie, "I remember now."

Tucker walked over to the real Fr. McNally and said with conviction, "You're the real priest, aren't you? I know from photos I saw. I knew the other guy was a fake. I just couldn't figure it out in time."

The priest asked, "What tipped you off?"

Tucker admitted, "My brother-in-law, Drew, is a real bum. I knew he was up to no good when he got out of prison. Then I saw him meeting with that guy." Tucker pointed to Paul.

Then he continued, "We aren't Catholic so it piqued my curiosity. I started following Drew. Everything about you checked out so I thought maybe Drew was seeking advice. Maybe he was trying to reform himself, I thought. I gave Drew the benefit of the doubt."

Hitching his jaw at Evan, Tucker added, "But then I saw Drew meet with that guy. I did my research on him. Found out his name, what he went to prison for. Found the connection in Chicago. Low and behold, I saw a photo of him with his brother, Paul. I was just starting to put the pieces together. Then I saw the articles online about Paul's arrest and trial and his escape to South America. I had heard rumors that my brother-in-law was burglarizing houses. I was so close. I was just trying to fit the last pieces together but then he killed me."

"Drew killed you," Hattie corrected and then quickly realized her mistake.

Paul advanced on her. "He's here. What's he saying?"

"He just wanted to know who killed him. He doesn't have a lot of memories from around the time he died," Hattie explained.

"I didn't kill him. Does he know that?" Paul asked. He was moving around the room, trying to figure out where Tucker was.

"He's right there," Hattie said, pointing to a spot a few feet directly in front of her.

"What do you mean Drew killed me?" Tucker asked confused.

Hattie looked at him sympathetically. "They found the gun in his storage unit. Drew was burglarizing homes that night, and they think he killed you right after."

Tucker rubbed at his chin. "That doesn't feel right. I still can't remember the details of that night, but that doesn't feel right to me. Why would Drew be at the Saints & Sinners Ball?"

Confronting Hattie, Paul demanded, "What's he saying?"

"Tucker's just confused about how Drew could have killed him. He said it's not making sense."

Waving the gun, Paul said, "I don't care about all that. What does he know about me? And more importantly who did he tell?"

Hattie looked to Tucker. She had no idea what to tell him. She felt like her every word was going to determine whether she lived or died. Since she felt like she didn't have much left, Hattie opted for the truth. "Tucker saw Drew meeting with you and Evan. He figured out who Evan was, then figured out who you are. He knew about your arrest and that you took off for South America before your trial." Hattie was connecting the dots herself. She locked eyes with Paul. "Is that when you killed Fr. McNally when he was in Brazil?"

Paul rubbed a hand across his head. "How do you know that? Did Tucker tell you that?"

"No," Hattie said, shaking her head. "Fr. McNally came from a mission in Brazil. If you escaped to South America, and now you're here assuming his identity, it makes sense."

Paul didn't confirm nor deny what Hattie said. He pointed the gun at Hattie and punctuated each word, "Who did Tucker tell about me?"

Hattie looked to Tucker again. "No one," he said. "I didn't have all the pieces together. Roxy knew I was looking into the priest. I still don't know why I let it slip, but I did. Lizzie knew I suspected her brother and was looking into the priest, but not any detail. I thought the priest was up to no good, but no one knew what I knew. I was still building my case. You don't drop a bombshell like that on the church and community without having all your evidence line up."

Hattie relayed the message to Paul.

Paul looked relieved. Then he coldly smirked at Hattie, "You know, now that you know, I'm going to have to kill you, right? I was hoping I wouldn't have to, but now I do."

For the first time, Hattie stood and so did Evan across the room. She knew she couldn't outrun them, but Hattie wasn't going to sit there and let Paul kill her.

Fr. McNally stood next to Hattie. "Ask Paul why he wasn't man enough to shoot me. Instead he waited until we were on his boat and my head was turned. He bashed me in the skull and pushed my body into the ocean. He watched me sink like it was nothing."

Hattie asked Paul the question and watched his eyes grow wide with fear. "How do you know that? No one would have known that!" Paul spun around the room frantically.

Hattie said quietly, "Even if you kill me, his spirit lives on. He'll tell someone else. He'll make his story known."

Paul turned back to Hattie and steadied his gun at her. Hattie counted the seconds. She wondered if it would hurt to be shot. At least she knew there was an afterlife.

A crash at the top of the steps disrupted Hattie's thoughts. They all turned their attention to the top of the stairs. Hattie wasted no time. She lunged for Paul's gun, knocking it out of his hands. Paul shoved her and Hattie fell to the ground as heavy-booted reinforcements clamored down the steps.

Hattie looked up to see Det. Granger followed by several uniformed officers. Hattie breathed a sigh of relief and looked up at Tucker and Fr. McNally. The priest said to her, "Thank you for telling my story. You're safe now," before his spirit vanished.

Chapter Sixty-Five

Two days after Hattie was taken by Paul Davidson, Harper was still reeling from what happened to her aunt. Harper had incredible guilt that she hadn't figured out who Paul was sooner and that she had left Hattie alone in the house. Hattie had assured Harper several times there was nothing more she could have done, and had Harper not gone to Dallas, the real identity of the man posing as Fr. McNally would have never been unmasked.

Harper knew her aunt was right but that didn't make her feel any better. After Det. Granger and his team stormed in and rescued Hattie, they had arrested Paul, his pregnant wife, and Evan. Carrie, the wife, was taken to the hospital under police custody, and Paul and Evan were taken directly to the station and then to jail.

During a thorough search of the storm shelter, way back in the multitude of rooms that Hattie had been held in, the police found millions of dollars in loose gemstones and jewelry, which given time would have been cut down. It turns out that Paul and his brother Evan had been running a regional operation. Drew was only the local thief. Paul and Evan were running the same across Texas and Tennessee. They carried all the stolen jewelry in the suitcases that Harper saw them bringing in.

Det. Granger said that he hadn't searched that far back when he was in the shelter the first time. He had no idea how complex the maze of halls and rooms was. Granger also said they found a key that Dan identified was to his office. They suspect it was Paul or Evan who planted the jewelry to distract away from them, and possibly to get Dan to stop digging deeper into the fake Fr. McNally.

The feds in Chicago fought for extradition to bring Paul back for his federal case there, and the Little Rock Police Department allowed it. Little Rock would be allowed to prosecute for kidnapping Hattie once the feds were done with him, if they so desired. Federal charges would also be brought against Paul, Evan and even Carrie in Little Rock federal court. It was likely the local Little Rock kidnapping case would be on hold for a long time.

Brazil was also talking to Det. Granger about what, if any, criminal charges they could levy against Paul. But with no body and no witnesses, the case was slim. The feds in Chicago assured Harper and Hattie that Paul and Evan were looking at what would amount to life sentences anyway. Justice would be served one way or another.

The most curious thing to Harper though was that as Hattie was giving her statement to Det. Granger, she had indicated that Paul told her the details of how he had killed Fr. McNally. She was clear that they had gone out on a fishing boat that

Paul rented. Once far out in open water, Paul hit Fr. McNally in the head and shoved him over the side of the boat. Paul had insisted, screaming in fact, that he hadn't told Hattie a single word. That instead Hattie had talked to the priest's ghost and got the story. It amounted to a confession, Det. Granger said, either way. Paul was essentially admitting that it was true just that he hadn't told Hattie.

When Harper had pressed her aunt, Hattie, with a wry smile on her face, had simply put her hands up and said, "You have your interview skills and I have mine," and left it at that. Harper knew there was more to the story, but she wasn't going to press for now. Harper was just glad the case was solved.

There were still many unanswered questions, but Harper assumed as Det. Granger laid out the case of Tucker's murder and more details became public, it would start to make sense. It seemed though that Paul had no idea that Drew had killed Tucker and Roxy. Paul was actually terrified that it would blow up his whole operation, and he was right, it did. That's why Paul went back to the spot so many times, he was trying to figure out who the killer was, too.

Today was Hattie's first day back to the shop. She gave herself a day to rest and then was back at it. Hattie had to go in, the shop was still brimming with more customers than before. And poor Beatrix couldn't handle it all. Many people were coming in to hear the details directly from Hattie. Harper promised that as soon as she went over to check on Lizzie Reese that she'd come help out. Harper still wasn't sure how she felt about Hattie's witchery. But Harper was at least starting to accept there were things she couldn't explain rationally.

Harper gave Sparkle and Shine a quick pet and a thanks for saving Hattie. It was them escaping and barking that brought attention to a missing Hattie. Once in the driveway, as Harper was getting in her Land Rover, she heard a man whistle seductively at her. She looked around and saw Jackson coming down his driveway.

"Is that your way of flirting?" Harper teased him. "Don't you know that catcalling women like that isn't allowed?"

"Not women, just you, and you love it," Jackson countered. He came over and wrapped her in a big hug. "Dinner tonight?" he asked.

Harper agreed and let herself enjoy Jackson's warm embrace. They weren't dating. They were friends who flirt and spend time together, which seemed silly at their age to have that many qualifiers. But it was what they had agreed upon. Neither was in a position to move any faster than that.

Harper assured Jackson she'd be ready for their dinner after a quick stop to check on Lizzie. Harper felt bad for the woman. First losing her husband and then her brother. It would be just a quick stop before getting ready for the evening.

Chapter Sixty-Six

Harper pulled up to Lizzie's house and patted the tin of chocolate chip cookies next to her. She had baked this time instead of making the faux pas of bringing store-bought. Harper really identified with Lizzie. There was something about Lizzie that struck close to home. If Harper hadn't left New York, she was sure this was how her life with Nick would have ended up.

They would have had money and power, but no love and warmth. Harper would have been stuck in a life she didn't want and wasn't happy in. In so many ways, Harper felt bad for Lizzie. A prisoner of her own choices is how Harper thought of it, but she knew too well what happened once you allowed yourself to start going down a certain path. It was hard to unmake the choice.

Lizzie was expecting her. Harper had called the day before and asked if she could stop over and visit. Lizzie was cautious but had agreed. The woman, dressed in a simple blue shift dress, adorned with a string of dainty pearls, greeted Harper at the door. Harper handed Lizzie the cookies and the two retreated to the family room off the kitchen. Lizzie had poured Harper a cup of coffee and the two sitting on opposite couches shared the cookies Harper brought.

Harper and Lizzie talked for about twenty minutes, making chit-chat and pleasantries. Feeling more comfortable, Harper said, "I really wanted to stop by to see how you're doing. It must be hard to know your brother killed your husband."

Lizzie smiled, but said pointedly, "You really don't know how to beat around the bush, do you? You'll do better here if you learn how to be less direct."

"Duly noted," Harper said, feeling chastised. "That isn't how it goes in New York. Few of us have the time for subtlety. We just want it straight. It's hard to undo years of that." What Harper didn't say was that it was ironic that the woman was being so direct with her insult of Harper's own directness, but she let it go.

Lizzie gestured with her hand as she spoke. "It's difficult, but we all have to move forward in life. I'm thinking of selling this house as it holds too many bad memories. I'm quite looking forward to being on my own."

"I can understand that. A fresh start is important. That's what I'm doing here in Little Rock."

"I heard you were quite persistent with finding out the truth about what happened to Tucker," Lizzie commented. The woman looked over her cup at Harper.

Harper felt some hostility and tension coming from the woman. "Yes, I was. I'm sorry it was your brother. I was thrown into the middle when I found Tucker's body."

Lizzie set her cup down. She picked up a cookie and took a bite. "Well gossip is one thing in this city, it's quite another to take action and get involved in things that are none of your business."

Harper wasn't sure what to say so she stayed silent.

Lizzie went on. "Let's take your aunt. Hattie stays out of other people's lives unless they ask her for help. I like that about her. Hattie has learned how it works here. You'd do well to learn from her example."

Lizzie took another bite of cookie. She added, "I am curious about one thing. Speaking of gossip, I heard that Hattie saw and talked to that priest's ghost. I wonder if she's talked to Tucker since his death."

Harper was caught off guard. She hadn't realized what Paul said had made its way beyond Det. Granger and some of the other police that were present. Skeptically, Harper said, "I wouldn't think so. Hattie hasn't said anything to me. That man pretending to be the priest was willing to say anything. I don't think he's someone I would believe."

"I'm just curious what tales Tucker would have to tell," Lizzie said.

"I can understand wanting to talk to a loved one after death, but I don't know if people can really do that."

"You misunderstand me, dear," Lizzie scolded. Her voice edgy and angry, she snapped, "I don't want to talk to Tucker. I want to find out what he is telling people. Is he trying to ruin me even in death?"

Harper was taken aback. She wasn't sure how to respond. Taking a last sip of her coffee, Harper said, "I should probably be going. I've taken up enough of your time. I just wanted to make sure you were okay, and you are. Do you have a restroom I can use before I go?"

"Down the hall, door is on the right," Lizzie said, remaining seated.

Harper followed the hall and quickly found the bathroom. She glanced by the mirror and noticed the dark circles under her eyes. She was tenser than she realized. Finishing up quickly, Harper washed her hands and headed out of the bathroom.

Turned around, Harper walked the wrong way and ended up going farther down the hall instead of back to the family room. As Harper turned to head in the right direction, she noticed a door was slightly ajar. She glimpsed a familiar person sitting behind a desk. Harper was going to pretend she hadn't seen him, but he called out to her.

"You really can't mind your own business can you," Matthew Inslee chided her. "Come in here, now, Harper."

Chapter Sixty-Seven

Harper hesitated in the hall. She thought about running out of the place but curiosity and poor judgment got the better of her. Harper turned back around and hesitantly pushed open the half-closed door. Peering inside, Harper said, "I really don't know what you mean. I'm just getting ready to leave. I had to go to the bathroom and walked out the wrong way."

Matthew Inslee was sitting behind the desk in what Harper assumed was Tucker's home office. There were awards Tucker had won from the city on the walls and a large bookshelf filled with books. Harper's eyes made it to the shelf that was second from the top. What she saw caused a wave of nausea to roll through her body. It was the devil mask, proudly displayed on a shelf. Why would Lizzie keep Drew's mask? Didn't the police find it when they searched his belongings?

Inslee followed Harper's gaze. He got up and picked up the mask and pulled it over his face. Inslee turned back around to Harper and stared at her menacingly. It was him. The killer. Harper knew for sure now. He was the right height. The mask fit the way it did that night.

Inslee started laughing. A dark menacing laugh that chilled Harper to her bones. Inslee said, "We didn't know if we were going to tell you or not. We were leaving it up to fate, but you came down here and found me."

"Tell me what?" Harper asked, confused and afraid. She started backing out of the office and bumped right into Lizzie. She was holding a gun and motioned for Harper to take steps back into the office.

"People know I'm here. You can't kill me. They will know," Harper warned. She thought about making a run for it, but they were in too close a range. A bullet would strike her for sure.

"We aren't going to kill you, Harper. At least not physically," Inslee explained.

Still wearing the devil mask, which was seriously making Harper uncomfortable, Inslee mocked, "But knowing what I'm going to tell you and not being able to do a damn thing about it is going to hurt you in another way. It's going to drive you crazy every single day."

"You are such a silly girl, and not very smart," Lizzie added with a mocking laugh. "It was right under your nose the whole time."

Turning to Inslee, Lizzie praised, "You were right. All we had to do was wait for Drew to give us the perfect night. It all worked out better than planned."

Inslee added, "See Lizzie found out Drew was burglarizing homes. When she did, Lizzie dropped enough hints that she knew Drew wouldn't be able to resist going out the night of the Saints & Sinners Ball to hit a few houses. We knew if we set Drew up and pinned Tucker's murder on him, he'd have no alibi without giving away his crimes. Lizzie found out Drew was going back out again the other night. All we had to do was drop a few bread crumbs in your lap, and you'd follow — literally. While you were chasing down Drew and getting him arrested, I planted the murder weapon in his storage unit. It worked out better than planned."

Inslee added, "Even with burglarizing homes, Drew still had no one to corroborate an alibi. He had no alibi, the murder weapon, a motive, and the means to do it. He's the perfect fall guy."

"Why suck up to the priest then?" Harper asked Inslee.

"He had to think I was on his side. When I found out who he really was, well that just made the whole thing sweeter. There were so many suspects that could have killed Tucker, nobody would be looking at us."

Turning to Lizzie, Harper inquired, "You worked together? You killed Roxy, too? Why?"

"Why wouldn't we?" Lizzie asked incredulously. "I've known Matthew for several years. I saw how dismissive my husband was of his work. Matthew knew of my husband's cheating. One night at a party about six months ago, we both had been drinking and admitted how much better our lives would be without

Tucker in it. This was a plan that was a long time in the making, Harper. Roxy was just revenge, plain and simple."

"The one thing we did not take into consideration was you," Inslee admitted. "You were the little wrench in our plan, but then you went after the wrong guy, and we let you. You just made it easier for us."

"You protected us, really," Lizzie added. "That's probably going to drive you crazy for years. You were hot on Drew's tail and then the fake priest. You weren't even paying attention to us."

Harper was frustrated. They were right. This was going to eat at her. They were also right that her focus was in the wrong direction. Drew and Paul made the obvious suspects. She was suspicious of Inslee but Det. Granger said he had an airtight alibi.

Locking eyes with Inslee, Harper asked, "What about your alibi?"

Inslee gave a sly smile and took off the mask. He set it down on the table. "You mean Mrs. Matthew Inslee? I proposed to her last night. We met up quickly that night at the party just to be seen and then left. I drove my car to her place right down the road and walked back. I confronted Tucker, killed him and I went back to her place. She lied for the man she loves and said I was there the whole time. She will be paid handsomely for it."

Lizzie shrugged her shoulder. "See, Harper, the perfect crime."

"There is no perfect crime," Harper countered.

"Of course, there is," Inslee stated. He sat down on the edge of Tucker's desk and detailed it out for her. "How could we not get away with it? It was a man that shot Tucker. You provided that evidence yourself. There is no one tied to Lizzie that she could have paid off. There's no money trail. Nothing. I've got a rock-solid alibi. Drew has done everything but confess. He has a known criminal record with a hatred of Tucker. Everyone knew they fought. He was robbing houses that night, mere blocks from the party. The murder weapon was found in his storage unit. It's a solid case."

Inslee folded his arms and looked at Harper with a smug expression on his face. "Now, Lizzie has all the money she needs and total freedom. Her louse of a husband is dead and that criminal for a brother will be locked up for the rest of his life. I'll see to that myself. And it paves the way for me to run for lead prosecutor. The way I see it, it's a win-win all the way around. The only loose end is you."

"I thought you said you weren't going to kill me?" Harper asked, the fear rising in her again.

"I'm not, unless you make too much noise and leave me no option," Inslee said. "Really I just want to watch you go crazy not being able to do anything with what you know. Oh, you'll tell some people. But no one will believe you. And even if they do, they are in the same position as you. You have no evidence. Nothing. It will be a wild accusation against the man running for public office and a grieving widow."

Inslee laughed at the predicament they left Harper in. "You can tell everyone you want."

Harper stared at the mask, wondering how she could use it.

Inslee read her thoughts. He picked up the mask, "You think this is evidence? It was Tucker's. There's no reason for it not to be in his house. And you'd have to prove it was this specific mask. Do you really want Manhattan all over again?"

Inslee stopped, waiting for Harper to respond. When she didn't, he added satisfied, "I didn't think so."

Harper stood for several moments. She took a deep breath and let it back out again. Her thoughts were swimming. Inslee was right on all counts. Harper felt defeated. Before she said anything, Inslee walked towards her.

"Now you should go and don't come back." Inslee warned, "If you come even close to Lizzie, I'll make sure the police slap a restraining order on you. I've got that power. Trust me, once I'm elected as lead prosecutor, that little shop of your aunt's is closing down. Enjoy it while you can."

Harper was numb. She walked out of the house without saying another word. She got into her SUV and picked up her phone. But Harper had no one to call. It was their word against hers, and the cops had a solid suspect in jail. Inslee was right. There was nothing she could do. Harper took one last look at the house. Harper had been wrong. She was nothing like Lizzie nor would she ever be.

Chapter Sixty-Eight

Hattie was faring far better after her ordeal than Harper was with her own. Hattie had watched Harper mope around the house and obsess over what Matthew Inslee and Lizzie had disclosed. Hattie had tried to refocus Harper's attention to other things like helping in the shop, which she did several times. The days seemed to pass slowly. Harper would spend time with Jackson. She'd help Dan with the magazine, but there was an edge to Harper that hadn't been there before. She was unsettled and restless and that worried Hattie to no end.

The day Harper left Lizzie after hearing the murder confession, she came straight back to the house and had gathered Hattie and Jackson in the kitchen. She told them what Inslee and Lizzie said. Neither Hattie nor Jackson were surprised, but even they told Harper there really wasn't anything she could do. Jackson had encouraged Harper to let life play out how it was supposed to, and that eventually it would come to light. Hattie had attempted to school Harper on karma, but the fact that Inslee and Lizzie would be free to live their lives gnawed at Harper. In the days following, she plotted and planned but all fell short.

Hattie and Jackson had taken Harper out for her fortieth birthday March 15, and the dinner was lovely until Matthew Inslee had walked in with a woman, presumably his alibi and date. Harper had grown sullen and angry again. She had vowed justice for Tucker and for the city.

Hattie had talked at length with Beau about what to do. He encouraged Hattie to just give Harper time. He reminded Hattie that Harper had so much happen in such a short period that she'd need time to process. He was sure eventually sweet Harper would return to normal. Hattie wasn't so sure. Harper pressed Hattie a few times about her ability to see the dead, but Hattie had remained tight-lipped. Harper had enough to deal with, and Hattie needed her in a better frame of mind.

The evening after Tucker Reese's funeral, which they all attended and watched Lizzie play the role of grieving widow to perfection, Harper asked Hattie if she could bring a few people together to meet at Hattie's shop. Hattie wasn't sure what Harper was up to, but she had agreed.

Hattie closed the shop early that Saturday. Harper had asked if Beatrix could stay and the young girl was more than happy to be included. Jackson had no more clue than Hattie as to why they were gathering, but he was there. Det. Granger was the first to arrive and then came in Dan. They said their hellos and Hattie and Beatrix went about bringing coffee, tea and snacks for their guests.

Granger asked Hattie if she could turn on the television she had mounted in the corner of the shop. It was rarely on so Hattie had to fish around for the remote control. After a few minutes, Hattie found it buried under some paperwork at the back of the counter.

Granger explained, "Matthew Inslee is holding a press conference to announce his candidacy for prosecutor. Bill Myers will hold the position until the election this November. Inslee is running against him."

Hattie watched Harper but her face didn't register surprise. It's what Inslee had told her.

Taking a seat at the table with them, Harper said, "I'm sure you're all wondering why I asked you to meet today. I have to tell you all something, but it can't leave this room for now."

Hattie watched as Harper looked at each of them and they all nodded in agreement. Harper went on, "You're going to have to take me at my word here. The story is crazy, and if I hadn't heard it myself, I might not believe me. But every word is the truth. I went to check on Lizzie a few days ago and Matthew Inslee was there. They admitted to killing Tucker and Roxy…"

Harper was interrupted when Dan and Granger both started to talk at once. Harper held her hand up. "Give me a chance to explain," she said. "Inslee said his alibi is only partially true. The woman he was with is going to marry him so she's covering for him. He wasn't with her the whole time. He also said he was running for prosecutor, which, Granger, you just saw he's announcing. Inslee killed Tucker and Roxy but Lizzie was behind it. She said it was something they had been plotting for a long time. The mask that Inslee wore that night is on a shelf in Tucker's home office. Apparently, it was Tucker's mask. Inslee put it on when I was there so even if you find his prints or DNA on the mask, he can explain it away. They covered every base to not get caught."

Det. Granger looked at Harper. "This is a very serious accusation you are leveling against them, you realize?"

"Yes, but that's why I'm not coming to you in an official capacity," Harper said sadly. "I can't prove it, and they told me as much. This is too big for me alone. I don't know that there is anything we can do, but I know if we work together, we have a better chance. We may never have the evidence to prove it, but at least we will all have our eyes and ears open."

Harper went over every detail of the visit with Lizzie. She explained in detail what Inslee had told her about the murder and the reasoning behind it. Harper also provided the explanation Inslee gave as to why they'd never be caught.

When Harper was done, no one spoke. Hattie thought it was probably as difficult for them to absorb as it was for Harper to retell the story.

Finally, Dan spoke. "I believe you. When I was the editor of the newspaper, I worked closely with Inslee. He was never someone I trusted, but I had gained his trust. Harper, when you came to my office that day the jewelry was found, Inslee wanted me to find out from you what you knew about the murder and stop you. He was very worried you had suspected him. He assured me over and over again that he hadn't killed Tucker. Until then, I hadn't suspected him at all. But he was so insistent you knew something you shouldn't, he made me suspicious. I'm in, whatever you need. My only question is what's the plan?"

Harper turned to him and smiled. "Thank you. Dan, if it wasn't for your research, we would have never stopped Paul or even known the real Fr. McNally had been murdered. I don't know the plan, that's why I'm coming to all of you. I think it's something we are going to have to work together when we can to find out what we can. Build a case over time. Be there when Inslee slips up."

Granger leveled a look at Harper. "You're telling me I've got an innocent man sitting in jail for a murder he didn't commit, and I have no way to prove?"

Harper nodded.

Granger thought for several moments and then said, "I'm in. The longer Inslee gets away with it, the cockier he will get. He'll slip eventually. But this is going to take time and teamwork."

Jackson reached for Harper's hand. He squeezed it and she smiled at him. Jackson said sincerely, "You know I'm in."

Beatrix and Hattie also agreed to lend support magical or otherwise. Harper went over and hugged her aunt. All of their attention was then turned to the television with the news breaking in and bringing them Matthew Inslee's press conference from the steps of the courthouse. He promised to fight crime and what he called "moral corruption" in the city.

Hattie knew there was a target on her back now, especially if Inslee won.

While everyone had their eyes fixed on the television, Hattie felt a presence. She turned towards the shop door and there was Tucker Reese.

"I remember, Hattie," Tucker said, coming close to her. "It was Matthew Inslee. He showed up to the Saints & Sinners Ball wearing a mask that had been given to me by the mayor of New Orleans. He called me over, and we argued about some recent cases. Then out of nowhere, he had a gun. Inslee shot me. Drew is innocent of my murder at least. I need justice."

All Hattie could do was mouth, "We know. We will fight for it."

"I'm not leaving until we get it," Tucker said.

Hattie offered Tucker a sympathetic smile. Together they all watched the last of the press conference.

As the group began to talk among themselves about the best plan of action, Harper walked back over to her aunt. Harper whispered, "I'm ready to learn whatever you can teach me. I want to tap into all of my powers."

This wasn't how Hattie wanted it all to go, but she saw a window opening, and she was going to take it.

READY BOOK #2
SECRETS TO TELL
NOW ON AMAZON

Access Stacy's Free Mystery Readers' Club Starter Library

Riley Sullivan Mystery Series prequel novella
(Meet Riley back when she was a journalist)
The 1922 Club Murder

Harper & Hattie Mystery Series prequel novella
Harper's Folly

Hit subscribe at

http://www.stacymjones.com/

Follow author Stacy M. Jones for exclusive information on book signings, events, fan giveaways, and her next novel.

Please leave a review for **Saints & Sinners Ball.**

Amazon: amazon.com/author/stacymjones
Facebook: StacyMJonesWriter
Goodreads: StacyMJonesWriter

Printed in Great Britain
by Amazon